Image Lecture Notebook

to accompany

PRINCIPLES OF

HIGH SCHOOL EDITION

Hillis • Sadava • Heller • Price

 Sinauer Associates, Inc.

 W. H. Freeman and Company

Cover photograph © Fred Bavendam/Minden Pictures.

Image Lecture Notebook to accompany *Principles of Life, High School Edition*

Address editorial correspondence to:
Sinauer Associates, Inc.
23 Plumtree Road
Sunderland, MA 01375 U.S.A.
Fax: 413-549-1118
Internet: www.sinauer.com; publish@sinauer.com

W.H. Freeman and Company
41 Madison Avenue
New York, NY 10010
Houndsmills, Basingstoke RG21 6XS, England
www.whfreeman.com

ISBN 978-1-4292-9614-4
Printed in U.S.A.

4 3 2 1

Table of Contents

Table of Contents (continued)

1 Principles of Life

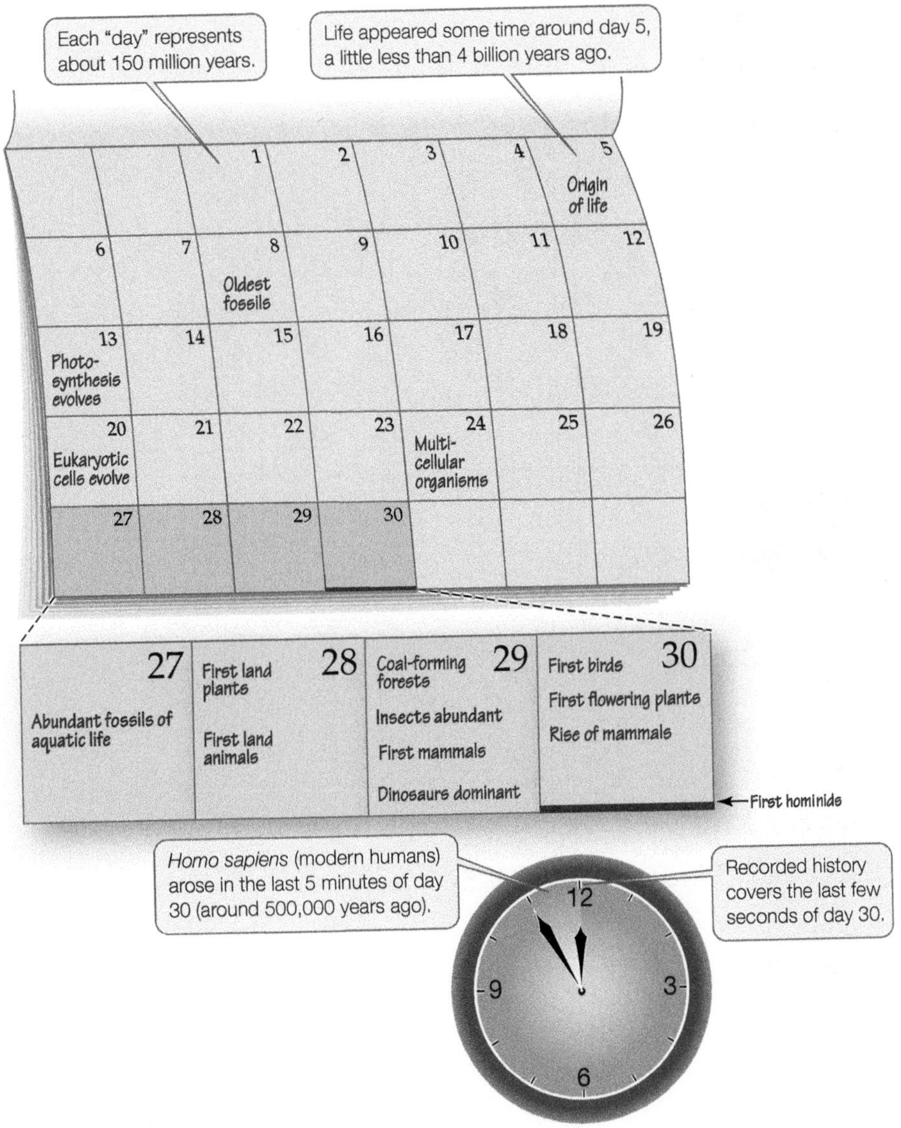

FIGURE 1.1 Life's Calendar *(Page 2)*

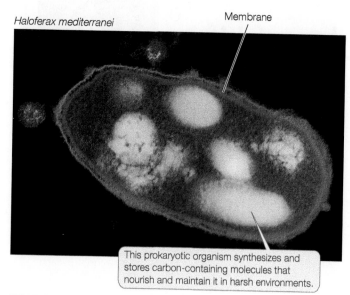

Haloferax mediterranei

Membrane

This prokaryotic organism synthesizes and stores carbon-containing molecules that nourish and maintain it in harsh environments.

FIGURE 1.2   The Basic Unit of Life is the Cell *(Page 3)*

(A)

(B)

FIGURE 1.3   Photosynthetic Organisms Changed Earth's Atmosphere *(Page 4)*

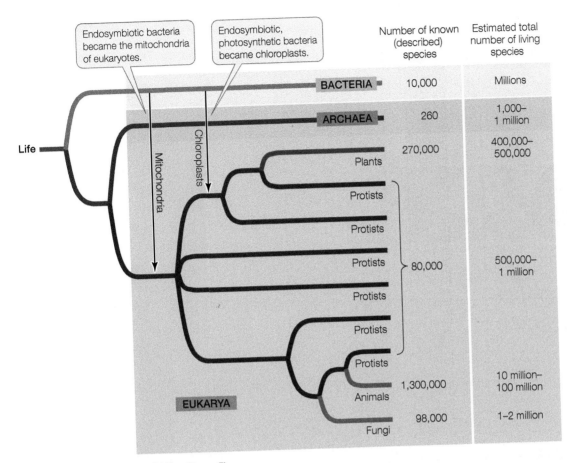

FIGURE 1.4   The Tree of Life *(Page 5)*

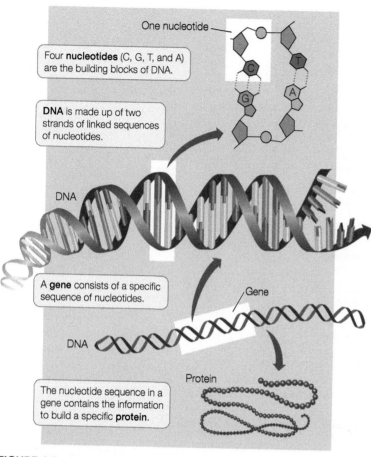

One nucleotide

Four **nucleotides** (C, G, T, and A) are the building blocks of DNA.

DNA is made up of two strands of linked sequences of nucleotides.

DNA

A **gene** consists of a specific sequence of nucleotides.

Gene

DNA

The nucleotide sequence in a gene contains the information to build a specific **protein**.

Protein

FIGURE 1.5   DNA Is Life's Blueprint *(Page 6)*

(A) Atoms to organisms

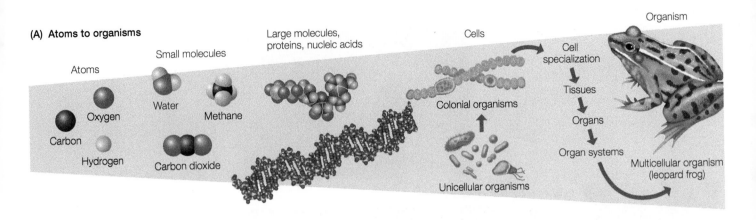

Atoms

Carbon

Oxygen

Hydrogen

Small molecules

Water

Methane

Carbon dioxide

Large molecules, proteins, nucleic acids

Cells

Colonial organisms

Unicellular organisms

Cell specialization

Tissues

Organs

Organ systems

Organism

Multicellular organism (leopard frog)

(B) Organisms to ecosystems

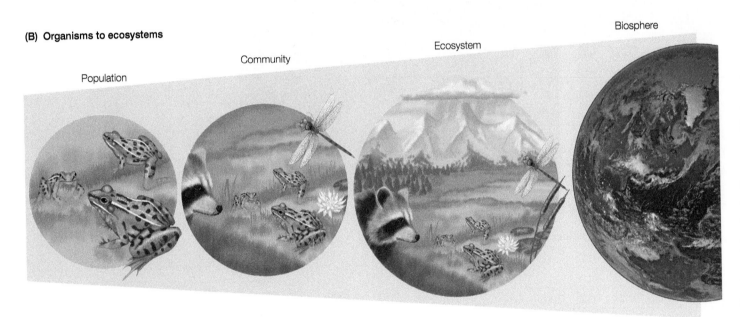

Population

Community

Ecosystem

Biosphere

FIGURE 1.6 Biology Is Studied at Many Levels of Organization *(Pages 6 and 7)*

(A) *Dyscophus guineti*

(B) *Xenopus laevis*

(C) *Agalychnis callidryas*

(D) *Rhacophorus nigropalmatus*

FIGURE 1.7 Adaptations to the Environment *(Page 9)*

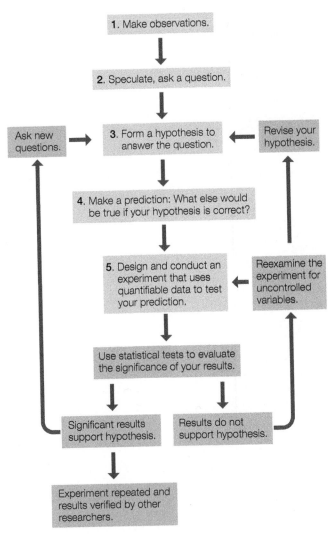

FIGURE 1.8   Scientific Methodology *(Page 11)*

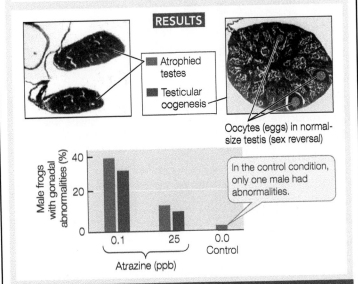

INVESTIGATION

FIGURE 1.9   Controlled Experiments Manipulate a Variable
The Hayes laboratory created controlled environments that differed only in the concentrations of atrazine in the water. Eggs from leopard frogs (*Rana pipiens*) raised specifically for laboratory use were allowed to hatch and the tadpoles were separated into experimental tanks containing water with different concentrations of atrazine.

HYPOTHESIS

Exposure to atrazine during larval development causes abnormalities in the reproductive tissues of male frogs.

METHOD

1. Establish 9 tanks in which all attributes are held constant except the water's atrazine concentration. Establish 3 atrazine conditions (3 replicate tanks per condition): 0 ppb (control condition), 0.1 ppb, and 25 ppb.
2. Place *Rana pipiens* tadpoles from laboratory-reared eggs in the 9 tanks (30 tadpoles per replicate).
3. When tadpoles have transitioned into adults, sacrifice the animals and evaluate their reproductive tissues.
4. Test for correlation of degree of atrazine exposure with the presence of abnormalities in the gonads (testes) of male frogs.

RESULTS

CONCLUSION

Exposure to atrazine at concentrations as low as 0.1 ppb induces abnormalities in the gonads of male frogs. The effect is not proportional to the level of exposure.

For more, go to Working with Data 1.1 at **yourBioPortal.com**.

Go to **yourBioPortal.com** for original citations, discussions, and relevant links for all INVESTIGATION figures.

INVESTIGATION

FIGURE 1.10 Comparative Experiments Look for Differences among Groups
To see whether the presence of atrazine correlates with testicular abnormalities in male frogs, the Hayes lab collected frogs and water samples from different locations around the U.S. The analysis that followed was "blind," meaning that the frogs and water samples were coded so that experimenters working with each specimen did not know which site the specimen came from.

HYPOTHESIS

Presence of the herbicide atrazine in environmental water correlates with gonadal abnormalities in frog populations.

METHOD

1. Based on commercial sales of atrazine, select 4 sites (sites 1–4) less likely and 4 sites (sites 5–8) more likely to be contaminated with atrazine.
2. Visit all sites in the spring (i.e., when frogs have transitioned from tadpoles into adults); collect frogs and water samples.
3. In the laboratory, sacrifice frogs and examine their reproductive tissues, documenting abnormalities.
4. Analyze the water samples for atrazine concentration (the sample for site 7 was not tested).
5. Quantify and correlate the incidence of reproductive abnormalities with environmental atrazine concentrations.

RESULTS

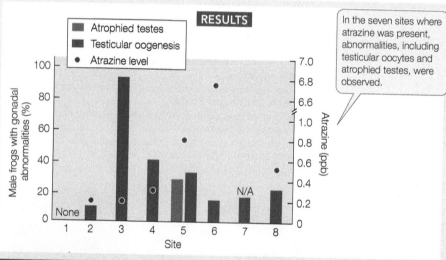

In the seven sites where atrazine was present, abnormalities, including testicular oocytes and atrophied testes, were observed.

CONCLUSION

Reproductive abnormalities exist in frogs from environments in which aqueous atrazine concentration is 0.2 ppb or above. The incidence of abnormalities does not appear to be proportional to atrazine concentration at the time of transition to adulthood.

Go to **yourBioPortal.com** for original citations, discussions, and relevant links for all INVESTIGATION figures.

Life Chemistry and Energy

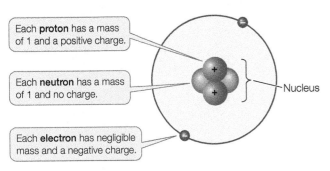

Each **proton** has a mass of 1 and a positive charge.

Each **neutron** has a mass of 1 and no charge.

Each **electron** has negligible mass and a negative charge.

Nucleus

IN-TEXT ART *(Page 17)*

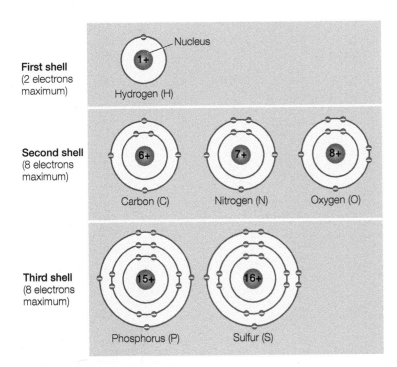

First shell
(2 electrons maximum)

Nucleus

Hydrogen (H)

Second shell
(8 electrons maximum)

Carbon (C)   Nitrogen (N)   Oxygen (O)

Third shell
(8 electrons maximum)

Phosphorus (P)   Sulfur (S)

FIGURE 2.1   Electron Shells *(Page 18)*

TABLE 2.1	Chemical Bonds and Interactions		
NAME	**BASIS OF INTERACTION**	**STRUCTURE**	**BOND ENERGY**[a]
Ionic attraction	Attraction of opposite charges		3–7
Covalent bond	Sharing of electron pairs		50–110
Hydrogen bond	Sharing of H atom		3–7
Hydrophobic interaction	Interaction of nonpolar substances in the presence of polar substances (especially water)		1–2
van der Waals interaction	Interaction of electrons of nonpolar substances		1

[a]Bond energy is the amount of energy (Kcal/mol) needed to separate two bonded or interacting atoms under physiological conditions.

(Page 18)

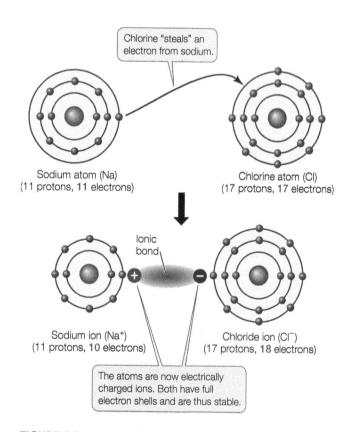

Chlorine "steals" an electron from sodium.

Sodium atom (Na)
(11 protons, 11 electrons)

Chlorine atom (Cl)
(17 protons, 17 electrons)

Ionic bond

Sodium ion (Na⁺)
(11 protons, 10 electrons)

Chloride ion (Cl⁻)
(17 protons, 18 electrons)

The atoms are now electrically charged ions. Both have full electron shells and are thus stable.

FIGURE 2.2 Ionic Bond between Sodium and Chlorine *(Page 19)*

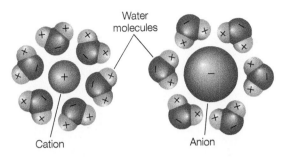

IN-TEXT ART *(Page 19)*

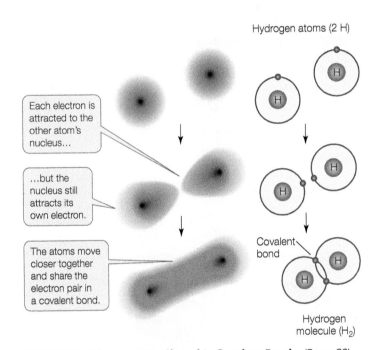

FIGURE 2.3   Electrons Are Shared in Covalent Bonds *(Page 20)*

(A)

1 C and 4 H

Methane (CH₄)

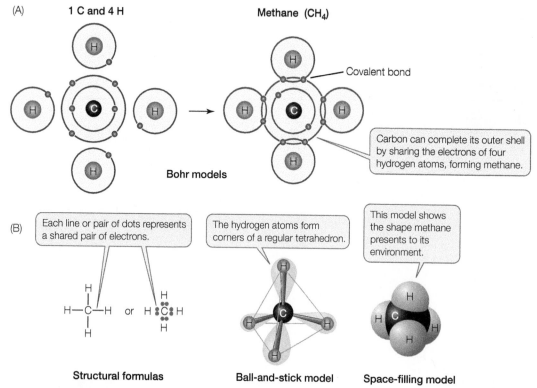

Covalent bond

Bohr models

Carbon can complete its outer shell by sharing the electrons of four hydrogen atoms, forming methane.

(B)

Each line or pair of dots represents a shared pair of electrons.

The hydrogen atoms form corners of a regular tetrahedron.

This model shows the shape methane presents to its environment.

Structural formulas

Ball-and-stick model

Space-filling model

FIGURE 2.4 Covalent Bonding *(Page 20)*

Bohr model

Space-filling model

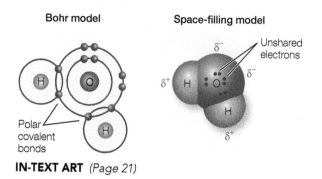

Unshared electrons

Polar covalent bonds

IN-TEXT ART *(Page 21)*

TABLE 2.2	Some Electronegativities
ELEMENT	**ELECTRONEGATIVITY**
Oxygen (O)	3.4
Chlorine (Cl)	3.2
Nitrogen (N)	3.0
Carbon (C)	2.6
Phosphorus (P)	2.2
Hydrogen (H)	2.2
Sodium (Na)	0.9
Potassium (K)	0.8

(Page 21)

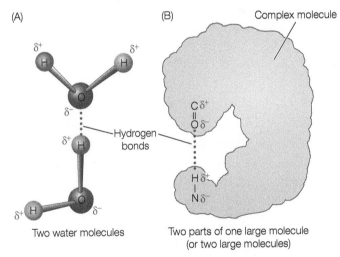

(A) Two water molecules

(B) Two parts of one large molecule (or two large molecules)

Hydrogen bonds

Complex molecule

FIGURE 2.5 Hydrogen Bonds Can Form between or within Molecules *(Page 21)*

Liquid water

IN-TEXT ART *(Page 22)*

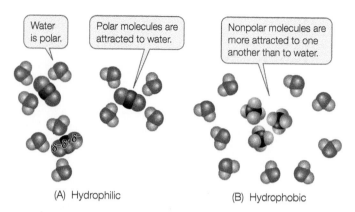

(A) Hydrophilic   (B) Hydrophobic

FIGURE 2.6   Hydrophilic and Hydrophobic *(Page 22)*

Functional group	Class of compounds and an example	Properties
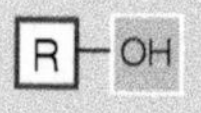 Hydroxyl — R—OH	Alcohols 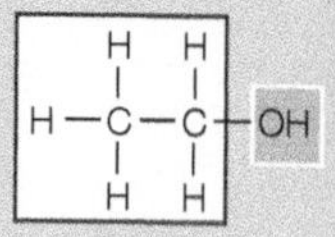 — Ethanol	Polar. Hydrogen bonds with water to help dissolve molecules. Enables linkage to other molecules by condensation.
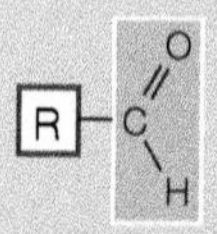 Aldehyde — R—C(=O)H	Aldehydes 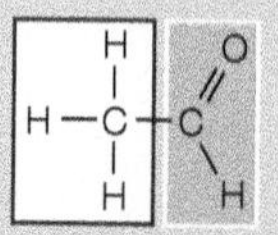 — Acetaldehyde	C=O group is very reactive. Important in building molecules and in energy-releasing reactions.
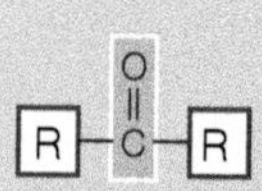 Keto — R—C(=O)—R	Ketones 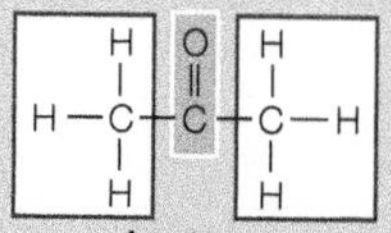 — Acetone	C=O group is important in carbohydrates and in energy reactions.
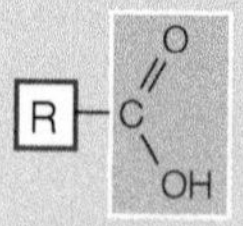 Carboxyl — R—C(=O)OH	Carboxylic acids 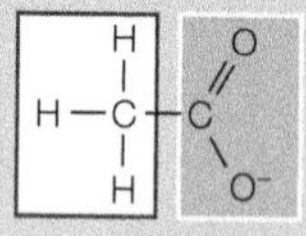 — Acetate	Acidic. Ionizes in living tissues to form —COO$^-$ and H$^+$. Enters into condensation reactions by giving up —OH. Some carboxylic acids important in energy-releasing reactions.
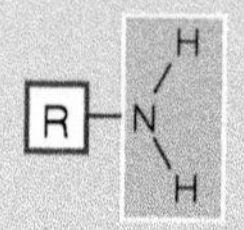 Amino — R—NH$_2$	Amines 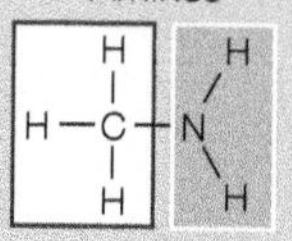 — Methylamine	Basic. Accepts H$^+$ in living tissues to form —NH$_3^+$. Enters into condensation reactions by giving up H$^+$.
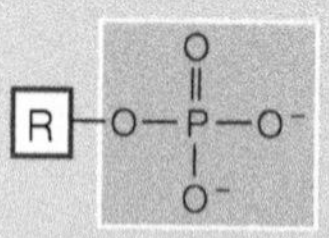 Phosphate — R—O—P(O$^-$)(O$^-$)—O$^-$	Organic phosphates 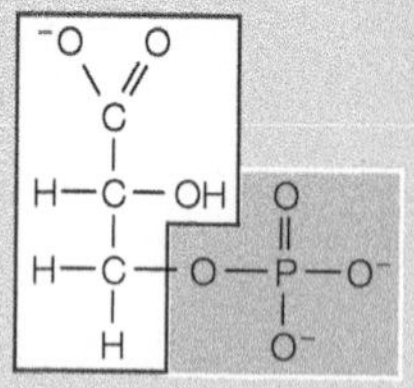 — 3-Phosphoglycerate	Negatively charged. Enters into condensation reactions by giving up —OH. When bonded to another phosphate, hydrolysis releases much energy.
 Sulfhydryl — R—SH	Thiols 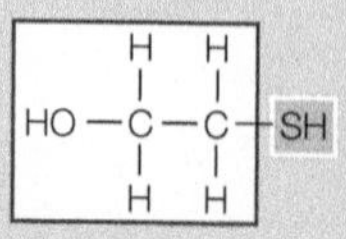 — Mercaptoethanol	By giving up H, two —SH groups can react to form a disulfide bridge (S—S), thus stabilizing protein structure.

FIGURE 2.7   Functional Groups Important to Living Systems
(Page 23)

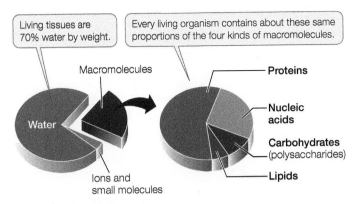

Living tissues are 70% water by weight.

Every living organism contains about these same proportions of the four kinds of macromolecules.

Macromolecules

Water

Ions and small molecules

Proteins

Nucleic acids

Carbohydrates (polysaccharides)

Lipids

IN-TEXT ART *(Page 23)*

(A) Condensation

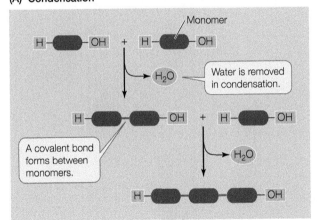

Monomer

Water is removed in condensation.

A covalent bond forms between monomers.

(B) Hydrolysis

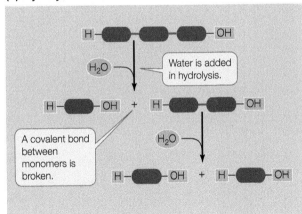

Water is added in hydrolysis.

A covalent bond between monomers is broken.

FIGURE 2.8 Condensation and Hydrolysis of Polymers *(Page 24)*

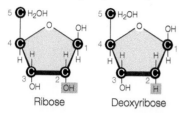

Five-carbon sugars (pentoses)

Ribose   Deoxyribose

Ribose and deoxyribose each have five carbons, but very different chemical properties and biological roles.

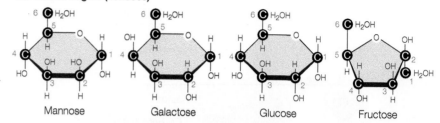

Six-carbon sugars (hexoses)

Mannose   Galactose   Glucose   Fructose

These hexoses all have the formula $C_6H_{12}O_6$, but each has distinct biochemical properties.

FIGURE 2.9 **Monosaccharides** *(Page 25)*

CH₂OH

Glucose   Fructose   Formation of linkage   Glucose   Fructose

Sucrose

H_2O

IN-TEXT ART *(Page 25)*

(A) Molecular structure

Starch and glycogen

Cellulose

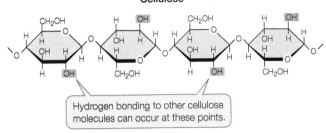

Hydrogen bonding to other cellulose molecules can occur at these points.

Cellulose is an unbranched polymer of glucose with linkages that are chemically very stable.

Branching occurs here.

Glycogen and starch are polymers of glucose, with branching at carbon 6 (see Figure 2.9).

(B) Macromolecular structure

Linear (cellulose)

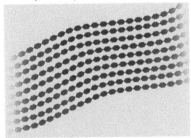

Parallel cellulose molecules form hydrogen bonds, resulting in thin fibrils.

Branched (starch)

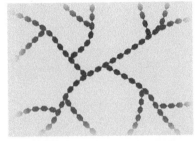

Branching limits the number of hydrogen bonds that can form in starch molecules, making starch less compact than cellulose.

Highly branched (glycogen)

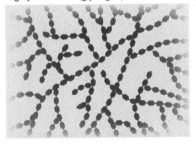

The high amount of branching in glycogen makes its solid deposits more compact than starch.

(C) Polysaccharides in cells

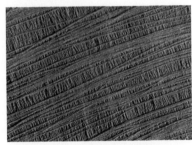

Layers of cellulose fibrils, as seen in this scanning electron micrograph, give plant cell walls great strength.

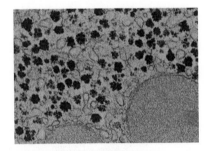

Within these potato cells, starch deposits (colored purple in this scanning electron micrograph) have a granular shape.

The dark clumps in this electron micrograph are glycogen deposits in a monkey liver cell.

FIGURE 2.10 Polysaccharides *(Page 26)*

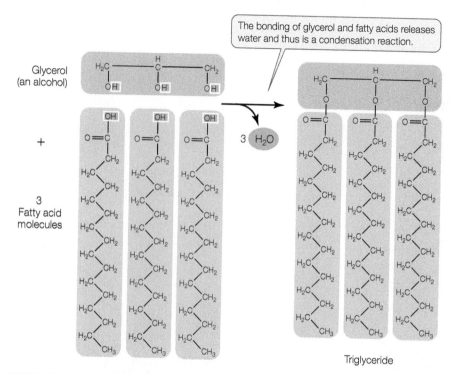

FIGURE 2.11 **Synthesis of a Triglyceride** *(Page 27)*

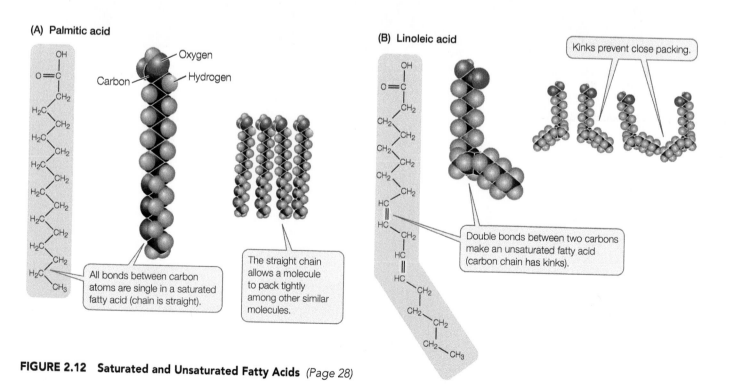

FIGURE 2.12 **Saturated and Unsaturated Fatty Acids** *(Page 28)*

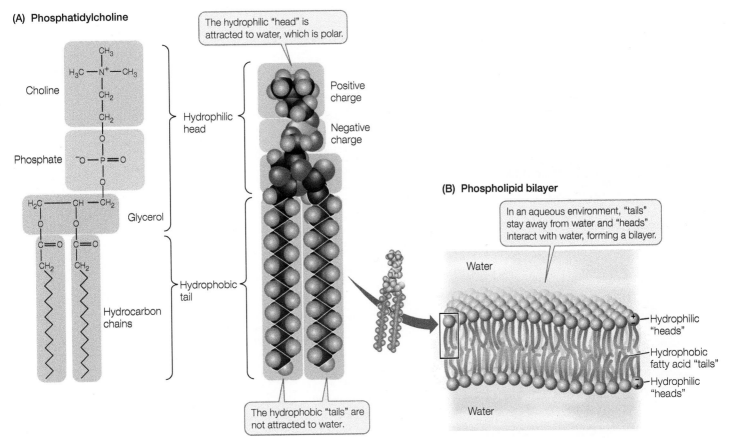

(A) Phosphatidylcholine

Choline

Phosphate

Glycerol

Hydrocarbon chains

Hydrophilic head

Hydrophobic tail

The hydrophilic "head" is attracted to water, which is polar.

Positive charge

Negative charge

The hydrophobic "tails" are not attracted to water.

(B) Phospholipid bilayer

In an aqueous environment, "tails" stay away from water and "heads" interact with water, forming a bilayer.

Water

Water

Hydrophilic "heads"

Hydrophobic fatty acid "tails"

Hydrophilic "heads"

FIGURE 2.13 Phospholipids *(Page 28)*

(A) Endergonic reaction

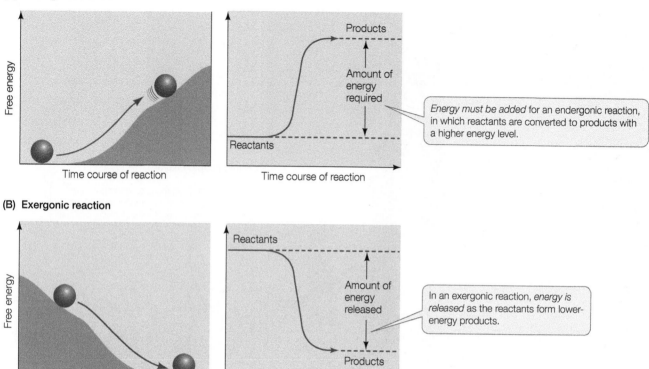

(B) Exergonic reaction

FIGURE 2.14   Energy Changes in Reactions *(Page 30)*

(A)

The First Law of Thermodynamics
The total amount of energy before a transformation equals the total amount after a transformation. No new energy is created, and no energy is lost.

(B)

The Second Law of Thermodynamics
Although a transformation does not change the total amount of energy within a closed system (one that is not exchanging matter or energy with the surroundings), after any transformation the amount of energy available to do work is always less than the original amount of energy.

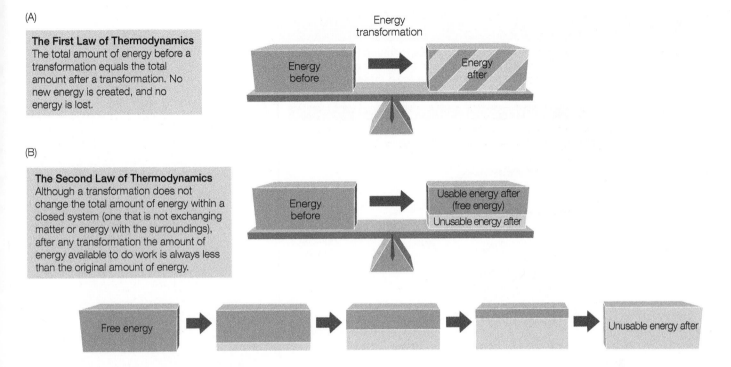

Another statement of the second law is that in a closed system, with repeated energy transformations, free energy decreases and unusable energy (disorder) increases—a phenomenon known as the increase in **entropy**.

FIGURE 2.15 The Laws of Thermodynamics *(Page 30)*

INVESTIGATION

FIGURE 2.16 Synthesis of Prebiotic Molecules in an Experimental Atmosphere
With an increased understanding of the atmospheric conditions that existed on primitive Earth, the researchers devised an experiment to see if these conditions could lead to the formation of organic molecules.

HYPOTHESIS

Organic chemical compounds can be generated under conditions similar to those that existed in the atmosphere of primitive Earth.

METHOD

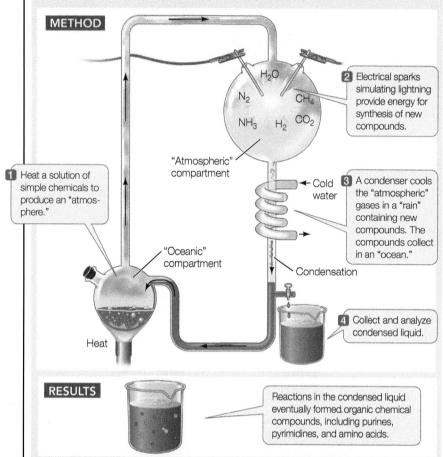

1 Heat a solution of simple chemicals to produce an "atmosphere."

"Atmospheric" compartment

H_2O N_2 CH_4 NH_3 H_2 CO_2

2 Electrical sparks simulating lightning provide energy for synthesis of new compounds.

← Cold water

3 A condenser cools the "atmospheric" gases in a "rain" containing new compounds. The compounds collect in an "ocean."

Condensation

"Oceanic" compartment

Heat

4 Collect and analyze condensed liquid.

RESULTS

Reactions in the condensed liquid eventually formed organic chemical compounds, including purines, pyrimidines, and amino acids.

CONCLUSION

The chemical building blocks of life could have been generated in the probable atmosphere of early Earth.

ANALYZE THE DATA

The following data show the amount of energy impinging on Earth in different forms.

Source	Energy (cal cm^{-2} yr^{-1})
Total radiation from sun	260,000
Ultraviolet light	
Wavelength <250 nm	570
Wavelength <200 nm	85
Wavelength <150 nm	3.5
Electric discharges	4
Cosmic rays	0.0015
Radioactivity	0.8
Volcanoes	0.13

A. Only a small fraction of the sun's energy is ultraviolet light (less than 250 nm). What is the rest of the solar energy?

B. The molecules CH_4, H_2O, NH_3, and CO_2 absorb light at wavelengths less than 200 nm. What fraction of total solar radiation is in this range?

C. Instead of electric discharges, what other sources of energy could be used in these experiments?

For more, go to Working with Data 2.1 at **yourBioPortal.com**.

Go to **yourBioPortal.com** for original citations, discussions, and relevant links for all INVESTIGATION figures.

Nucleic Acids, Proteins, and Enzymes

3

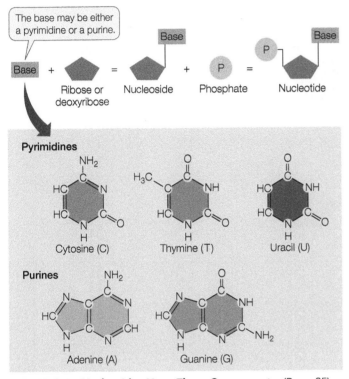

FIGURE 3.1 Nucleotides Have Three Components *(Page 35)*

TABLE 3.1	Distinguishing RNA from DNA		
NUCLEIC ACID	**SUGAR**	**BASES**	**STRANDS**
RNA	Ribose	Adenine	Single
		Cytosine	
		Guanine	
		Uracil	
DNA	Deoxyribose	Adenine	Double
		Cytosine	
		Guanine	
		Thymine	

(Page 35)

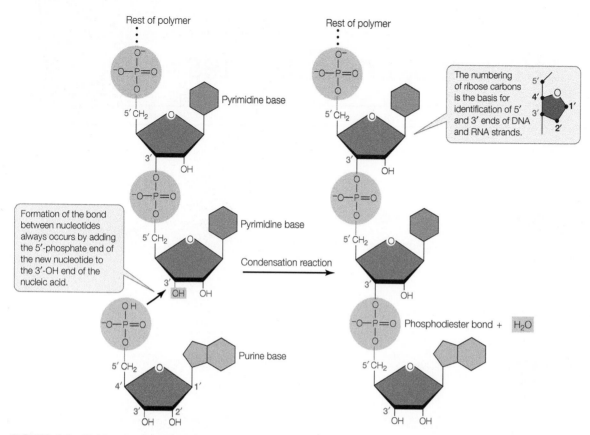

FIGURE 3.2   Linking Nucleotides Together *(Page 36)*

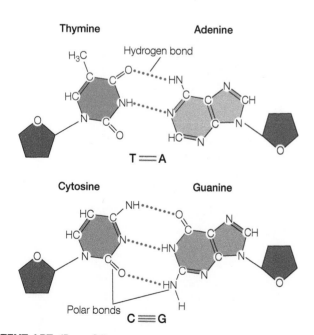

(A)

RNA (single-stranded)

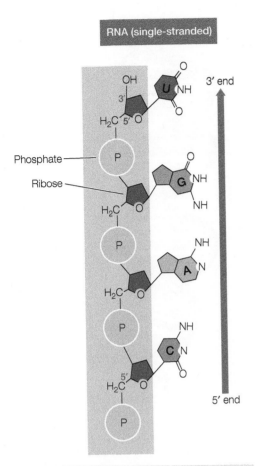

3′ end

Phosphate

Ribose

5′ end

In RNA, the bases are attached to ribose. The bases in RNA are the purines adenine (A) and guanine (G) and the pyrimidines cytosine (C) and uracil (U).

FIGURE 3.3   RNA *(Page 37)*

(B)

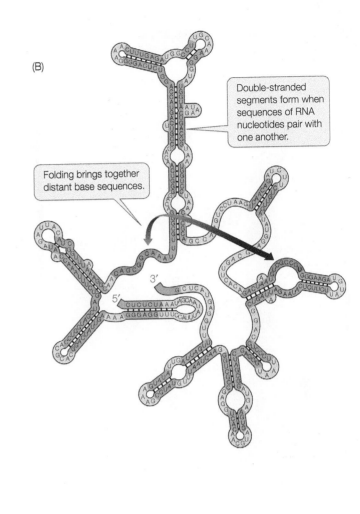

Double-stranded segments form when sequences of RNA nucleotides pair with one another.

Folding brings together distant base sequences.

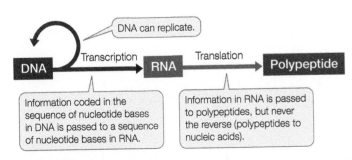

DNA can replicate.

DNA → Transcription → RNA → Translation → Polypeptide

Information coded in the sequence of nucleotide bases in DNA is passed to a sequence of nucleotide bases in RNA.

Information in RNA is passed to polypeptides, but never the reverse (polypeptides to nucleic acids).

IN-TEXT ART *(Page 37)*

(A)

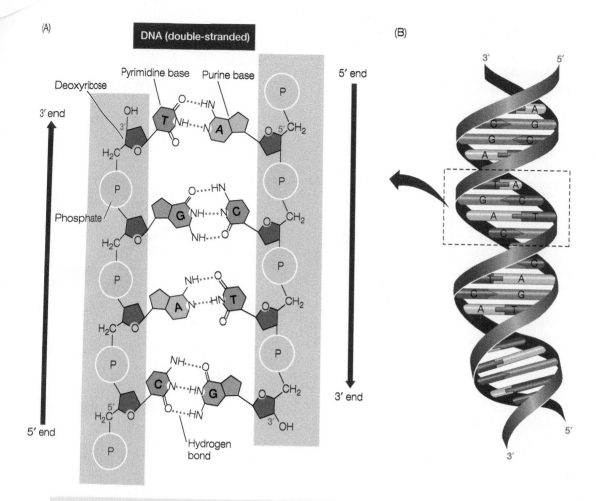

In DNA, the bases are attached to deoxyribose, and the base thymine (T) is found instead of uracil. Hydrogen bonds between purines and pyrimidines hold the two strands of DNA together.

FIGURE 3.4   DNA *(Page 38)*

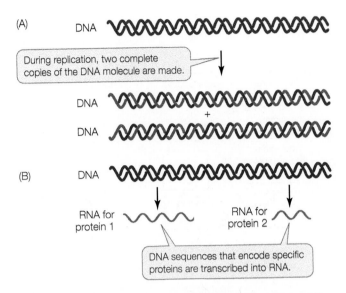

(A)

DNA

During replication, two complete copies of the DNA molecule are made.

DNA

+

DNA

(B)

DNA

RNA for protein 1

RNA for protein 2

DNA sequences that encode specific proteins are transcribed into RNA.

FIGURE 3.5 DNA Replication and Transcription *(Page 39)*

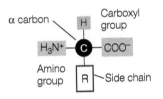

α carbon

H Carboxyl group

H_3N^+ C COO^-

Amino group

R Side chain

IN-TEXT ART *(Page 39)*

TABLE 3.2 The Twenty Amino Acids in Proteins

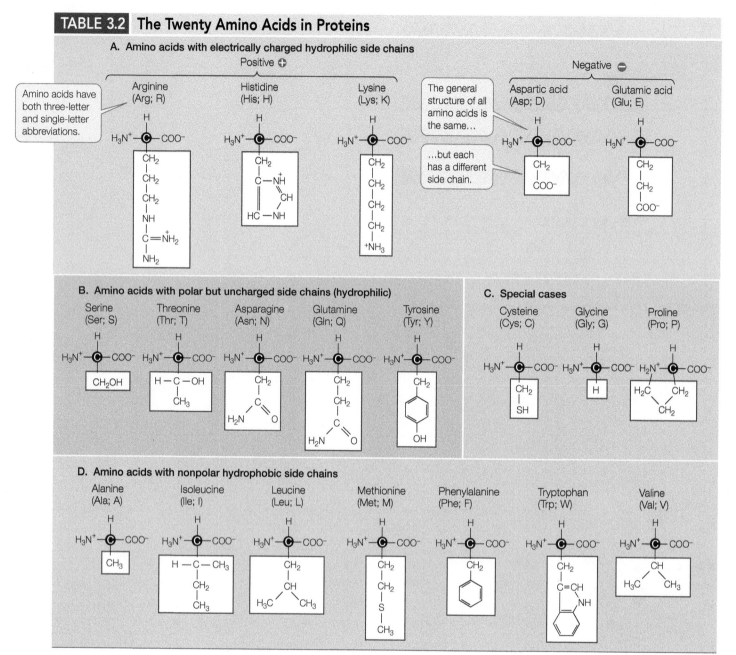

A. Amino acids with electrically charged hydrophilic side chains

Positive ⊕

Negative ⊖

Amino acids have both three-letter and single-letter abbreviations.

Arginine (Arg; R)

Histidine (His; H)

Lysine (Lys; K)

The general structure of all amino acids is the same...

...but each has a different side chain.

Aspartic acid (Asp; D)

Glutamic acid (Glu; E)

B. Amino acids with polar but uncharged side chains (hydrophilic)

Serine (Ser; S)

Threonine (Thr; T)

Asparagine (Asn; N)

Glutamine (Gln; Q)

Tyrosine (Tyr; Y)

C. Special cases

Cysteine (Cys; C)

Glycine (Gly; G)

Proline (Pro; P)

D. Amino acids with nonpolar hydrophobic side chains

Alanine (Ala; A)

Isoleucine (Ile; I)

Leucine (Leu; L)

Methionine (Met; M)

Phenylalanine (Phe; F)

Tryptophan (Trp; W)

Valine (Val; V)

(Page 40)

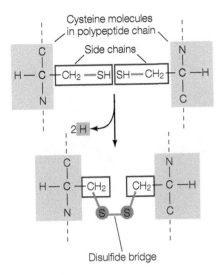

IN-TEXT ART *(Page 41)*

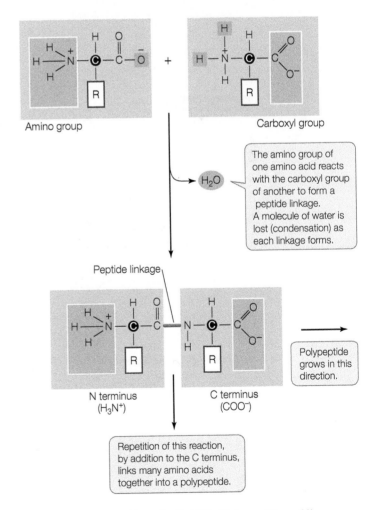

FIGURE 3.6 Formation of a Peptide Linkage *(Page 41)*

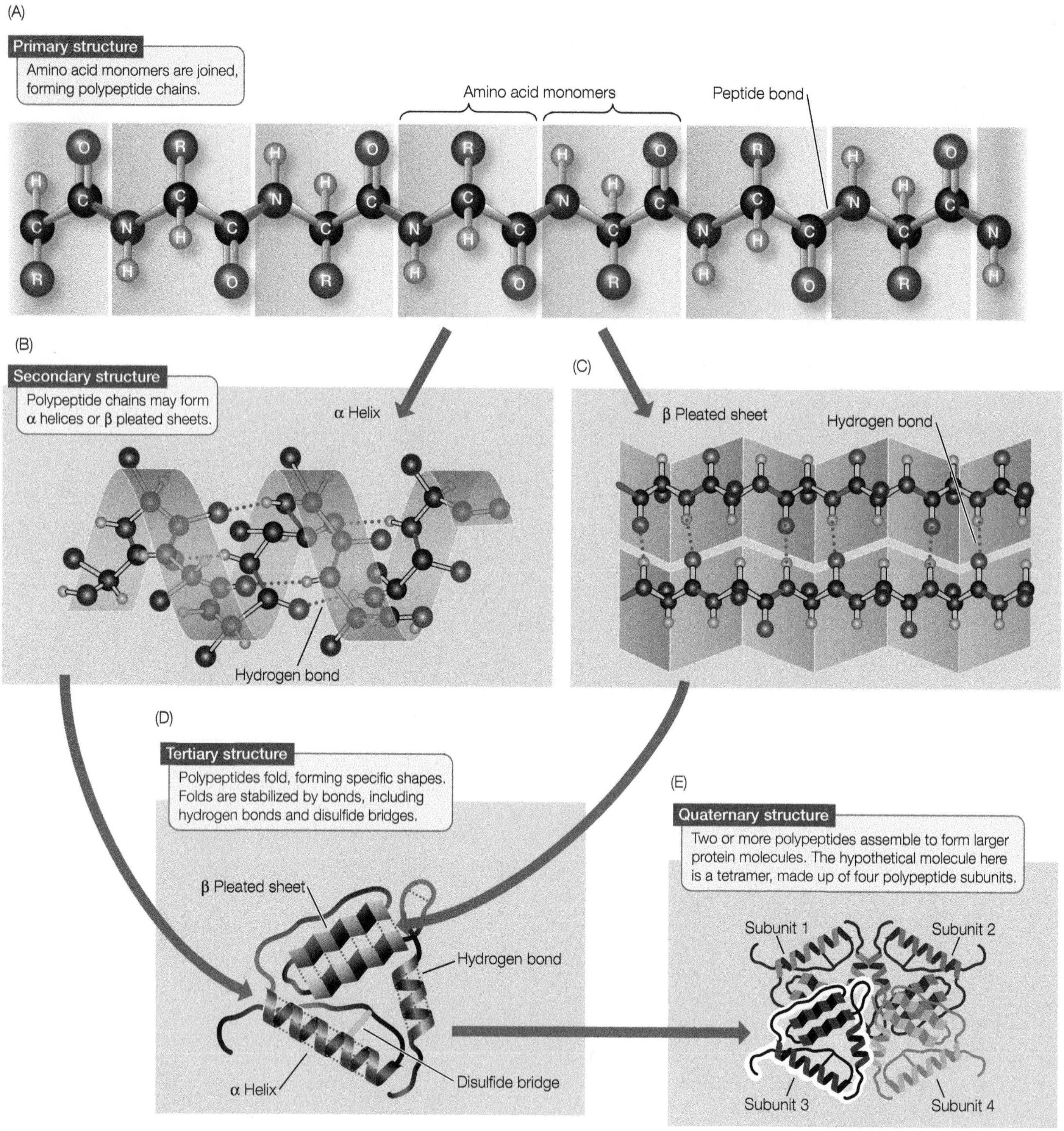

(A)

Primary structure
Amino acid monomers are joined, forming polypeptide chains.

Amino acid monomers

Peptide bond

(B)

Secondary structure
Polypeptide chains may form α helices or β pleated sheets.

α Helix

Hydrogen bond

(C)

β Pleated sheet

Hydrogen bond

(D)

Tertiary structure
Polypeptides fold, forming specific shapes. Folds are stabilized by bonds, including hydrogen bonds and disulfide bridges.

β Pleated sheet

Hydrogen bond

α Helix

Disulfide bridge

(E)

Quaternary structure
Two or more polypeptides assemble to form larger protein molecules. The hypothetical molecule here is a tetramer, made up of four polypeptide subunits.

Subunit 1

Subunit 2

Subunit 3

Subunit 4

FIGURE 3.7 The Four Levels of Protein Structure *(Page 42)*

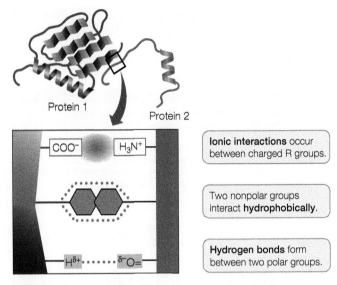

FIGURE 3.8   Noncovalent Interactions between Proteins and Other Molecules *(Page 43)*

Ionic interactions occur between charged R groups.

Two nonpolar groups interact **hydrophobically.**

Hydrogen bonds form between two polar groups.

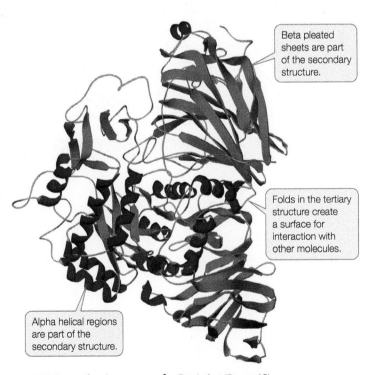

Beta pleated sheets are part of the secondary structure.

Folds in the tertiary structure create a surface for interaction with other molecules.

Alpha helical regions are part of the secondary structure.

FIGURE 3.9   The Structure of a Protein *(Page 43)*

INVESTIGATION

FIGURE 3.10 Primary Structure Specifies Tertiary Structure   Using the protein ribonuclease, Christian Anfinsen showed that proteins spontaneously fold into a functionally correct three-dimensional configuration. As long as the primary structure is not disrupted, the information for correct folding under the right conditions is retained.

HYPOTHESIS

Under controlled conditions that simulate normal cellular environment in the laboratory, the primary structure of a denatured protein can reestablish the protein's three-dimensional structure.

METHOD   Chemically denature functional ribonuclease, disrupting disulfide bridges and other intramolecular interactions that maintain the protein's shape, so that only primary structure (i.e., the amino acid sequence) remains. Once denaturation is complete, remove the disruptive chemicals.

RESULTS   When the disruptive agents are removed, three-dimensional structure is restored and the protein once again is functional.

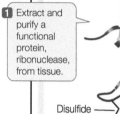

1 Extract and purify a functional protein, ribonuclease, from tissue.

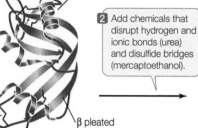

α helix

Disulfide bridge

β pleated sheet

2 Add chemicals that disrupt hydrogen and ionic bonds (urea) and disulfide bridges (mercaptoethanol).

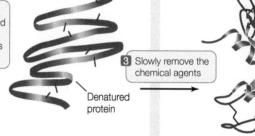

Denatured protein

3 Slowly remove the chemical agents

CONCLUSION

In normal cellular conditions, the primary structure of a protein specifies how it folds into a functional, three-dimensional structure.

ANALYZE THE DATA

Initially, disulfide bonds (S—S) in RNase A were eliminated because the sulfur atoms in cysteine were reduced (—SH). At time 0, reoxidation began and at various times, the amount of disulfide bond re-formation (blue circles) and the function of ribonuclease (enzyme activity; red circles) were measured by chemical methods. Here are the data:

A. At what time did disulfide bonds begin to form?

B. At what time did enzyme activity begin to appear?

C. Explain the difference between your answers for the times of (A) and (B).

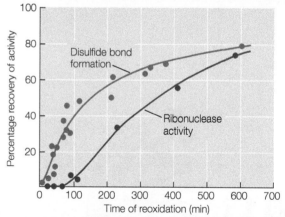

For more, go to Working with Data 3.1 at **yourBioPortal.com**.

Go to **yourBioPortal.com** for original citations, discussions, and relevant links for all INVESTIGATION figures.

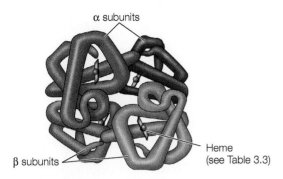

α subunits

β subunits

Heme
(see Table 3.3)

IN-TEXT ART *(Page 44)*

(A)

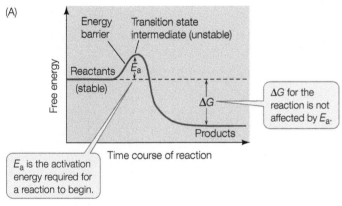

Energy
barrier

Transition state
intermediate (unstable)

Free energy

E_a

Reactants
(stable)

ΔG

Products

Time course of reaction

ΔG for the
reaction is not
affected by E_a.

E_a is the activation
energy required for
a reaction to begin.

(B)

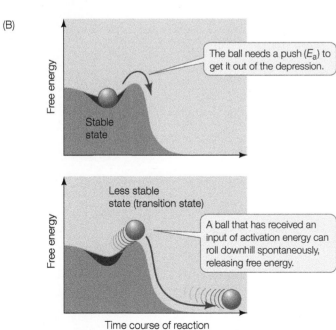

Free energy

The ball needs a push (E_a) to
get it out of the depression.

Stable
state

Free energy

Less stable
state (transition state)

A ball that has received an
input of activation energy can
roll downhill spontaneously,
releasing free energy.

Time course of reaction

FIGURE 3.11 Activation Energy Initiates Reactions *(Page 46)*

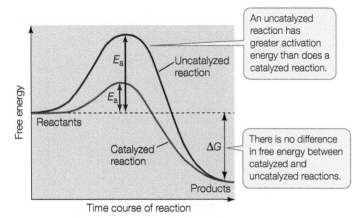

FIGURE 3.12 **Enzymes Lower the Energy Barrier** *(Page 47)*

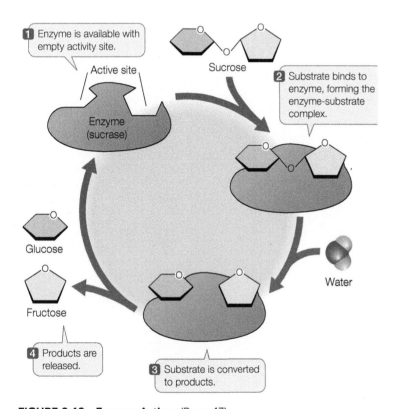

FIGURE 3.13 **Enzyme Action** *(Page 47)*

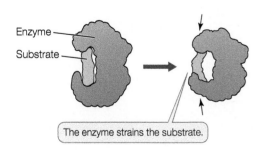

IN-TEXT ART *(Page 47)*

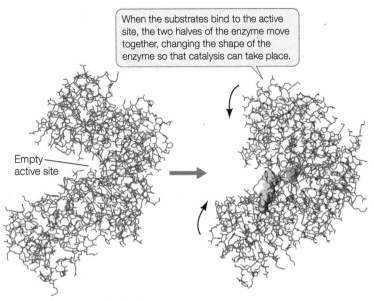

FIGURE 3.14 Some Enzymes Change Shape When Substrate Binds to Them *(Page 48)*

TABLE 3.3	Some Examples of Nonprotein "Partners" of Enzymes	
TYPE OF MOLECULE	**ROLE IN CATALYZED REACTIONS**
Cofactors	
Iron (Fe^{2+} or Fe^{3+})	Oxidation/reduction
Copper (Cu^+ or Cu^{2+})	Oxidation/reduction
Zinc (Zn^{2+})	Helps bind NAD
Coenzymes	
Biotin	Carries —COO^-
Coenzyme A	Carries —CO—CH_3
NAD	Carries electrons
FAD	Carries electrons
ATP	Provides/extracts energy
Prosthetic groups	
Heme	Binds ions, O_2, and electrons; contains iron cofactor
Flavin	Binds electrons
Retinal	Converts light energy

(Page 48)

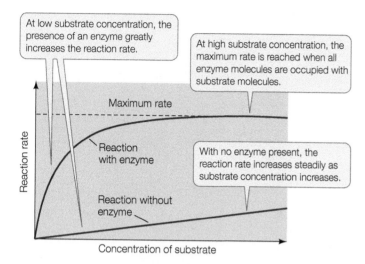

FIGURE 3.15 Catalyzed Reactions Reach a Maximum Rate
(Page 49)

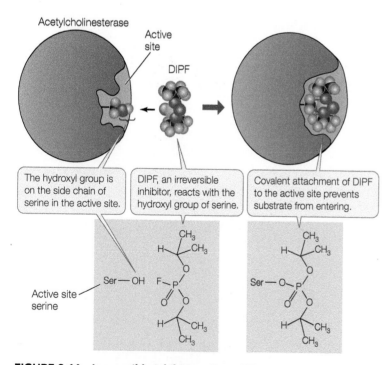

FIGURE 3.16 Irreversible Inhibition *(Page 50)*

(A) Competitive inhibition

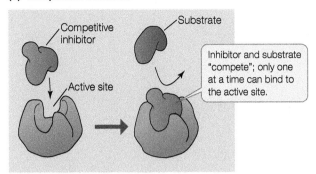

(B) Noncompetitive inhibition

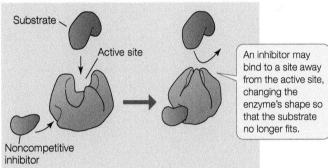

FIGURE 3.17 Reversible Inhibition *(Page 50)*

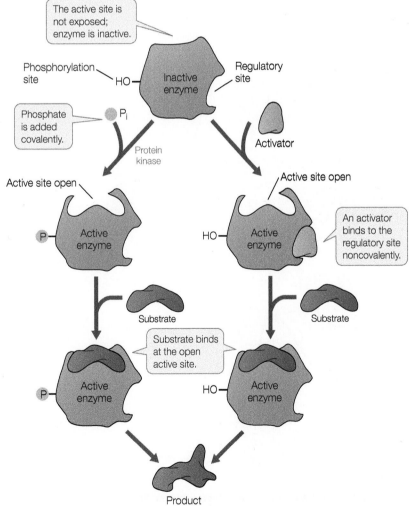

FIGURE 3.18 Allosteric Regulation of Enzyme Activity *(Page 51)*

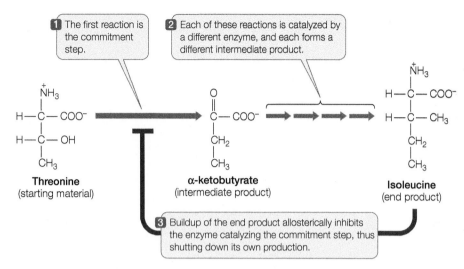

FIGURE 3.19   Feedback Inhibition of Metabolic Pathways *(Page 52)*

(A)

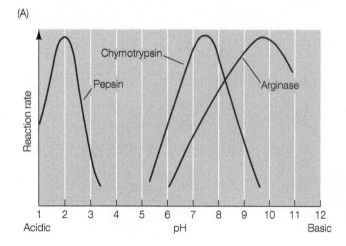

(B)

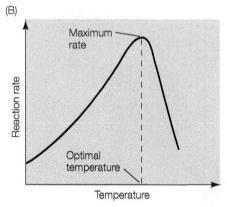

FIGURE 3.20   Enzyme Activity Is Affected by the Environment
(Page 52)

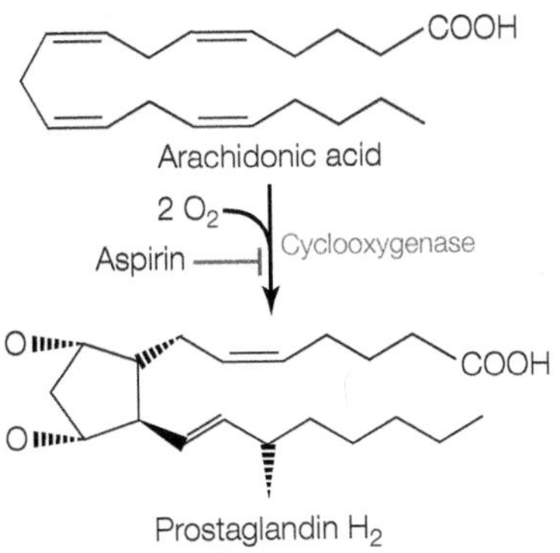

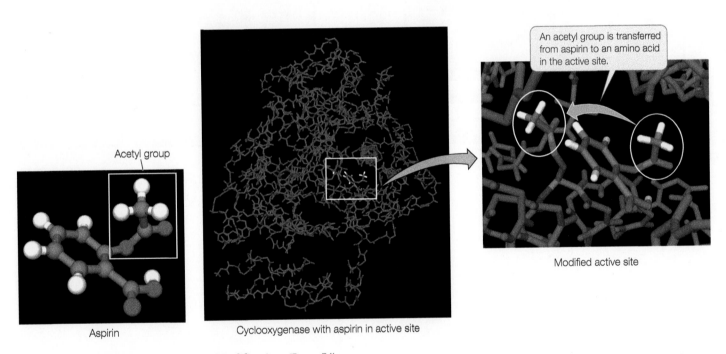

COOH

Arachidonic acid

2 O$_2$

Aspirin —| Cyclooxygenase

COOH

Prostaglandin H$_2$

FIGURE 3.21 Aspirin: An Enzyme Inhibitor *(Page 53)*

Acetyl group

An acetyl group is transferred from aspirin to an amino acid in the active site.

Modified active site

Aspirin

Cyclooxygenase with aspirin in active site

FIGURE 3.22 Inhibition by Covalent Modification *(Page 54)*

Cells: The Working Units of Life

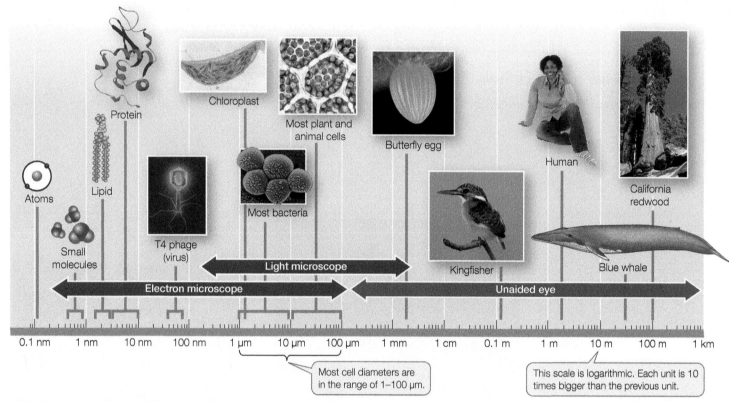

4

Atoms · Small molecules · Lipid · Protein · T4 phage (virus) · Chloroplast · Most bacteria · Most plant and animal cells · Butterfly egg · Kingfisher · Human · Blue whale · California redwood

Electron microscope · Light microscope · Unaided eye

0.1 nm · 1 nm · 10 nm · 100 nm · 1 μm · 10 μm · 100 μm · 1 mm · 1 cm · 0.1 m · 1 m · 10 m · 100 m · 1 km

Most cell diameters are in the range of 1–100 μm.

This scale is logarithmic. Each unit is 10 times bigger than the previous unit.

FIGURE 4.1 The Scale of Life *(Page 57)*

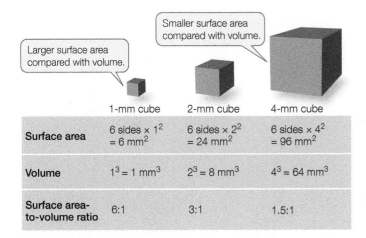

	1-mm cube	2-mm cube	4-mm cube
Surface area	6 sides × 1^2 = 6 mm^2	6 sides × 2^2 = 24 mm^2	6 sides × 4^2 = 96 mm^2
Volume	1^3 = 1 mm^3	2^3 = 8 mm^3	4^3 = 64 mm^3
Surface area-to-volume ratio	6:1	3:1	1.5:1

FIGURE 4.2   Why Cells Are Small *(Page 58)*

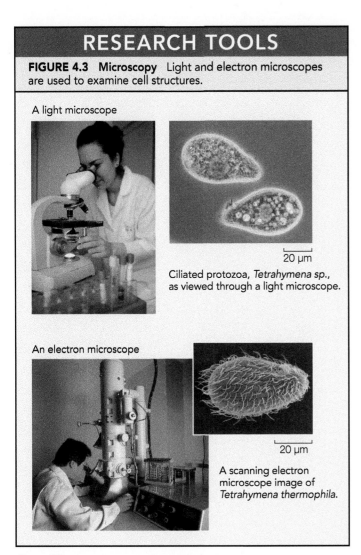

RESEARCH TOOLS

FIGURE 4.3   Microscopy Light and electron microscopes are used to examine cell structures.

A light microscope

20 μm

Ciliated protozoa, *Tetrahymena sp.*, as viewed through a light microscope.

An electron microscope

20 μm

A scanning electron microscope image of *Tetrahymena thermophila.*

RESEARCH TOOLS

FIGURE 4.4 Centrifugation Structures within cells can be separated from one another on the basis of size and density, and the isolated structures can then be analyzed chemically.

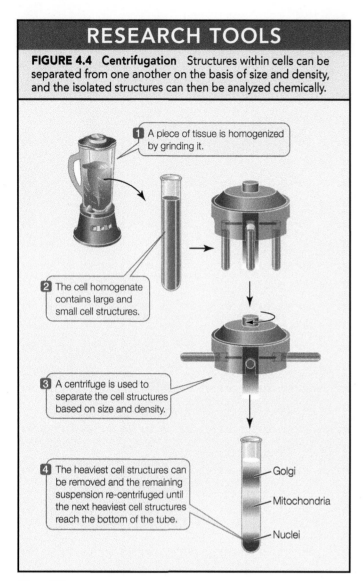

1 A piece of tissue is homogenized by grinding it.

2 The cell homogenate contains large and small cell structures.

3 A centrifuge is used to separate the cell structures based on size and density.

4 The heaviest cell structures can be removed and the remaining suspension re-centrifuged until the next heaviest cell structures reach the bottom of the tube.

— Golgi

— Mitochondria

— Nuclei

(Page 59)

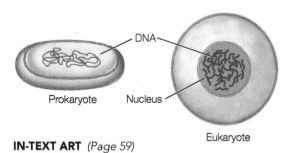

DNA

Prokaryote   Nucleus

Eukaryote

IN-TEXT ART *(Page 59)*

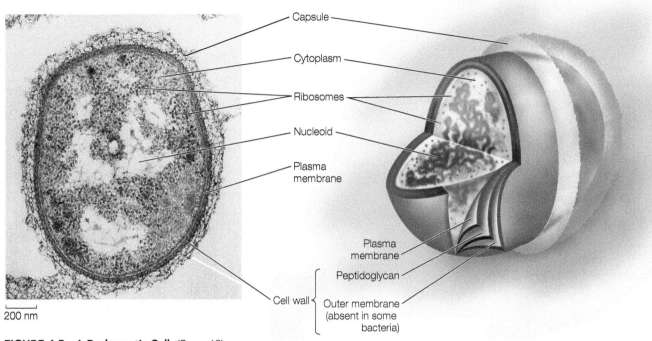

FIGURE 4.5   A Prokaryotic Cell *(Page 60)*

(A)

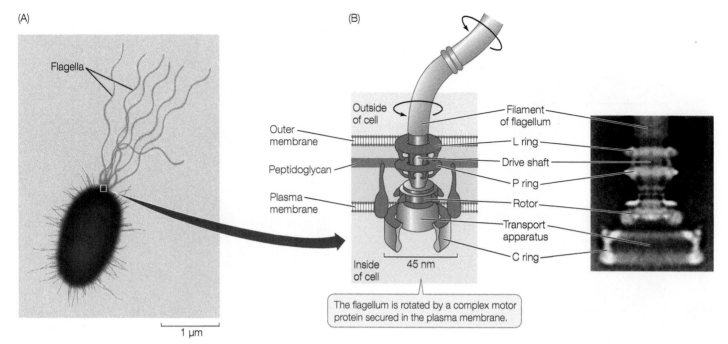

Flagella

1 µm

(B)

Outside of cell

Outer membrane

Peptidoglycan

Plasma membrane

Inside of cell

Filament of flagellum

L ring

Drive shaft

P ring

Rotor

Transport apparatus

C ring

45 nm

The flagellum is rotated by a complex motor protein secured in the plasma membrane.

FIGURE 4.6 Prokaryotic Flagella *(Page 61)*

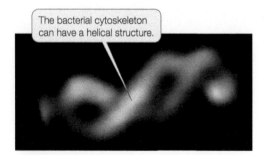

The bacterial cytoskeleton can have a helical structure.

IN-TEXT ART *(Page 61)*

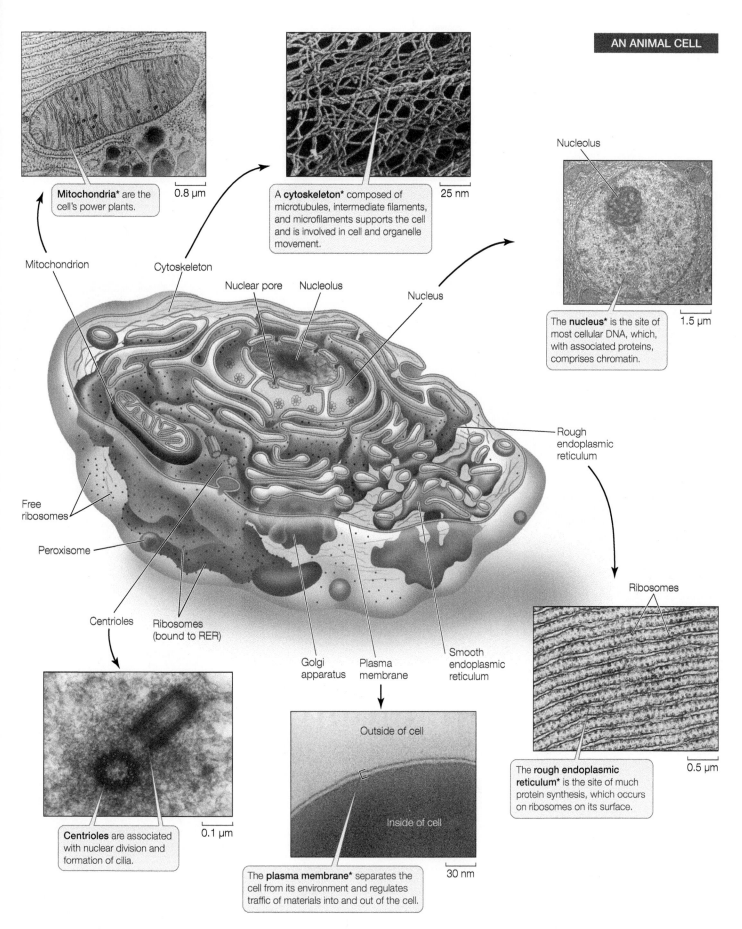

AN ANIMAL CELL

Mitochondria* are the cell's power plants.

0.8 µm

A **cytoskeleton*** composed of microtubules, intermediate filaments, and microfilaments supports the cell and is involved in cell and organelle movement.

25 nm

Nucleolus

The **nucleus*** is the site of most cellular DNA, which, with associated proteins, comprises chromatin.

1.5 µm

Mitochondrion

Cytoskeleton

Nuclear pore   Nucleolus

Nucleus

Rough endoplasmic reticulum

Free ribosomes

Peroxisome

Centrioles

Ribosomes (bound to RER)

Golgi apparatus

Plasma membrane

Smooth endoplasmic reticulum

Ribosomes

Centrioles are associated with nuclear division and formation of cilia.

0.1 µm

Outside of cell

Inside of cell

The **plasma membrane*** separates the cell from its environment and regulates traffic of materials into and out of the cell.

30 nm

The **rough endoplasmic reticulum*** is the site of much protein synthesis, which occurs on ribosomes on its surface.

0.5 µm

FIGURE 4.7 Eukaryotic Cells (Pages 62 and 63)

A PLANT CELL

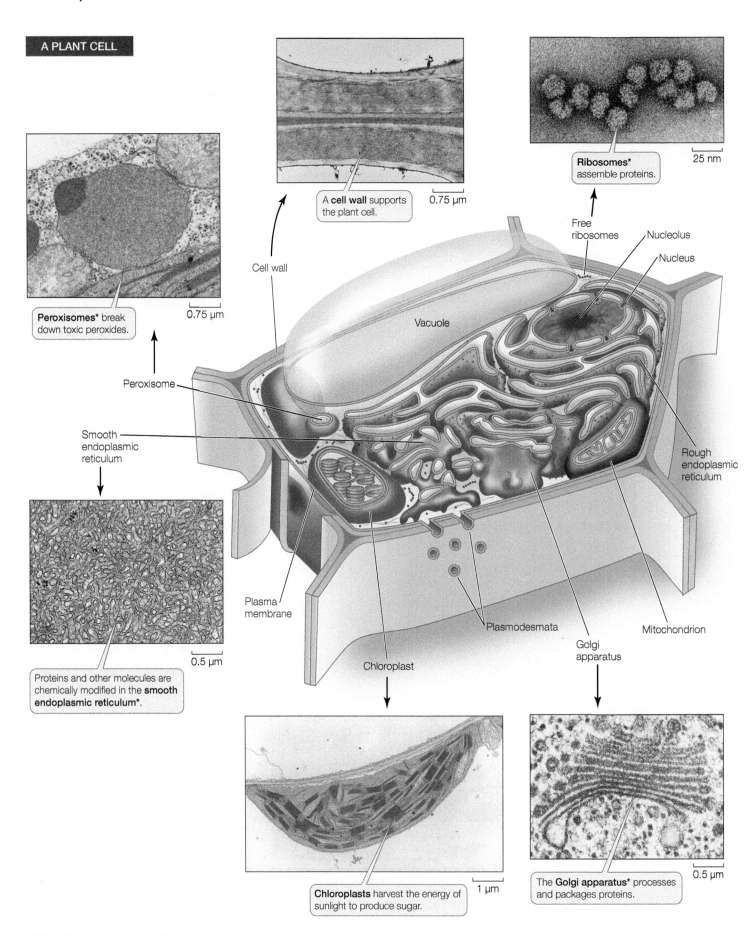

A **cell wall** supports the plant cell.

0.75 μm

Ribosomes* assemble proteins.

25 nm

Free ribosomes

Nucleolus

Nucleus

Cell wall

Vacuole

Peroxisomes* break down toxic peroxides.

0.75 μm

Peroxisome

Smooth endoplasmic reticulum

Rough endoplasmic reticulum

Proteins and other molecules are chemically modified in the **smooth endoplasmic reticulum***.

0.5 μm

Plasma membrane

Plasmodesmata

Mitochondrion

Chloroplast

Golgi apparatus

Chloroplasts harvest the energy of sunlight to produce sugar.

1 μm

The **Golgi apparatus*** processes and packages proteins.

0.5 μm

FIGURE 4.7   Eukaryotic Cells *(continued)*

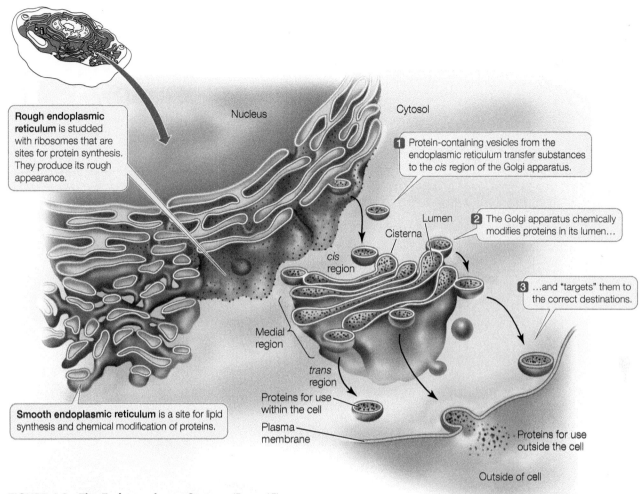

Rough endoplasmic reticulum is studded with ribosomes that are sites for protein synthesis. They produce its rough appearance.

Nucleus

Cytosol

1 Protein-containing vesicles from the endoplasmic reticulum transfer substances to the *cis* region of the Golgi apparatus.

Lumen

2 The Golgi apparatus chemically modifies proteins in its lumen…

Cisterna

cis region

3 …and "targets" them to the correct destinations.

Medial region

trans region

Proteins for use within the cell

Plasma membrane

Smooth endoplasmic reticulum is a site for lipid synthesis and chemical modification of proteins.

Proteins for use outside the cell

Outside of cell

FIGURE 4.8   The Endomembrane System *(Page 65)*

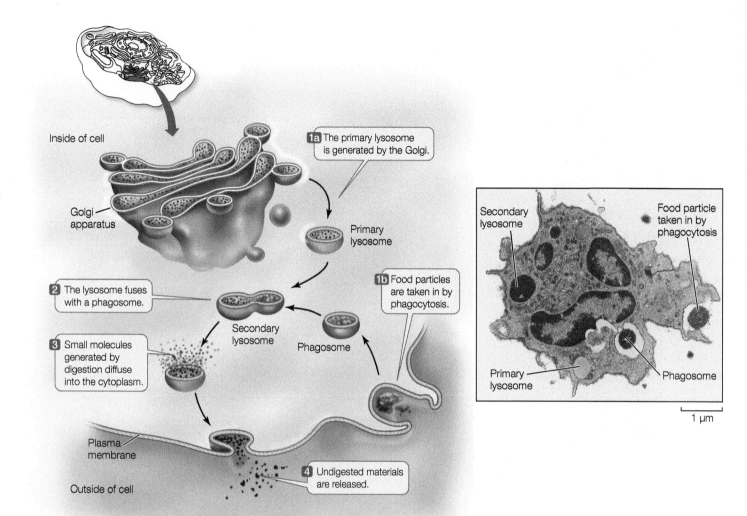

Inside of cell

Golgi apparatus

1a The primary lysosome is generated by the Golgi.

Primary lysosome

2 The lysosome fuses with a phagosome.

1b Food particles are taken in by phagocytosis.

Secondary lysosome

Phagosome

3 Small molecules generated by digestion diffuse into the cytoplasm.

Plasma membrane

Outside of cell

4 Undigested materials are released.

Secondary lysosome

Food particle taken in by phagocytosis

Primary lysosome

Phagosome

1 μm

FIGURE 4.9 Lysosomes Isolate Digestive Enzymes from the Cytoplasm *(Page 67)*

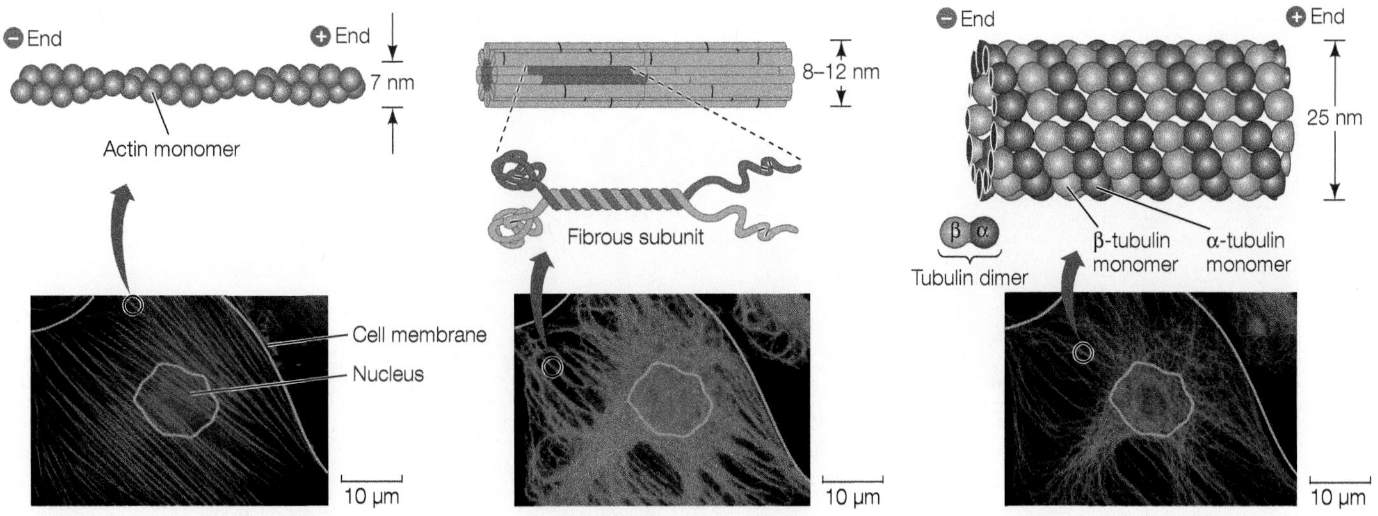

(A) **Microfilaments**
Made up of strands of the protein actin; often interact with strands of other proteins.

(B) **Intermediate filaments**
Made up of fibrous proteins organized into tough, ropelike assemblages that stabilize a cell's structure and help maintain its shape.

(C) **Microtubules**
Long, hollow cylinders made up of many molecules of the protein tubulin. Tubulin consists of two subunits, α-tubulin and β-tubulin.

FIGURE 4.10   The Cytoskeleton *(Page 69)*

(A)

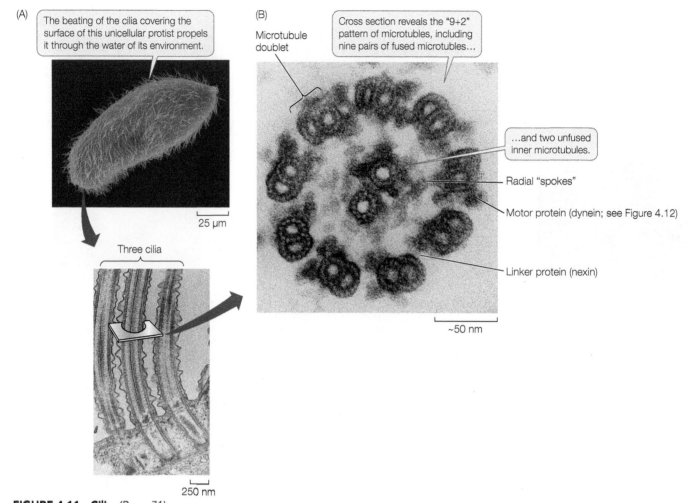

The beating of the cilia covering the surface of this unicellular protist propels it through the water of its environment.

25 μm

Three cilia

250 nm

(B)

Microtubule doublet

Cross section reveals the "9+2" pattern of microtubules, including nine pairs of fused microtubules...

...and two unfused inner microtubules.

Radial "spokes"

Motor protein (dynein; see Figure 4.12)

Linker protein (nexin)

~50 nm

FIGURE 4.11 Cilia *(Page 71)*

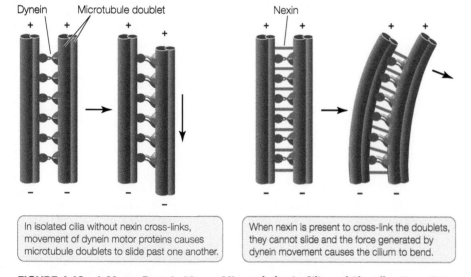

Dynein   Microtubule doublet

Nexin

In isolated cilia without nexin cross-links, movement of dynein motor proteins causes microtubule doublets to slide past one another.

When nexin is present to cross-link the doublets, they cannot slide and the force generated by dynein movement causes the cilium to bend.

FIGURE 4.12 A Motor Protein Moves Microtubules in Cilia and Flagella *(Page 71)*

(A)

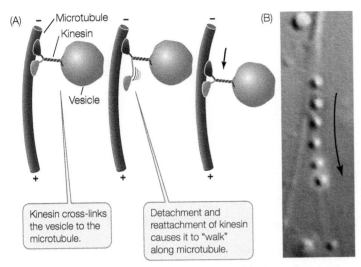

Kinesin cross-links the vesicle to the microtubule.

Detachment and reattachment of kinesin causes it to "walk" along microtubule.

(B)

FIGURE 4.13   A Motor Protein Drives Vesicles along Microtubules *(Page 72)*

INVESTIGATION

FIGURE 4.14   The Role of Microfilaments in Cell Movement: Showing Cause and Effect in Biology   In test tubes, the drug cytochalasin B prevents microfilament formation from monomeric precursors. This led to the question: Will the drug work like this in living cells and inhibit the movement of *Amoeba*?

HYPOTHESIS

Amoeboid cell movements are caused by the cytoskeleton.

METHOD

Amoeba proteus is a single-celled eukaryote that moves by extending its membrane.

Cytochalasin B is a drug that blocks the formation of microfilaments, part of the cytoskeleton.

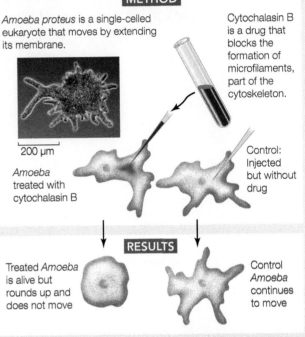

200 µm

Amoeba treated with cytochalasin B

Control: Injected but without drug

RESULTS

Treated *Amoeba* is alive but rounds up and does not move

Control *Amoeba* continues to move

CONCLUSION

Microfilaments of the cytoskeleton are essential for amoeboid cell movement

ANALYZE THE DATA

Several important controls were done to validate the conclusions of this experiment. The experiment was repeated in the presence of the following drugs: cycloheximide, which inhibits new protein synthesis; dinitrophenol, which inhibits new ATP formation (energy); and colchicine, which inhibits the polymerization of microtubules. Here are the results:

Condition	Rounded cells (%)
No drug	3
Cytochalasin B	95
Colchicine	4
Cycloheximide	3
Cycloheximide + cytochalasin B	94
Dinitrophenol	5
Dinitrophenol + cytochalasin B	85

Explain each experiment. What can you conclude about *Amoeba* and the cytoskeleton?

Go to **yourBioPortal.com** for original citations, discussions, and relevant links for all INVESTIGATION figures.

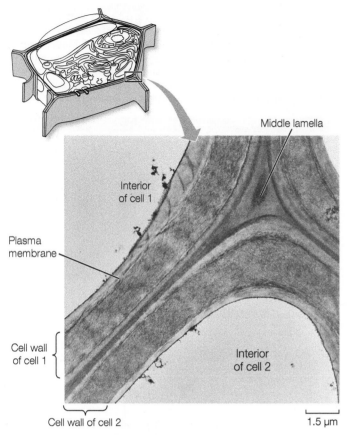

Middle lamella

Interior of cell 1

Plasma membrane

Cell wall of cell 1

Interior of cell 2

Cell wall of cell 2

1.5 μm

FIGURE 4.15 The Plant Cell Wall *(Page 73)*

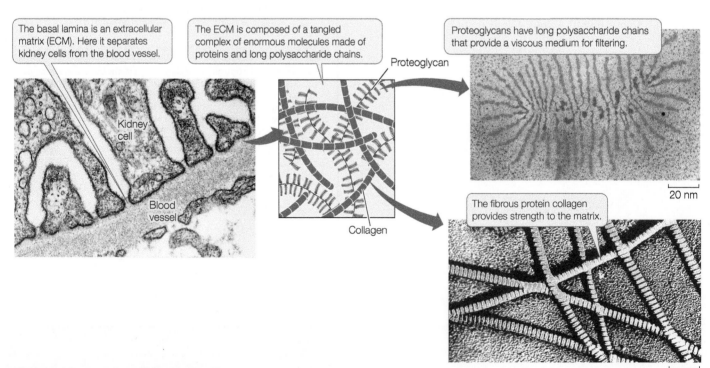

The basal lamina is an extracellular matrix (ECM). Here it separates kidney cells from the blood vessel.

The ECM is composed of a tangled complex of enormous molecules made of proteins and long polysaccharide chains.

Proteoglycans have long polysaccharide chains that provide a viscous medium for filtering.

Kidney cell

Blood vessel

Proteoglycan

Collagen

20 nm

The fibrous protein collagen provides strength to the matrix.

100 nm

FIGURE 4.16 An Extracellular Matrix *(Page 74)*

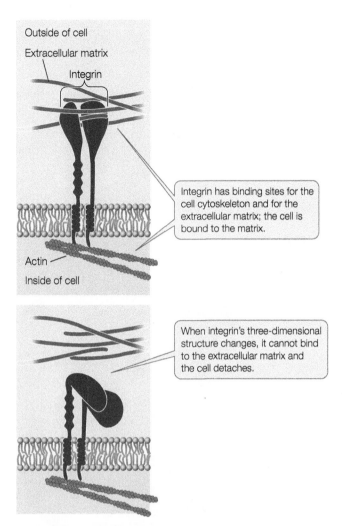

Outside of cell

Extracellular matrix

Integrin

Integrin has binding sites for the cell cytoskeleton and for the extracellular matrix; the cell is bound to the matrix.

Actin

Inside of cell

When integrin's three-dimensional structure changes, it cannot bind to the extracellular matrix and the cell detaches.

FIGURE 4.17 Cell Membrane Proteins Interact with the Extracellular Matrix *(Page 74)*

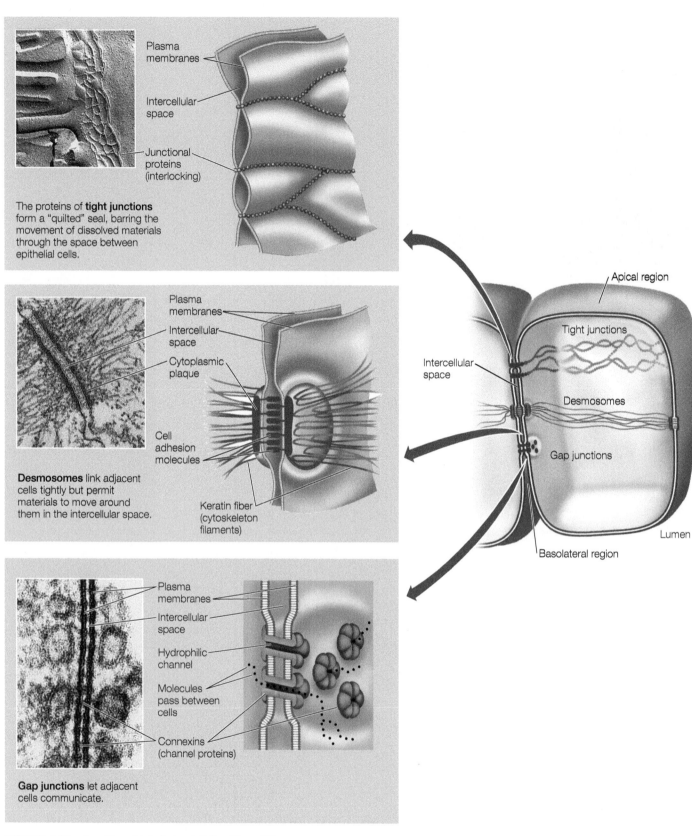

The proteins of **tight junctions** form a "quilted" seal, barring the movement of dissolved materials through the space between epithelial cells.

Plasma membranes

Intercellular space

Junctional proteins (interlocking)

Desmosomes link adjacent cells tightly but permit materials to move around them in the intercellular space.

Plasma membranes

Intercellular space

Cytoplasmic plaque

Cell adhesion molecules

Keratin fiber (cytoskeleton filaments)

Gap junctions let adjacent cells communicate.

Plasma membranes

Intercellular space

Hydrophilic channel

Molecules pass between cells

Connexins (channel proteins)

Apical region

Tight junctions

Intercellular space

Desmosomes

Gap junctions

Basolateral region

Lumen

FIGURE 4.18   Junctions Link Animal Cells *(Page 75)*

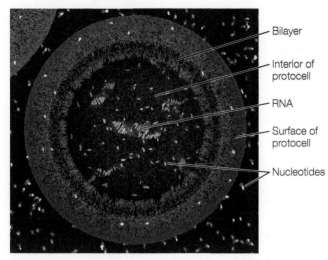

Bilayer

Interior of protocell

RNA

Surface of protocell

Nucleotides

FIGURE 4.19 A Protocell *(Page 76)*

Cell Membranes and Signaling

5

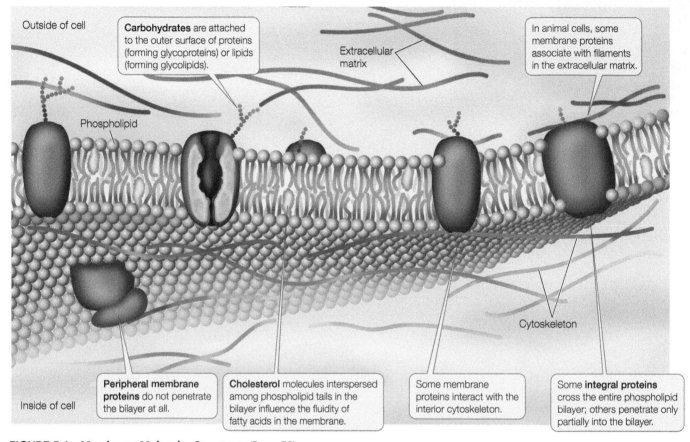

Outside of cell

Phospholipid

Carbohydrates are attached to the outer surface of proteins (forming glycoproteins) or lipids (forming glycolipids).

Extracellular matrix

In animal cells, some membrane proteins associate with filaments in the extracellular matrix.

Cytoskeleton

Inside of cell

Peripheral membrane proteins do not penetrate the bilayer at all.

Cholesterol molecules interspersed among phospholipid tails in the bilayer influence the fluidity of fatty acids in the membrane.

Some membrane proteins interact with the interior cytoskeleton.

Some **integral proteins** cross the entire phospholipid bilayer; others penetrate only partially into the bilayer.

FIGURE 5.1 **Membrane Molecular Structure** *(Page 79)*

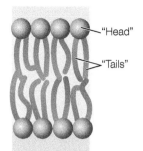

"Head"

"Tails"

IN-TEXT ART *(Page 80)*

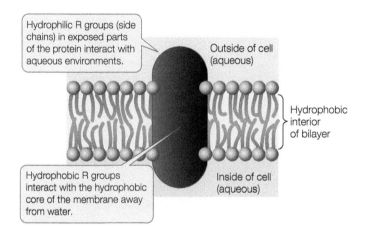

Hydrophilic R groups (side chains) in exposed parts of the protein interact with aqueous environments.

Outside of cell (aqueous)

Hydrophobic interior of bilayer

Hydrophobic R groups interact with the hydrophobic core of the membrane away from water.

Inside of cell (aqueous)

IN-TEXT ART *(Page 81)*

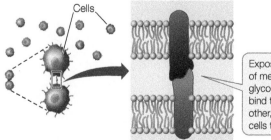

Cells

Exposed regions of membrane glycoproteins bind to each other, causing cells to adhere.

IN-TEXT ART *(Page 82)*

INVESTIGATION

FIGURE 5.2 Rapid Diffusion of Membrane Proteins
A human cell can be fused to a mouse cell in the laboratory, forming a single large cell (heterokaryon). This phenomenon was used to test whether membrane proteins can diffuse independently in the plane of the plasma membrane.

HYPOTHESIS

Proteins embedded in a membrane can diffuse freely within the membrane.

METHOD

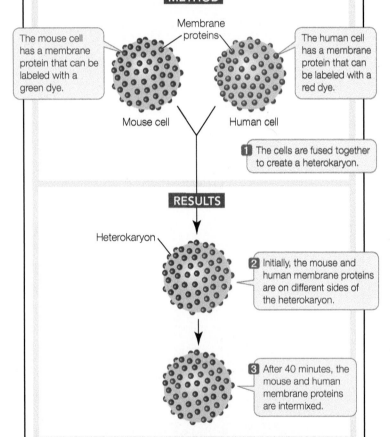

Membrane proteins

The mouse cell has a membrane protein that can be labeled with a green dye.

The human cell has a membrane protein that can be labeled with a red dye.

Mouse cell   Human cell

1 The cells are fused together to create a heterokaryon.

RESULTS

Heterokaryon

2 Initially, the mouse and human membrane proteins are on different sides of the heterokaryon.

3 After 40 minutes, the mouse and human membrane proteins are intermixed.

CONCLUSION

Membrane proteins can diffuse rapidly in the plane of the membrane.

ANALYZE THE DATA

The experiment was repeated at various temperatures with the following results:

Temperature (°C)	Cells with mixed proteins (%)
0	0
15	8
20	42
26	77

Plot these data on a graph of Percentage Mixed vs. Temperature. Explain these data, relating the results to the concepts of diffusion and membrane fluidity.

Go to **yourBioPortal.com** for original citations, discussions, and relevant links for all INVESTIGATION figures.

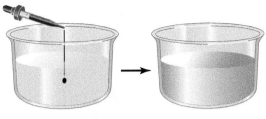

IN-TEXT ART *(Page 83)*

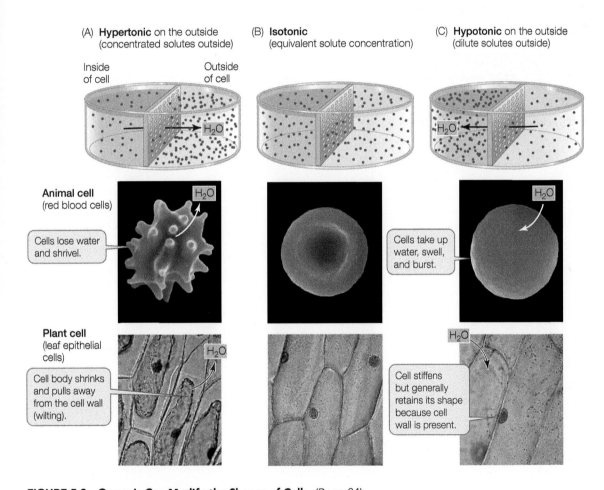

(A) **Hypertonic** on the outside
(concentrated solutes outside)

(B) **Isotonic**
(equivalent solute concentration)

(C) **Hypotonic** on the outside
(dilute solutes outside)

Inside
of cell

Outside
of cell

H_2O

H_2O

Animal cell
(red blood cells)

H_2O

Cells lose water
and shrivel.

H_2O

Cells take up
water, swell,
and burst.

Plant cell
(leaf epithelial
cells)

H_2O

Cell body shrinks
and pulls away
from the cell wall
(wilting).

H_2O

Cell stiffens
but generally
retains its shape
because cell
wall is present.

FIGURE 5.3 Osmosis Can Modify the Shapes of Cells *(Page 84)*

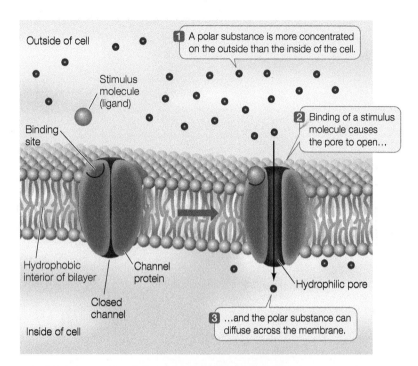

FIGURE 5.4   A Ligand-Gated Channel Protein Opens in Response to a Stimulus *(Page 85)*

INVESTIGATION

FIGURE 5.5 Aquaporins Increase Membrane Permeability to Water A protein was isolated from the membranes of cells in which water diffuses rapidly across the membranes. When the protein was inserted into oocytes, which do not normally have it, the water permeability of the oocytes was greatly increased.

HYPOTHESIS

Aquaporin increases membrane permeability to water.

METHOD

Aquaporin mRNA   Aquaporin channel

Protein synthesis

This oocyte does not have aquaporins in the cell membrane.

This oocyte has aquaporins inserted experimentally into the cell membrane.

RESULTS

3.5 minutes in hypotonic solution

Water does not diffuse into the cell, so it does not swell.

Water diffuses into the cell through the aquaporin channels, and it swells.

CONCLUSION

Aquaporin increases the rate of water diffusion across the cell membrane.

ANALYZE THE DATA

Oocytes were injected with aquaporin mRNA (red circles) or a solution without mRNA (blue circles). Water permeability was tested by incubating the oocytes in hypotonic solution and measuring cell volume. After time X in the upper curve, intact oocytes were not visible:

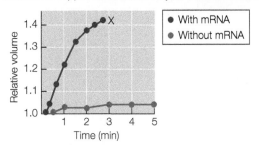

- With mRNA
- Without mRNA

A. Why did the cells with aquaporin mRNA increase in volume?
B. What happened at time X?
C. Calculate the relative rates (volume increase per minute) of swelling in the control and experimental curves. What does this show about the effectiveness of mRNA injection?

For more, go to Working with Data 5.1 at **yourBioPortal.com**.

Go to **yourBioPortal.com** for original citations, discussions, and relevant links for all INVESTIGATION figures.

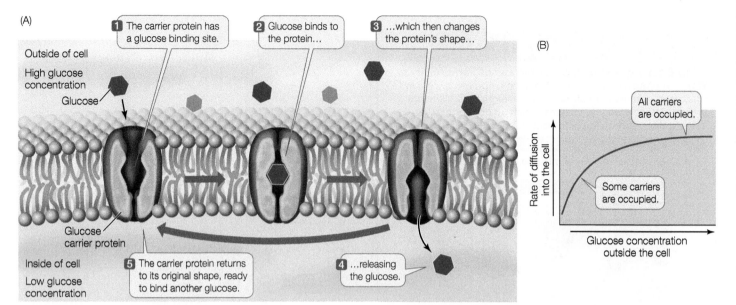

FIGURE 5.6   A Carrier Protein Facilitates Diffusion *(Page 87)*

TABLE 5.1	Membrane Transport Mechanisms		
	SIMPLE DIFFUSION	FACILITATED DIFFUSION (CHANNEL OR CARRIER PROTEIN)	ACTIVE TRANSPORT
Cellular energy required?	No	No	Yes
Driving force	Concentration gradient	Concentration gradient	ATP hydrolysis (against concentration gradient)
Membrane protein required?	No	Yes	Yes
Specificity	No	Yes	Yes

(Page 87)

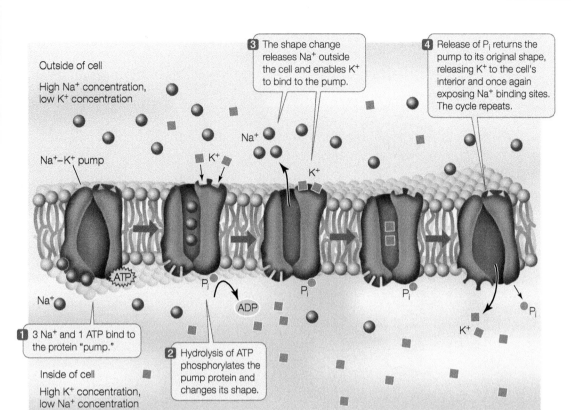

FIGURE 5.7   Primary Active Transport: The Sodium–Potassium Pump *(Page 88)*

(A) Endocytosis

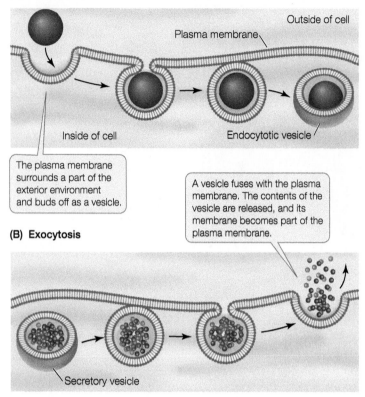

Outside of cell

Plasma membrane

Inside of cell

Endocytotic vesicle

The plasma membrane surrounds a part of the exterior environment and buds off as a vesicle.

A vesicle fuses with the plasma membrane. The contents of the vesicle are released, and its membrane becomes part of the plasma membrane.

(B) Exocytosis

Secretory vesicle

FIGURE 5.8 Endocytosis and Exocytosis *(Page 89)*

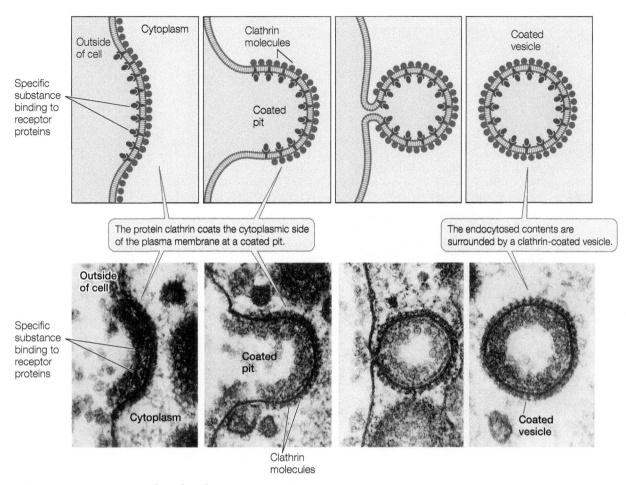

FIGURE 5.9   Receptor-Mediated Endocytosis *(Page 90)*

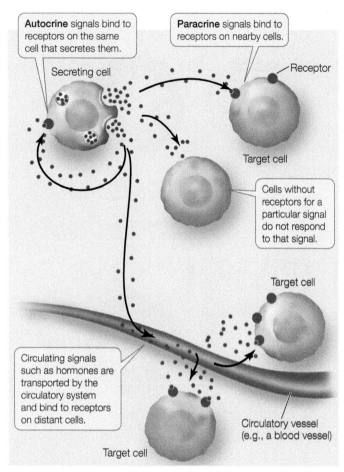

FIGURE 5.10 Chemical Signaling Concepts (Page 91)

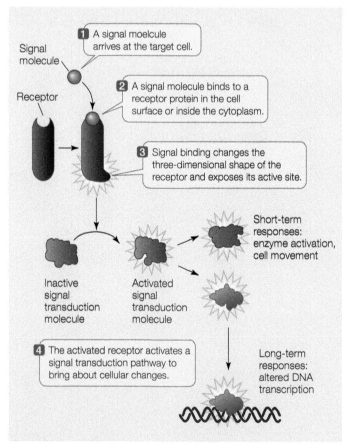

FIGURE 5.11 Signal Transduction Concepts (Page 92)

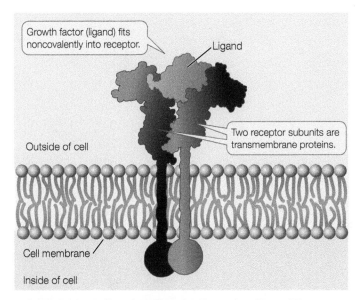

FIGURE 5.12 A Signal Binds to Its Receptor *(Page 92)*

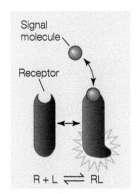

IN-TEXT ART *(Page 92)*

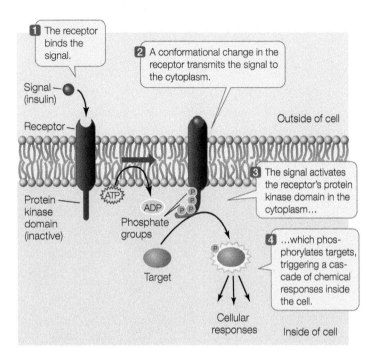

1. The receptor binds the signal.

2. A conformational change in the receptor transmits the signal to the cytoplasm.

Signal (insulin)

Receptor

Outside of cell

3. The signal activates the receptor's protein kinase domain in the cytoplasm...

Protein kinase domain (inactive)

ATP

ADP

Phosphate groups

Target

4. ...which phosphorylates targets, triggering a cascade of chemical responses inside the cell.

Cellular responses

Inside of cell

FIGURE 5.13   A Protein Kinase Receptor *(Page 93)*

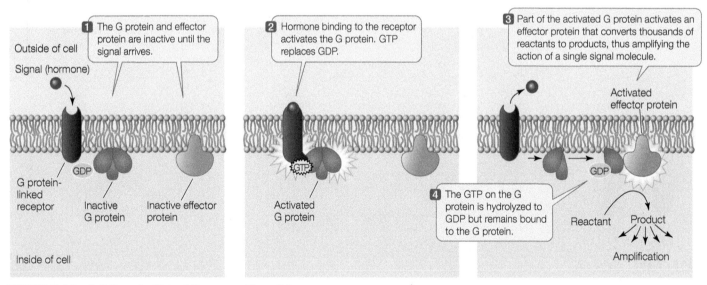

1. The G protein and effector protein are inactive until the signal arrives.

Outside of cell

Signal (hormone)

G protein-linked receptor

GDP

Inactive G protein

Inactive effector protein

Inside of cell

2. Hormone binding to the receptor activates the G protein. GTP replaces GDP.

GTP

Activated G protein

3. Part of the activated G protein activates an effector protein that converts thousands of reactants to products, thus amplifying the action of a single signal molecule.

Activated effector protein

4. The GTP on the G protein is hydrolyzed to GDP but remains bound to the G protein.

GDP

Reactant   Product

Amplification

FIGURE 5.14   A G Protein–Linked Receptor *(Page 94)*

INVESTIGATION

FIGURE 5.15 The Discovery of a Second Messenger Glycogen phosphorylase is activated in liver cells after epinephrine binds to a membrane receptor. Sutherland and his colleagues observed that this activation could occur in vivo only if fragments of the plasma membrane were present. They designed experiments to show that a second messenger caused the activation of glycogen phosphorylase.

HYPOTHESIS

A second messenger mediates between receptor activation at the plasma membrane and enzyme activation in the cytoplasm.

METHOD

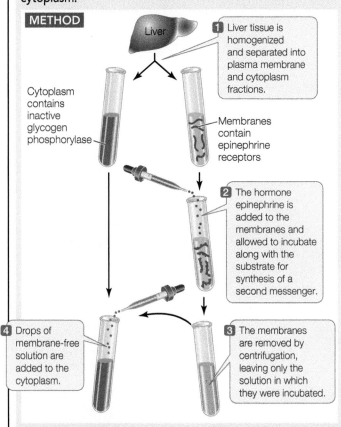

Cytoplasm contains inactive glycogen phosphorylase

1 Liver tissue is homogenized and separated into plasma membrane and cytoplasm fractions.

Membranes contain epinephrine receptors

2 The hormone epinephrine is added to the membranes and allowed to incubate along with the substrate for synthesis of a second messenger.

3 The membranes are removed by centrifugation, leaving only the solution in which they were incubated.

4 Drops of membrane-free solution are added to the cytoplasm.

RESULTS

Active glycogen phosphorylase is present in the cytoplasm.

CONCLUSION

A soluble second messenger, produced by hormone-activated membranes, is present in the solution and activates enzymes in the cytoplasm.

ANALYZE THE DATA

The activity of previously inactive liver glycogen phosphorylase was measured with and without epinephrine incubation, with these results:

Condition	Enzyme activity (units)
Homogenate	0.4
Homogenate + epinephrine	2.5
Cytoplasm fraction	0.2
Cytoplasm + epinephrine	0.4
Membranes + epinephrine	0.4
Cytoplasm + membranes + epinephrine	2.0

A. What do these data show?

B. Propose an experiment to show that the factor that activates the enzyme is stable on heating and give predicted data.

C. Propose an experiment to show that cAMP can replace the membrane fraction and hormone treatment and give predicted data.

For more, go to Working with Data 5.2 at **yourBioPortal.com**.

Go to **yourBioPortal.com** for original citations, discussions, and relevant links for all INVESTIGATION figures.

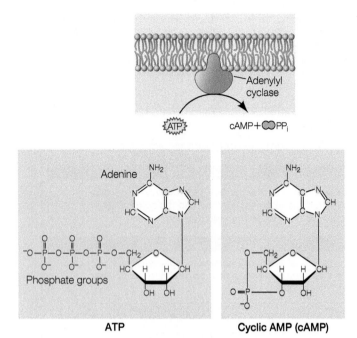

FIGURE 5.16 The Formation of Cyclic AMP *(Page 95)*

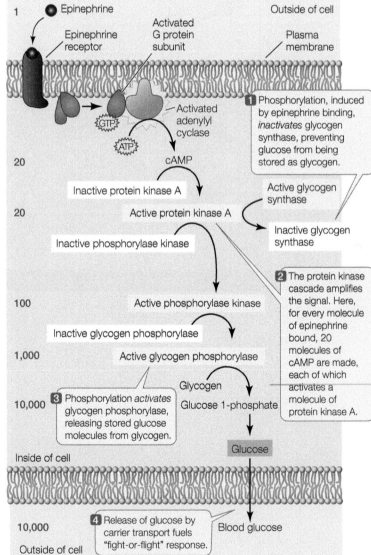

FIGURE 5.17 A Cascade of Reactions Leads to Altered Enzyme Activity *(Page 96)*

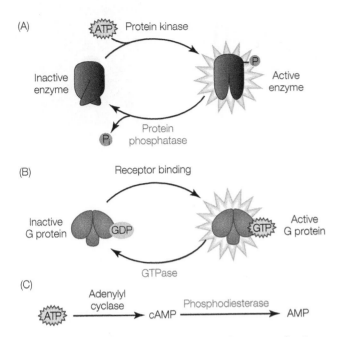

FIGURE 5.18   Signal Transduction Regulatory Mechanisms *(Page 97)*

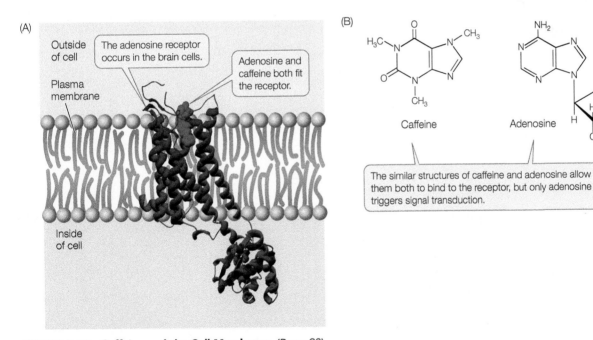

FIGURE 5.19   Caffeine and the Cell Membrane *(Page 98)*

Pathways that Harvest and Store Chemical Energy

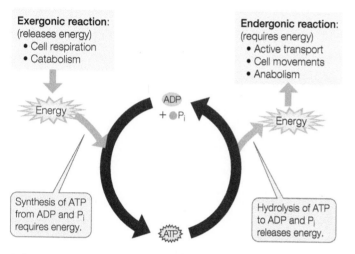

Exergonic reaction:
(releases energy)
- Cell respiration
- Catabolism

Energy

Endergonic reaction:
(requires energy)
- Active transport
- Cell movements
- Anabolism

Energy

ADP
+ P_i

Synthesis of ATP from ADP and P_i requires energy.

Hydrolysis of ATP to ADP and P_i releases energy.

ATP

FIGURE 6.1   The Concept of Coupling Reactions *(Page 101)*

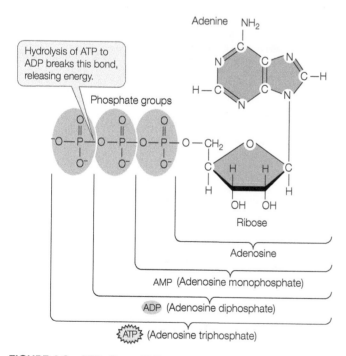

Hydrolysis of ATP to ADP breaks this bond, releasing energy.

Phosphate groups

Adenine NH_2

Ribose

Adenosine

AMP (Adenosine monophosphate)

ADP (Adenosine diphosphate)

ATP (Adenosine triphosphate)

FIGURE 6.2   ATP *(Page 101)*

Adenine—ribose—O—P—O ~ P—O ~ P—O⁻ + H₂O

ATP

↓

Adenine—ribose—O—P—O ~ P—OH + HO—P—O⁻

ADP   **P$_i$**

IN-TEXT ART *(Page 102)*

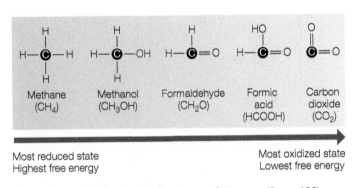

| Methane (CH_4) | Methanol (CH_3OH) | Formaldehyde (CH_2O) | Formic acid (HCOOH) | Carbon dioxide (CO_2) |

Most reduced state
Highest free energy

Most oxidized state
Lowest free energy

FIGURE 6.3   Oxidation, Reduction, and Energy *(Page 102)*

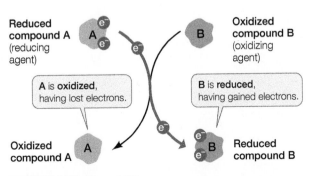

Reduced compound A (reducing agent)

Oxidized compound B (oxidizing agent)

A is **oxidized**, having lost electrons.

B is **reduced**, having gained electrons.

Oxidized compound A

Reduced compound B

IN-TEXT ART *(Page 102)*

(A)

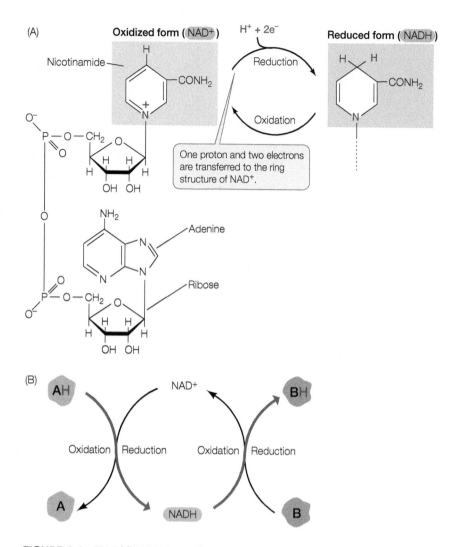

One proton and two electrons are transferred to the ring structure of NAD+.

(B)

FIGURE 6.4 **NAD+/NADH Is an Electron Carrier in Redox Reactions** *(Page 103)*

(A)

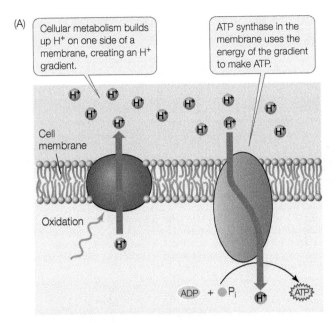

Cellular metabolism builds up H⁺ on one side of a membrane, creating an H⁺ gradient.

ATP synthase in the membrane uses the energy of the gradient to make ATP.

Cell membrane

Oxidation

H^+

ADP + P$_i$ ATP

(B)

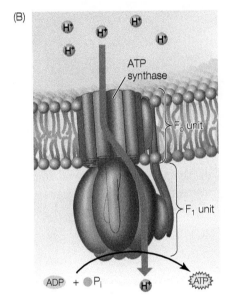

ATP synthase

F$_o$ unit

F$_1$ unit

ADP + P$_i$ H⁺   ATP

FIGURE 6.5   Chemiosmosis *(Page 104)*

INVESTIGATION

FIGURE 6.6 An Experiment Demonstrates the Chemiosmotic Mechanism The chemiosmosis hypothesis was a bold departure from the conventional scientific thinking of the time. It required an intact compartment separated by a membrane. Could a proton gradient drive the synthesis of ATP?

HYPOTHESIS

A H^+ gradient can drive ATP synthesis by isolated mitochondria or chloroplasts.

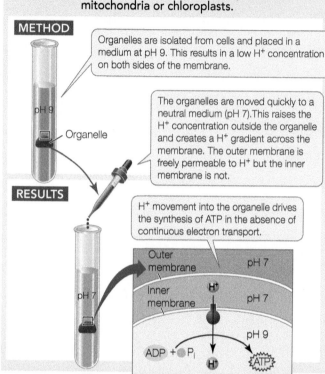

METHOD

Organelles are isolated from cells and placed in a medium at pH 9. This results in a low H^+ concentration on both sides of the membrane.

pH 9

Organelle

The organelles are moved quickly to a neutral medium (pH 7).This raises the H^+ concentration outside the organelle and creates a H^+ gradient across the membrane. The outer membrane is freely permeable to H^+ but the inner membrane is not.

RESULTS

H^+ movement into the organelle drives the synthesis of ATP in the absence of continuous electron transport.

pH 7

Outer membrane — pH 7

Inner membrane — pH 7

pH 9

$ADP + P_i$

H^+

ATP

CONCLUSION

In the absence of electron transport, an artificial H^+ gradient is sufficient for ATP synthesis by organelles.

ANALYZE THE DATA

In another experiment, chloroplast thylakoids were added to an acid solution at pH 3.8. After a short time to equilibrate, they were then transferred back to a solution at pH 8 in the presence of ADP, phosphate (P_i), and magnesium ions (Mg^{2+}). Some thylakoids were not transferred to pH 3.8, but instead kept at pH 7.0. ATP formation was measured using luciferase, which catalyzes the formation of a luminescent (light-emitting) molecule if ATP is present. Here are the data from the paper:

Reaction mixture	Luciferase activity (light emission)	
	Raw data	Corrected data
Complete, pH 3.8	141	
Complete, pH 7.0	12	
Complete, pH 3.8 – P_i	12	
" " – ADP	4	
" " – Mg^{2+}	60	
" " – chloroplasts	7	

A. Which reaction mixture is the control? Use the control data to correct the raw data for the other, experimental reaction mixtures and fill in the table.

B. Why did ATP production go down in the absence of P_i?

For more, go to Working with Data 6.1 at **yourBioPortal.com**.

Go to **yourBioPortal.com** for original citations, discussions, and relevant links for all INVESTIGATION figures.

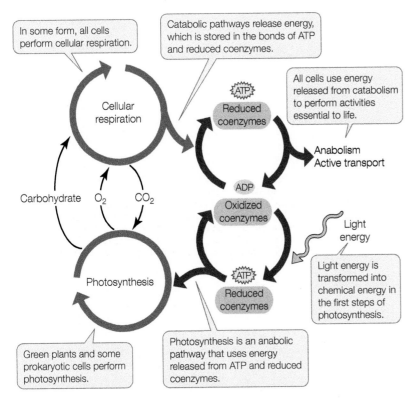

FIGURE 6.7   ATP, Reduced Coenzymes, and Metabolism *(Page 106)*

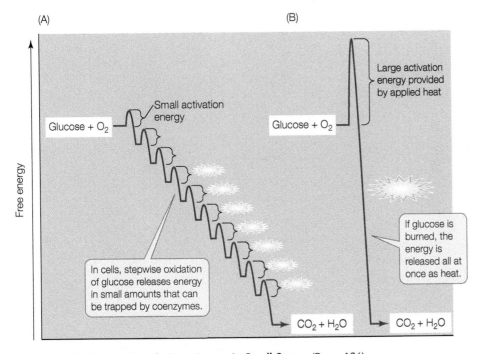

FIGURE 6.8   Energy Metabolism Occurs in Small Steps *(Page 106)*

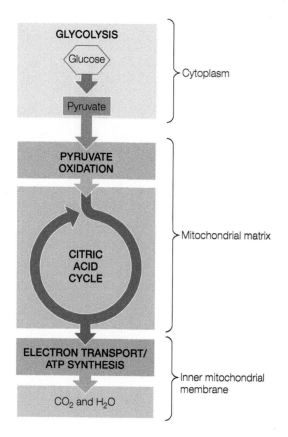

FIGURE 6.9   Energy-Releasing Metabolic Pathways *(Page 107)*

Glyceraldehyde
3-phosphate
dehydrogenase

Phospho-
glycerate
kinase

NAD$^+$

P_i

NADH

ADP

ATP

Glyceraldehyde
3-phosphate

1,3-Bisphospho-
glycerate

3-Phospho-
glycerate

IN-TEXT ART *(Page 107)*

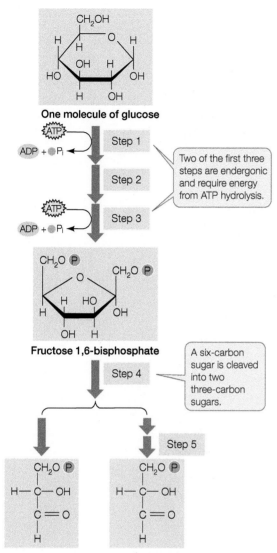

One molecule of glucose

Step 1

Step 2

Step 3

Two of the first three steps are endergonic and require energy from ATP hydrolysis.

Fructose 1,6-bisphosphate

Step 4

A six-carbon sugar is cleaved into two three-carbon sugars.

Step 5

Two molecules of glyceraldehyde 3-phosphate

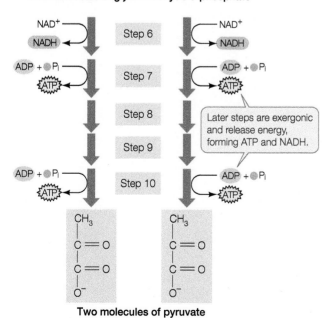

Step 6

Step 7

Step 8

Step 9

Step 10

Later steps are exergonic and release energy, forming ATP and NADH.

Two molecules of pyruvate

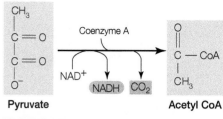

Pyruvate   Acetyl CoA

IN-TEXT ART *(Page 108)*

FIGURE 6.10   Glycolysis Converts Glucose into Pyruvate
(Page 107)

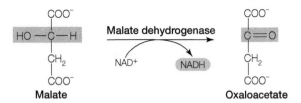

Malate dehydrogenase

Malate

Oxaloacetate

IN-TEXT ART *(Page 108)*

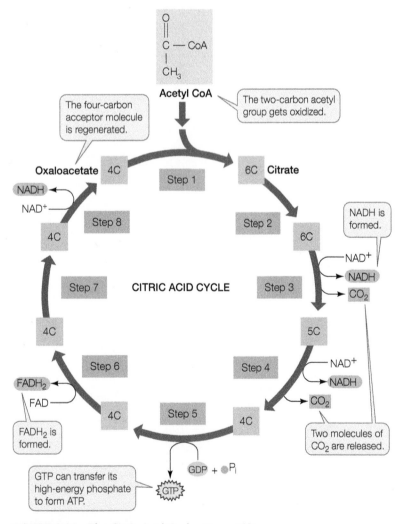

FIGURE 6.11 The Citric Acid Cycle *(Page 108)*

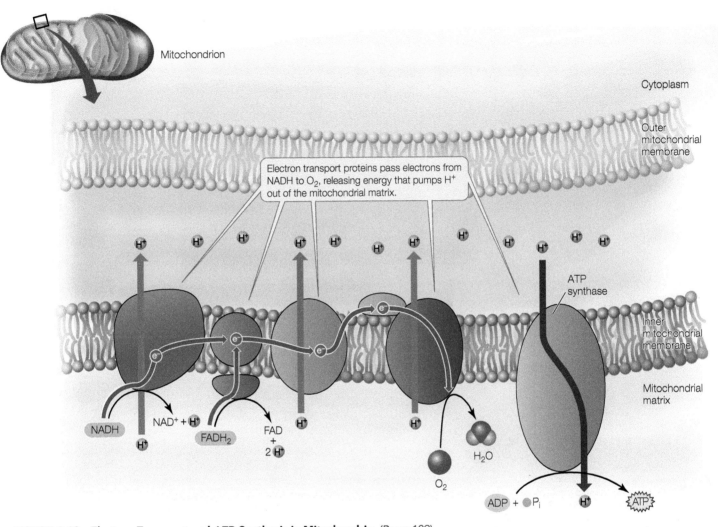

Mitochondrion

Cytoplasm

Outer mitochondrial membrane

Electron transport proteins pass electrons from NADH to O_2, releasing energy that pumps H^+ out of the mitochondrial matrix.

ATP synthase

Inner mitochondrial membrane

Mitochondrial matrix

NADH

NAD$^+$ + H$^+$

FADH$_2$

FAD + 2 H$^+$

H$_2$O

O$_2$

ADP + P$_i$

ATP

FIGURE 6.12   Electron Transport and ATP Synthesis in Mitochondria *(Page 109)*

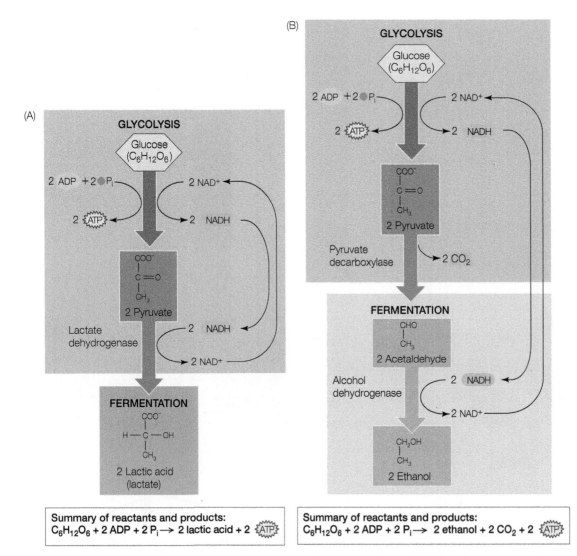

FIGURE 6.13 Fermentation *(Page 110)*

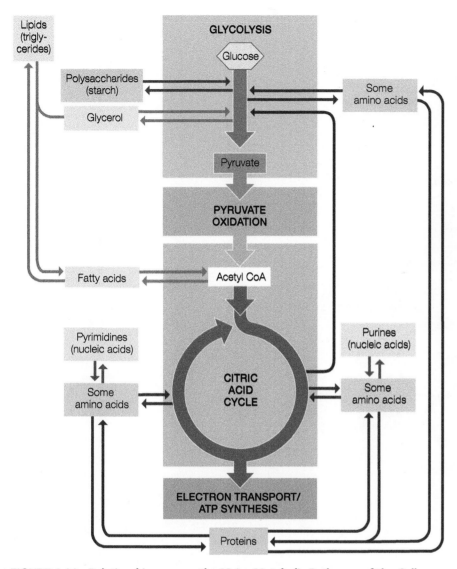

FIGURE 6.14 Relationships among the Major Metabolic Pathways of the Cell
(Page 112)

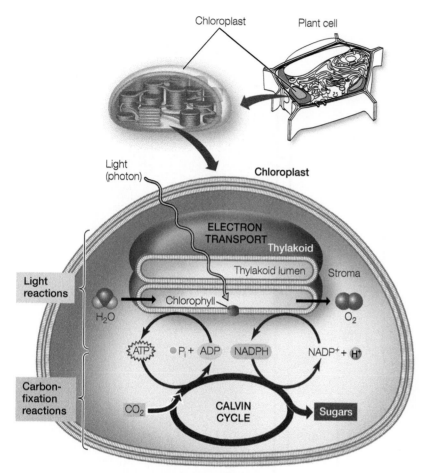

Chloroplast   Plant cell

Chloroplast

Light
(photon)

**ELECTRON
TRANSPORT**   Thylakoid

Thylakoid lumen   Stroma

Light
reactions   Chlorophyll

H_2O O_2

ATP P_i + ADP   NADPH $NADP^+$ + H^+

Carbon-
fixation
reactions

CO_2 **CALVIN
CYCLE**   Sugars

FIGURE 6.15   An Overview of Photosynthesis *(Page 113)*

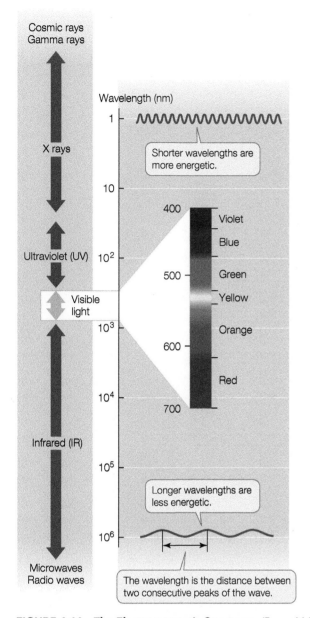

FIGURE 6.16 The Electromagnetic Spectrum *(Page 114)*

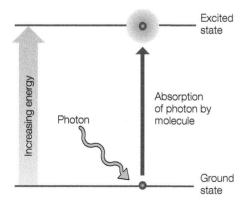

IN-TEXT ART *(Page 114)*

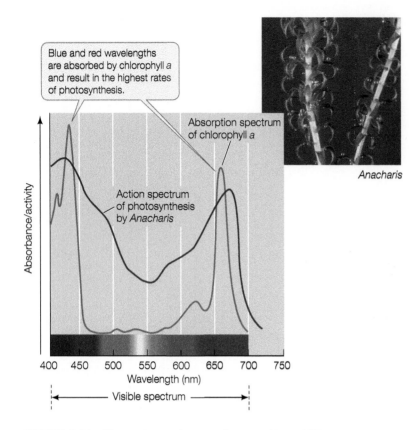

Blue and red wavelengths are absorbed by chlorophyll *a* and result in the highest rates of photosynthesis.

Absorption spectrum of chlorophyll *a*

Action spectrum of photosynthesis by *Anacharis*

Anacharis

Absorbance/activity

Wavelength (nm)

400   450   500   550   600   650   700   750

Visible spectrum

FIGURE 6.17   Absorption and Action Spectra *(Page 115)*

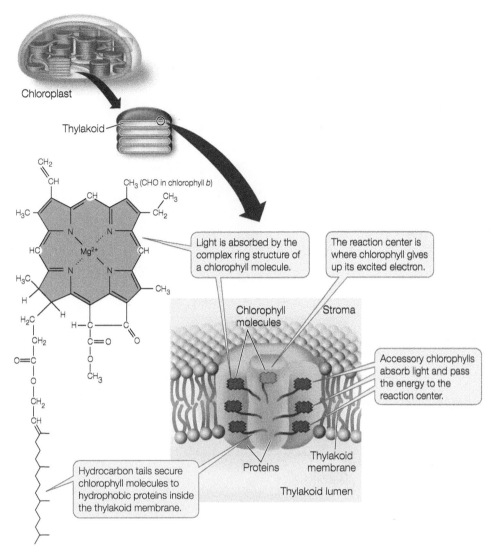

Chloroplast

Thylakoid

CH₂
CH
CH₃ (CHO in chlorophyll *b*)
CH₃
CH₂
H₃C
N   N
HC   Mg²⁺   CH
N   N
H₃C   CH₃
H
H₂C   H
H—C—C
CH₂   C=O
C=O   O
O   CH₃
O
CH₂
CH
CH₂

Light is absorbed by the complex ring structure of a chlorophyll molecule.

The reaction center is where chlorophyll gives up its excited electron.

Chlorophyll molecules

Stroma

Accessory chlorophylls absorb light and pass the energy to the reaction center.

Proteins

Thylakoid membrane

Thylakoid lumen

Hydrocarbon tails secure chlorophyll molecules to hydrophobic proteins inside the thylakoid membrane.

FIGURE 6.18   The Molecular Structure of Chlorophyll *(Page 115)*

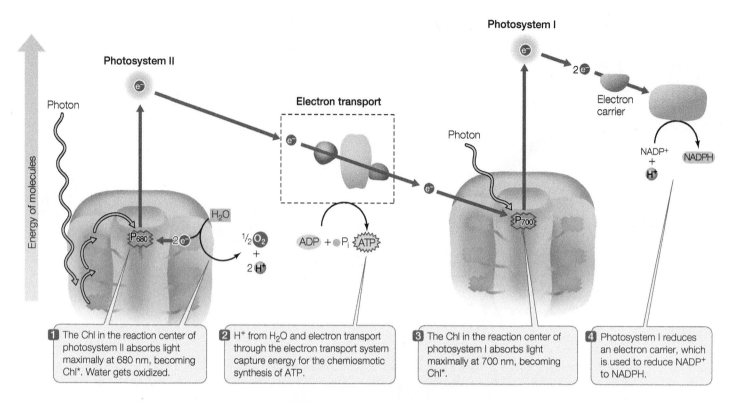

FIGURE 6.19   Noncyclic Electron Transport Uses Two Photosystems *(Page 116)*

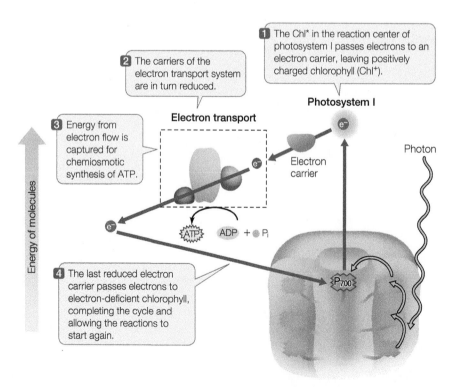

FIGURE 6.20   Cyclic Electron Transport Traps Light Energy as ATP *(Page 117)*

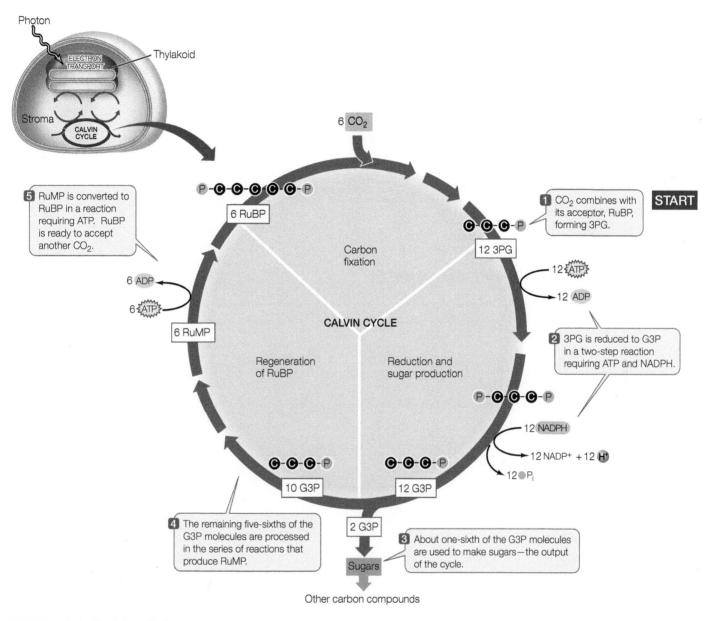

FIGURE 6.21   The Calvin Cycle   (Page 118)

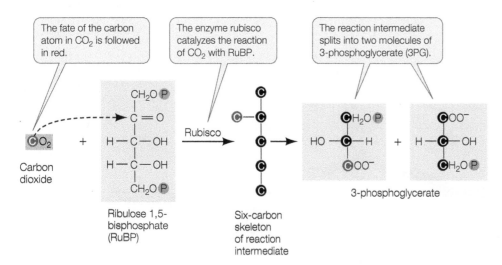

FIGURE 6.22 **RuBP Is the Carbon Dioxide Acceptor** *(Page 119)*

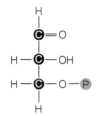

Glyceraldehyde 3-phosphate (G3P)

IN-TEXT ART *(Page 119)*

FIGURE 6.23 **Products of Glucose Metabolism** *(Page 120)*

The Cell Cycle and Cell Division

7

(A) Reproduction

(B) Growth

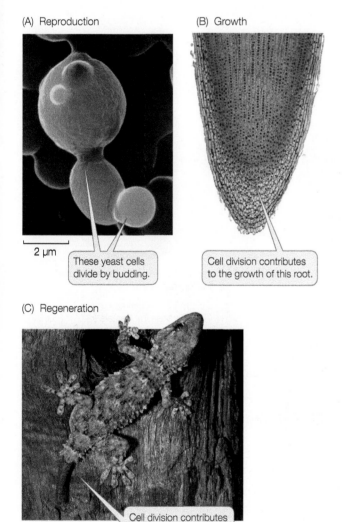

2 μm

These yeast cells divide by budding.

Cell division contributes to the growth of this root.

(C) Regeneration

Cell division contributes to the regeneration of a lizard's tail.

FIGURE 7.1 The Importance of Cell Division *(Page 125)*

FIGURE 7.2   Asexual Reproduction on a Large Scale *(Page 125)*

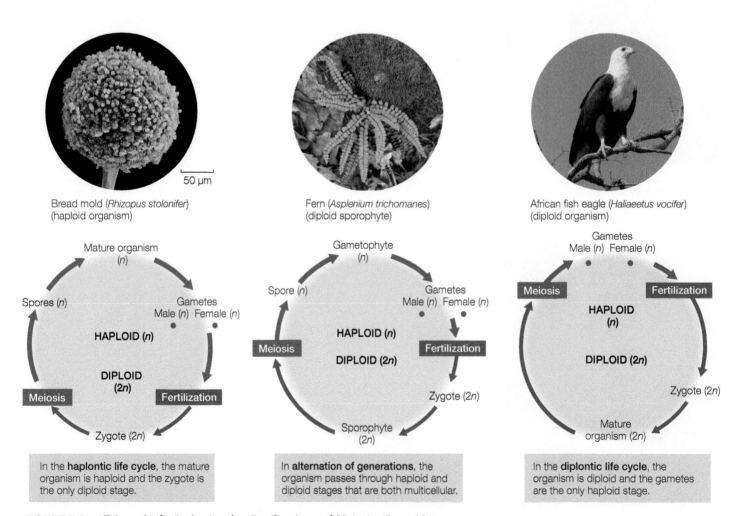

Bread mold (*Rhizopus stolonifer*)
(haploid organism)

50 µm

Fern (*Asplenium trichomanes*)
(diploid sporophyte)

African fish eagle (*Haliaeetus vocifer*)
(diploid organism)

Mature organism
(*n*)

Spores (*n*)

Gametes
Male (*n*) Female (*n*)

HAPLOID (*n*)

**DIPLOID
(2*n*)**

Meiosis

Fertilization

Zygote (2*n*)

In the **haplontic life cycle**, the mature organism is haploid and the zygote is the only diploid stage.

Gametophyte
(*n*)

Spore (*n*)

Gametes
Male (*n*) Female (*n*)

HAPLOID (*n*)

DIPLOID (2*n*)

Meiosis

Fertilization

Zygote (2*n*)

Sporophyte
(2*n*)

In **alternation of generations**, the organism passes through haploid and diploid stages that are both multicellular.

Gametes
Male (*n*) Female (*n*)

Meiosis

Fertilization

**HAPLOID
(*n*)**

DIPLOID (2*n*)

Zygote (2*n*)

Mature
organism (2*n*)

In the **diplontic life cycle**, the organism is diploid and the gametes are the only haploid stage.

FIGURE 7.3   All Sexual Life Cycles Involve Fertilization and Meiosis *(Page 126)*

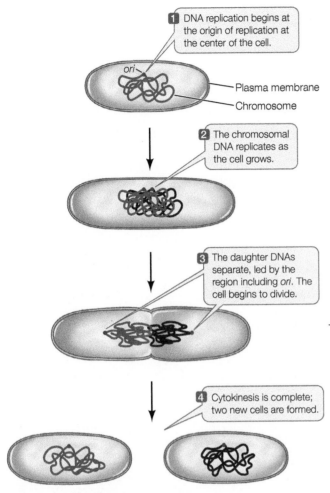

1 DNA replication begins at the origin of replication at the center of the cell.

ori

Plasma membrane

Chromosome

2 The chromosomal DNA replicates as the cell grows.

3 The daughter DNAs separate, led by the region including *ori*. The cell begins to divide.

4 Cytokinesis is complete; two new cells are formed.

FIGURE 7.4   Prokaryotic Cell Division *(Page 128)*

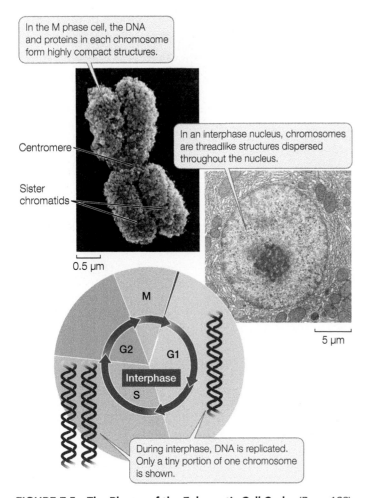

In the M phase cell, the DNA and proteins in each chromosome form highly compact structures.

In an interphase nucleus, chromosomes are threadlike structures dispersed throughout the nucleus.

Centromere

Sister chromatids

0.5 µm

5 µm

M

G2

G1

Interphase

S

During interphase, DNA is replicated. Only a tiny portion of one chromosome is shown.

FIGURE 7.5   The Phases of the Eukaryotic Cell Cycle *(Page 129)*

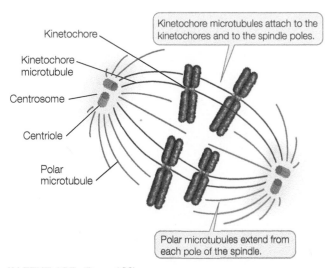

Kinetochore

Kinetochore microtubule

Centrosome

Centriole

Polar microtubule

Kinetochore microtubules attach to the kinetochores and to the spindle poles.

Polar microtubules extend from each pole of the spindle.

IN-TEXT ART *(Page 129)*

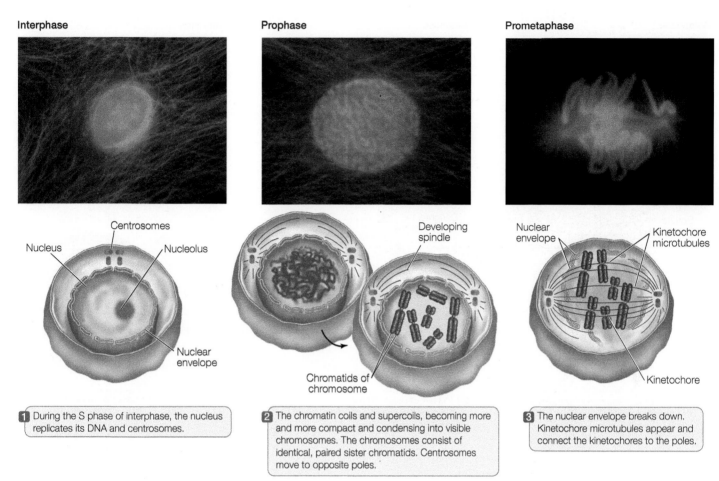

Interphase

Prophase

Prometaphase

Centrosomes

Nucleus

Nucleolus

Nuclear
envelope

Developing
spindle

Chromatids of
chromosome

Nuclear
envelope

Kinetochore
microtubules

Kinetochore

1 During the S phase of interphase, the nucleus replicates its DNA and centrosomes.

2 The chromatin coils and supercoils, becoming more and more compact and condensing into visible chromosomes. The chromosomes consist of identical, paired sister chromatids. Centrosomes move to opposite poles.

3 The nuclear envelope breaks down. Kinetochore microtubules appear and connect the kinetochores to the poles.

FIGURE 7.6 The Phases of Mitosis *(Pages 130 and 131)*

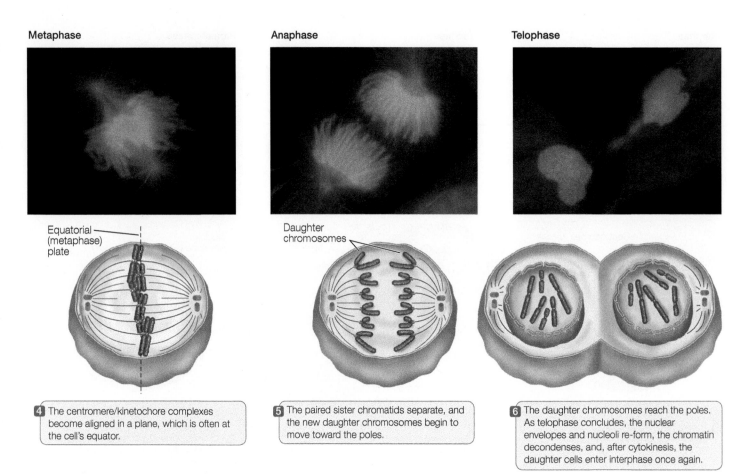

Metaphase

Equatorial
(metaphase)
plate

4 The centromere/kinetochore complexes become aligned in a plane, which is often at the cell's equator.

Anaphase

Daughter
chromosomes

5 The paired sister chromatids separate, and the new daughter chromosomes begin to move toward the poles.

Telophase

6 The daughter chromosomes reach the poles. As telophase concludes, the nuclear envelopes and nucleoli re-form, the chromatin decondenses, and, after cytokinesis, the daughter cells enter interphase once again.

FIGURE 7.6   The Phases of Mitosis *(continued)*

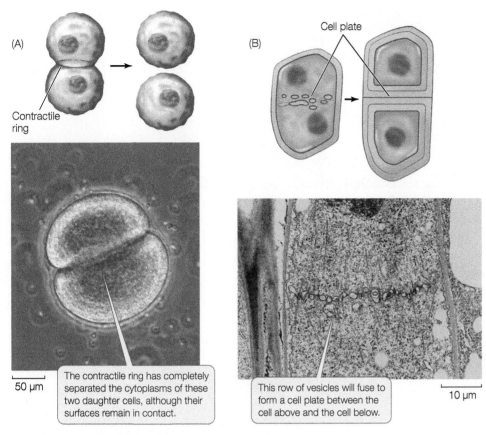

(A)

Contractile ring

50 µm

The contractile ring has completely separated the cytoplasms of these two daughter cells, although their surfaces remain in contact.

(B)

Cell plate

This row of vesicles will fuse to form a cell plate between the cell above and the cell below.

10 µm

FIGURE 7.7   Cytokinesis Differs in Animal and Plant Cells *(Page 132)*

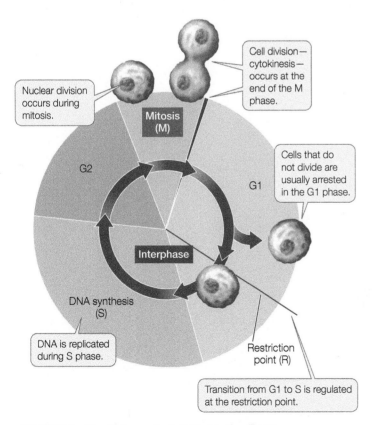

Nuclear division occurs during mitosis.

Cell division— cytokinesis— occurs at the end of the M phase.

Mitosis (M)

G2

Cells that do not divide are usually arrested in the G1 phase.

G1

Interphase

DNA synthesis (S)

DNA is replicated during S phase.

Restriction point (R)

Transition from G1 to S is regulated at the restriction point.

FIGURE 7.8   The Eukaryotic Cell Cycle *(Page 133)*

INVESTIGATION

FIGURE 7.9 Regulation of the Cell Cycle Nuclei in G1 do not undergo DNA replication, but nuclei in S phase do. To determine if there is some signal in the S cells that stimulates G1 cells to replicate their DNA, cells in the G1 and S phases were fused together, creating cells with both G1 and S properties.

HYPOTHESIS

A cell in S phase contains an activator
of DNA replication.

METHOD

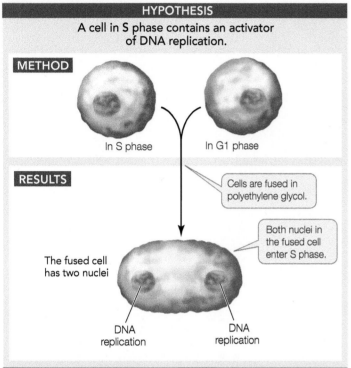

In S phase   In G1 phase

RESULTS

Cells are fused in
polyethylene glycol.

Both nuclei in
the fused cell
enter S phase.

The fused cell
has two nuclei

DNA   DNA
replication   replication

CONCLUSION

The S phase cell produces a substance that diffuses to the
G1 nucleus and activates DNA replication.

ANALYZE THE DATA

The experiment used mammalian cells undergoing the cell cycle synchronously. Radioactive labeling and microscopy were used to determine which nuclei were synthesizing DNA.
Here are counts of the cell nuclei that were labeled:

Type of cells	Cells with labeled nuclei/total cells
Unfused G1:	6/300
Unfused S:	435/500
Fused G1 and S cells:	17*/19

*Both nuclei labeled

A. What were the percentages of cells in S phase in each of the three experiments?
B. What does this mean in terms of control of the cell cycle?

Go to **yourBioPortal.com** for original citations, discussions,
and relevant links for all INVESTIGATION figures.

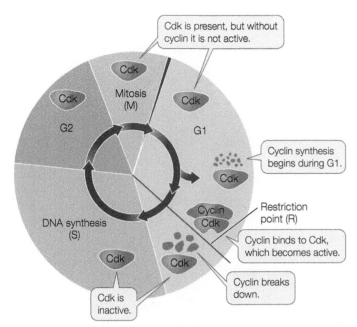

FIGURE 7.10   Cyclins Are Transient in the Cell Cycle (Page 134)

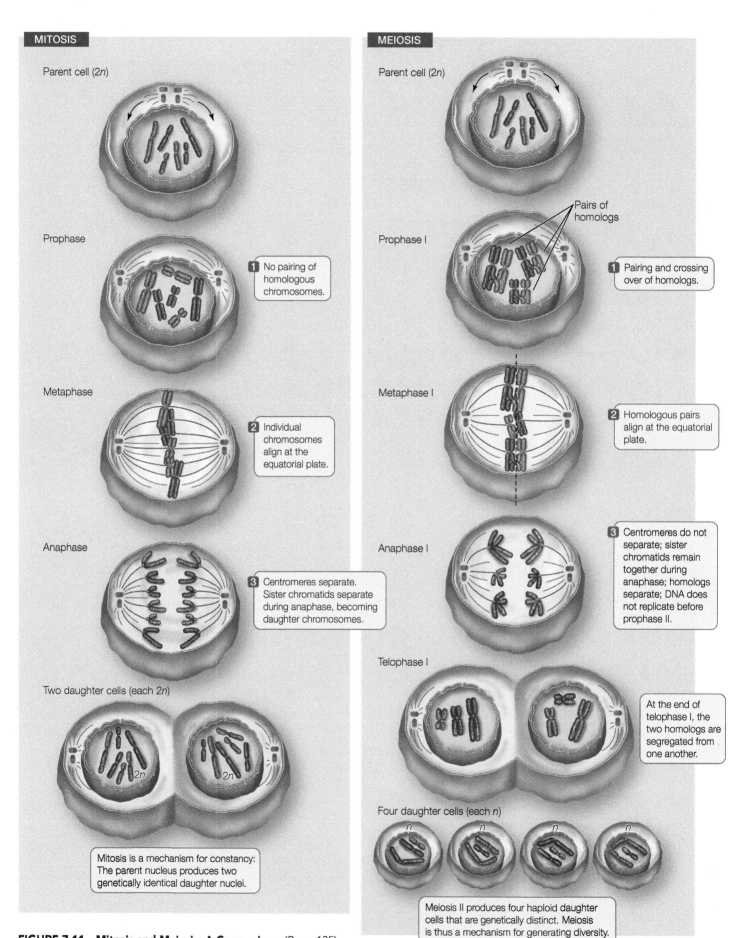

FIGURE 7.11 Mitosis and Meiosis: A Comparison *(Page 135)*

MEIOSIS I

Early prophase I

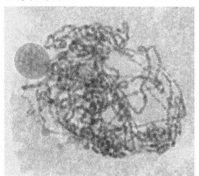

Centrosomes

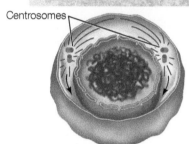

1 The chromatin begins to condense following interphase.

Mid-prophase I

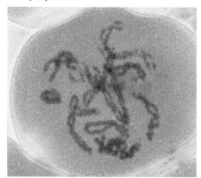

Pairs of homologs

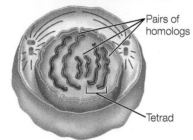

Tetrad

2 Synapsis aligns homologs, and chromosomes condense further.

Late prophase I–Prometaphase

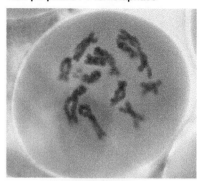

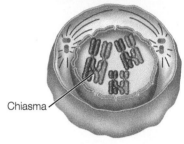

Chiasma

3 The chromosomes continue to coil and shorten. The chiasmata reflect crossing over, the exchange of genetic material between nonsister chromatids in a homologous pair. In prometaphase the nuclear envelope breaks down.

MEIOSIS II

Prophase II

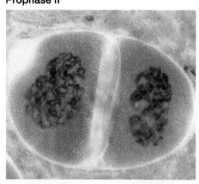

7 The chromosomes condense again, following a brief interphase (interkinesis) in which DNA does not replicate.

Metaphase II

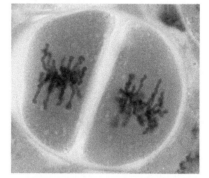

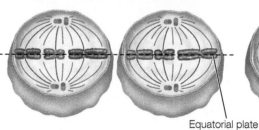

Equatorial plate

8 The centromeres of the paired chromatids line up across the equatorial plates of each cell.

Anaphase II

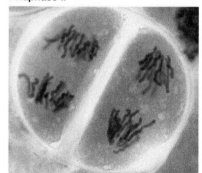

9 The chromatids finally separate, becoming chromosomes in their own right, and are pulled to opposite poles. Because of crossing over and independent assortment, each new cell will have a different genetic makeup.

FIGURE 7.12 Meiosis: Generating Haploid Cells *(Pages 136 and 137)*

Metaphase I

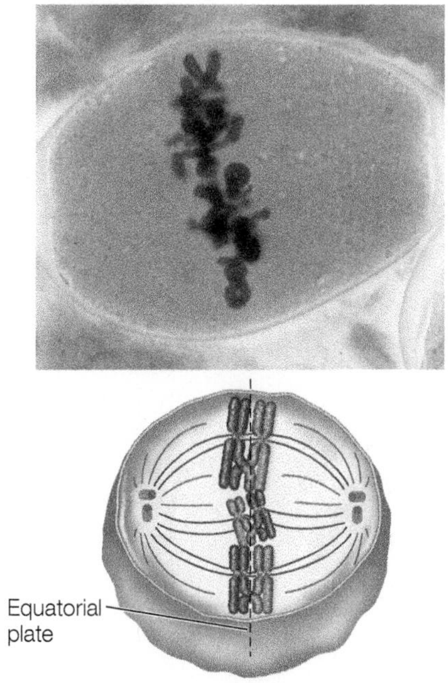

Equatorial plate

4 The homologous pairs line up on the equatorial (metaphase) plate.

Anaphase I

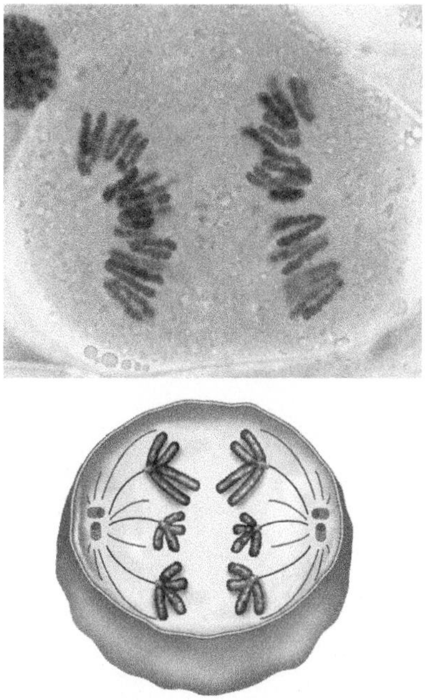

5 The homologous chromosomes (each with two chromatids) move to opposite poles of the cell.

Telophase I

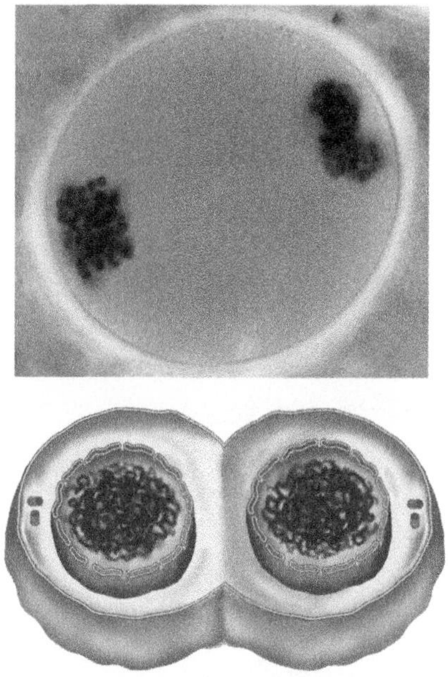

6 The chromosomes gather into nuclei, and the original cell divides.

Telophase II

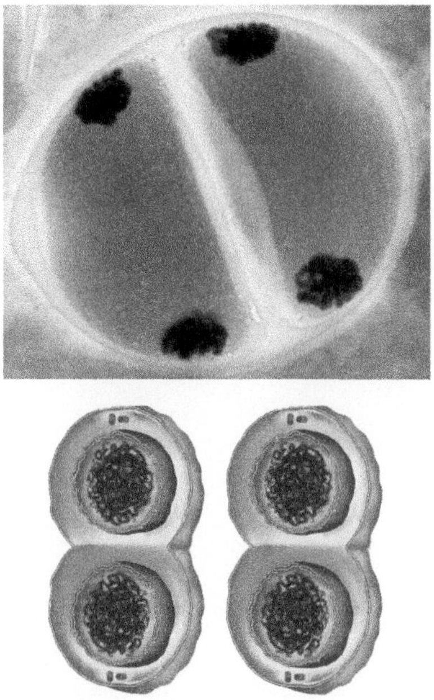

10 The chromosomes gather into nuclei, and the cells divide.

Products

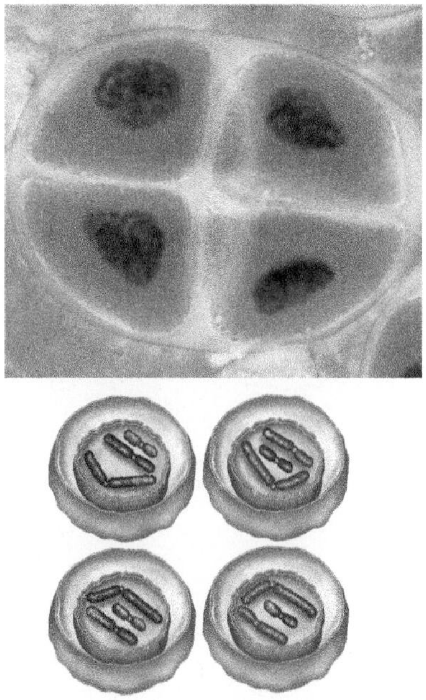

11 Each of the four cells has a nucleus with a haploid number of chromosomes.

FIGURE 7.12   Meiosis: Generating Haploid Cells (continued)

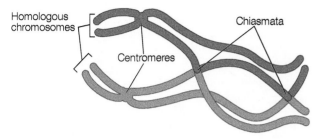

IN-TEXT ART *(Page 138)*

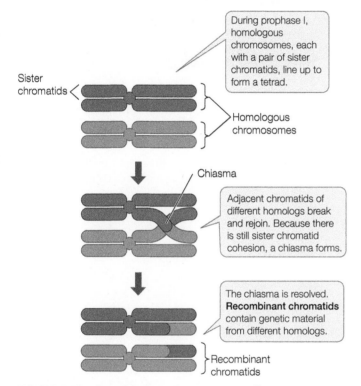

> During prophase I, homologous chromosomes, each with a pair of sister chromatids, line up to form a tetrad.

Sister chromatids

Homologous chromosomes

Chiasma

> Adjacent chromatids of different homologs break and rejoin. Because there is still sister chromatid cohesion, a chiasma forms.

> The chiasma is resolved. **Recombinant chromatids** contain genetic material from different homologs.

Recombinant chromatids

FIGURE 7.13   Crossing Over Forms Genetically Diverse Chromosomes *(Page 139)*

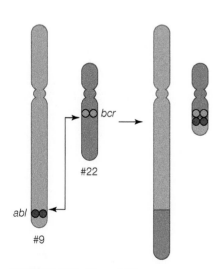

bcr

#22

abl

#9

IN-TEXT ART *(Page 140)*

(A)

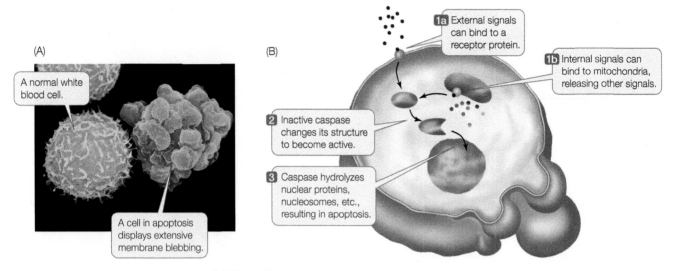

A normal white blood cell.

A cell in apoptosis displays extensive membrane blebbing.

(B)

1a External signals can bind to a receptor protein.

1b Internal signals can bind to mitochondria, releasing other signals.

2 Inactive caspase changes its structure to become active.

3 Caspase hydrolyzes nuclear proteins, nucleosomes, etc., resulting in apoptosis.

FIGURE 7.14   Apoptosis: Programmed Cell Death *(Page 141)*

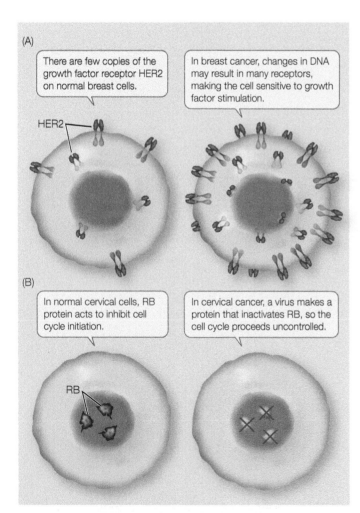

(A)

There are few copies of the growth factor receptor HER2 on normal breast cells.

In breast cancer, changes in DNA may result in many receptors, making the cell sensitive to growth factor stimulation.

HER2

(B)

In normal cervical cells, RB protein acts to inhibit cell cycle initiation.

In cervical cancer, a virus makes a protein that inactivates RB, so the cell cycle proceeds uncontrolled.

RB

FIGURE 7.15   Molecular Changes Regulate the Cell Cycle in Cancer Cells *(Page 142)*

Inheritance, Genes, and Chromosomes

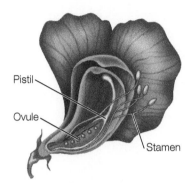

Pistil

Ovule

Stamen

IN-TEXT ART *(Page 145)*

INVESTIGATION

FIGURE 8.1 Mendel's Monohybrid Experiments
Mendel performed crosses with pea plants and carefully analyzed the outcomes to show that genetic determinants are particulate.

HYPOTHESIS

When two strains of peas with contrasting traits are bred, their characteristics are irreversibly blended in succeeding generations.

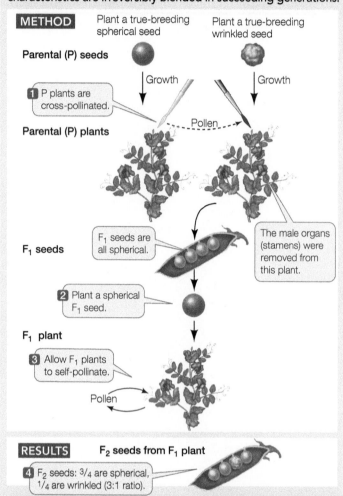

METHOD

Plant a true-breeding spherical seed

Plant a true-breeding wrinkled seed

Parental (P) seeds

↓ Growth   ↓ Growth

1 P plants are cross-pollinated.

Pollen →

Parental (P) plants

F₁ seeds

F₁ seeds are all spherical.

The male organs (stamens) were removed from this plant.

2 Plant a spherical F₁ seed.

F₁ plant

3 Allow F₁ plants to self-pollinate.

Pollen

RESULTS   F₂ seeds from F₁ plant

4 F₂ seeds: 3/4 are spherical, 1/4 are wrinkled (3:1 ratio).

CONCLUSION

The hypothesis is rejected. No irreversible blending of characteristics, and a recessive trait can reappear in succeeding generations.

ANALYZE THE DATA

Here are Mendel's data (the number of offspring showing each trait) for the F₂ from crosses between plants with contrasting traits:

Characteristic	Dominant	Recessive
Seed shape	5474 spherical	1850 wrinkled
Seed color	6022 yellow	2001 green
Flower color	705 purple	224 white
Pod color	428 green	152 yellow
Stem height	787 tall	277 short

A. Calculate the phenotypic ratio of dominant:recessive in the F₂ offspring.
B. What can you conclude about the behavior of alleles during gamete formation in a plant that is heterozygous for a trait?
C. Perform a chi square analysis to evaluate the statistical significance of these data (refer to Appendix B).

Go to **yourBioPortal.com** for original citations, discussions, and relevant links for all INVESTIGATION figures.

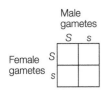

IN-TEXT ART *(Page 147)*

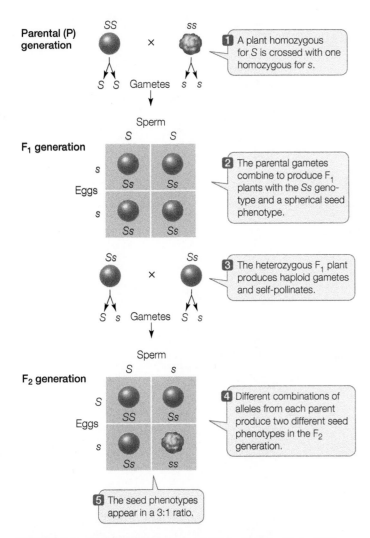

FIGURE 8.2   Mendel's Explanation of Inheritance *(Page 147)*

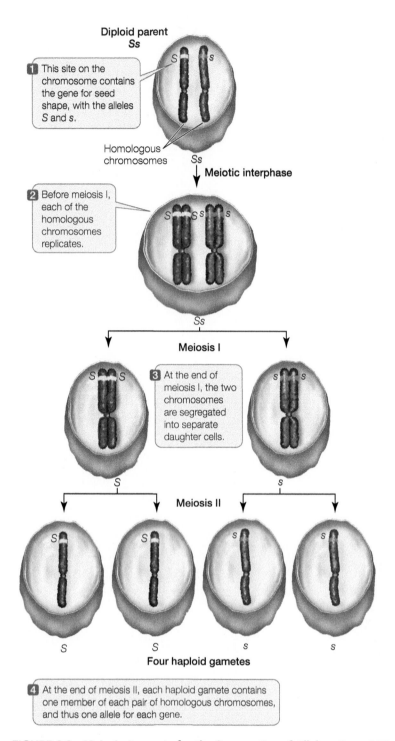

Diploid parent
Ss

1 This site on the chromosome contains the gene for seed shape, with the alleles *S* and *s*.

Homologous chromosomes

Ss

Meiotic interphase

2 Before meiosis I, each of the homologous chromosomes replicates.

Ss

Meiosis I

3 At the end of meiosis I, the two chromosomes are segregated into separate daughter cells.

S   *s*

Meiosis II

S   *S*   *s*   *s*

Four haploid gametes

4 At the end of meiosis II, each haploid gamete contains one member of each pair of homologous chromosomes, and thus one allele for each gene.

FIGURE 8.3   Meiosis Accounts for the Segregation of Alleles *(Page 148)*

INVESTIGATION

FIGURE 8.4 Homozygous or Heterozygous?   An individual with a dominant phenotype may have either a homozygous or a heterozygous genotype. The test cross determines which.

HYPOTHESIS

The progeny of a test cross can reveal whether an organism is homozygous or heterozygous.

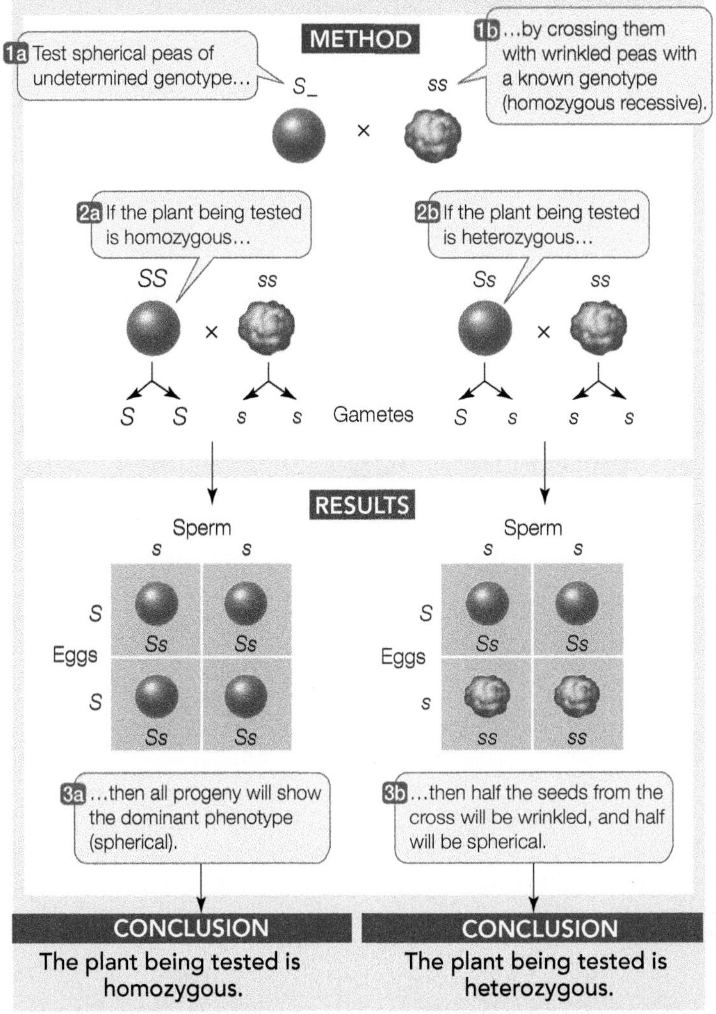

METHOD

1a Test spherical peas of undetermined genotype...

1b ...by crossing them with wrinkled peas with a known genotype (homozygous recessive).

$S\_$ × ss

2a If the plant being tested is homozygous...

SS × ss

2b If the plant being tested is heterozygous...

Ss × ss

S S s s Gametes S s s s

RESULTS

Sperm
s s

Eggs
S Ss Ss
S Ss Ss

Sperm
s s

Eggs
S Ss Ss
s ss ss

3a ...then all progeny will show the dominant phenotype (spherical).

3b ...then half the seeds from the cross will be wrinkled, and half will be spherical.

CONCLUSION

The plant being tested is homozygous.

CONCLUSION

The plant being tested is heterozygous.

ANALYZE THE DATA

A tall plant was crossed with a short plant to produce three F_1 plants (A, B, and C). Each of the F_1 plants was test crossed with these results:

F_1	Tall progeny	Short progeny
A	34	0
B	18	15
C	21	0

A. For each test cross, what were the genotypes and phenotypes of both parents?

B. Choose and perform a statistical test from Appendix B to evaluate the significance of these data.

Go to **yourBioPortal.com** for original citations, discussions, and relevant links for all INVESTIGATION figures.

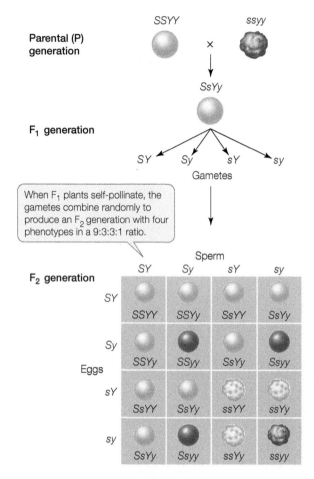

FIGURE 8.5 **Independent Assortment** *(Page 149)*

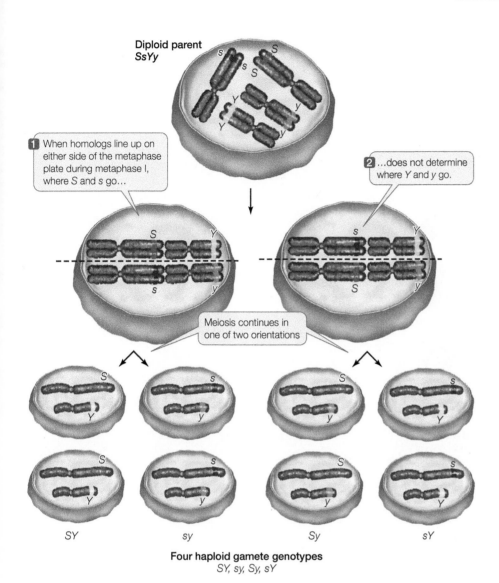

FIGURE 8.6   Meiosis Accounts for Independent Assortment of Alleles *(Page 150)*

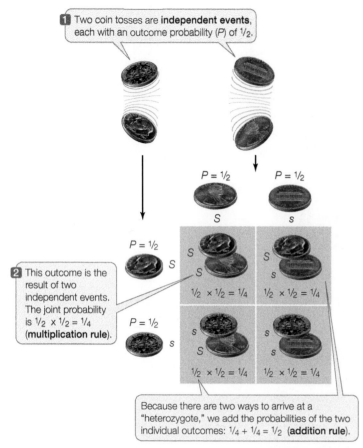

FIGURE 8.7 **Using Probability Calculations in Genetics** *(Page 151)*

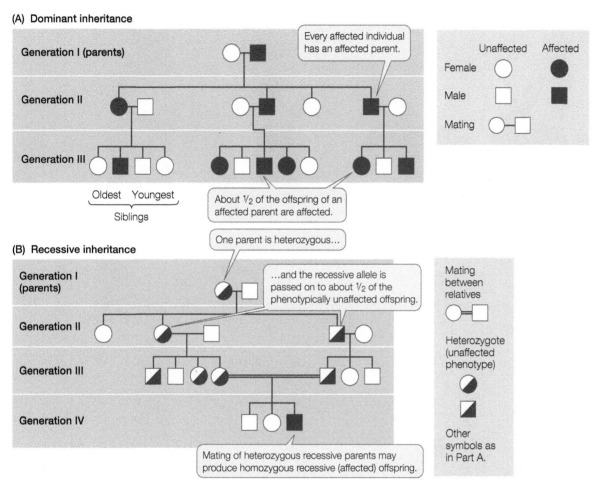

FIGURE 8.8 Pedigree Analysis and Inheritance *(Page 151)*

Possible genotypes	CC, Cc^{chd}, Cc^h, Cc	$c^{chd}c^{chd}$, $c^{chd}c$	c^hc^h, c^hc	cc
Phenotype	Dark gray	Chinchilla	Point restricted	Albino

FIGURE 8.9 Multiple Alleles for Coat Color in Rabbits (Page 152)

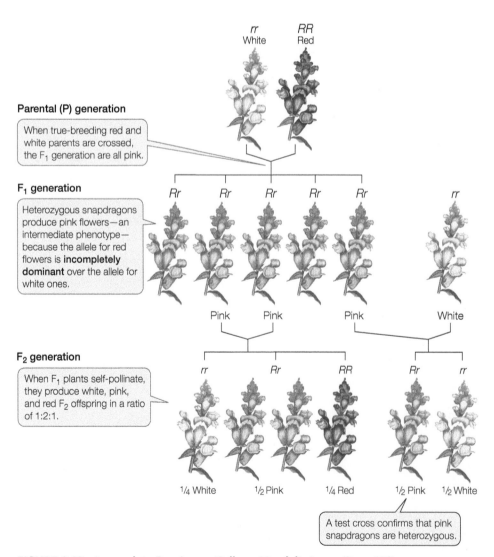

Parental (P) generation

When true-breeding red and white parents are crossed, the F₁ generation are all pink.

rr White   *RR* Red

F₁ generation

Heterozygous snapdragons produce pink flowers—an intermediate phenotype—because the allele for red flowers is **incompletely dominant** over the allele for white ones.

Rr   *Rr*   *Rr*   *Rr*   *Rr*   *rr*

Pink   Pink   Pink   White

F₂ generation

When F₁ plants self-pollinate, they produce white, pink, and red F₂ offspring in a ratio of 1:2:1.

rr   *Rr*   *RR*   *Rr*   *rr*

¼ White   ½ Pink   ¼ Red   ½ Pink   ½ White

A test cross confirms that pink snapdragons are heterozygous.

FIGURE 8.10 Incomplete Dominance Follows Mendel's Laws (Page 153)

Blood type of cells	Genotype	Blood cell types that body rejects	Reaction to added antibodies	
			Anti-A	Anti-B
A	$I^A I^A$ or $I^A I^O$	B		
B	$I^B I^B$ or $I^B I^O$	A		
AB	$I^A I^B$	Neither A nor B		
O	$I^O I^O$	A, B, and AB		

Red blood cells that do not react with antibody remain evenly dispersed.

Red blood cells that react with antibody clump together (speckled appearance).

FIGURE 8.11   ABO Blood Reactions Are Important in Transfusions *(Page 153)*

Parent: *B73*   Hybrid   Parent: *Mo17*

IN-TEXT ART *(Page 154)*

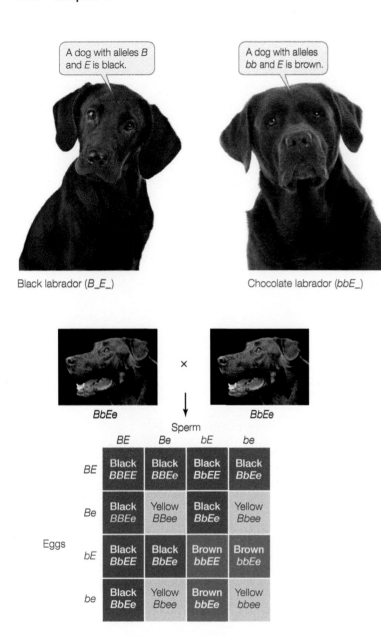

A dog with alleles *B* and *E* is black.

Black labrador (*B_E_*)

A dog with alleles *bb* and *E* is brown.

Chocolate labrador (*bbE_*)

A dog with *ee* is yellow, regardless of its *Bb* alleles.

Yellow labrador (*_ _ee*)

BbEe × *BbEe*

Sperm

Eggs		*BE*	*Be*	*bE*	*be*
	BE	Black *BBEE*	Black *BBEe*	Black *BbEE*	Black *BbEe*
	Be	Black *BBEe*	Yellow *BBee*	Black *BbEe*	Yellow *Bbee*
	bE	Black *BbEE*	Black *BbEe*	Brown *bbEE*	Brown *bbEe*
	be	Black *BbEe*	Yellow *Bbee*	Brown *bbEe*	Yellow *bbee*

FIGURE 8.12   Genes Interact Epistatically *(Page 155)*

INVESTIGATION

FIGURE 8.13 Some Alleles Do Not Assort Independently
Morgan's studies showed that the genes for body color and wing size in *Drosophila* are linked, so that their alleles do not assort independently.

HYPOTHESIS

Alleles for different characteristics always assort independently.

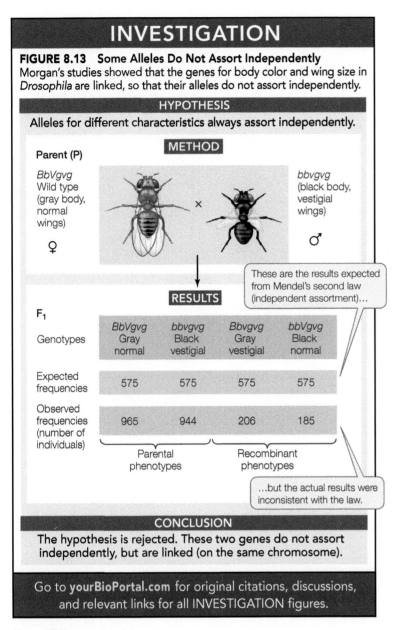

METHOD

Parent (P)

BbVgvg
Wild type
(gray body,
normal
wings)
♀

×

bbvgvg
(black body,
vestigial
wings)
♂

These are the results expected from Mendel's second law (independent assortment)...

RESULTS

F₁

Genotypes	*BbVgvg* Gray normal	*bbvgvg* Black vestigial	*Bbvgvg* Gray vestigial	*bbVgvg* Black normal
Expected frequencies	575	575	575	575
Observed frequencies (number of individuals)	965	944	206	185

Parental phenotypes   Recombinant phenotypes

...but the actual results were inconsistent with the law.

CONCLUSION

The hypothesis is rejected. These two genes do not assort independently, but are linked (on the same chromosome).

Go to **yourBioPortal.com** for original citations, discussions, and relevant links for all INVESTIGATION figures.

(Page 156)

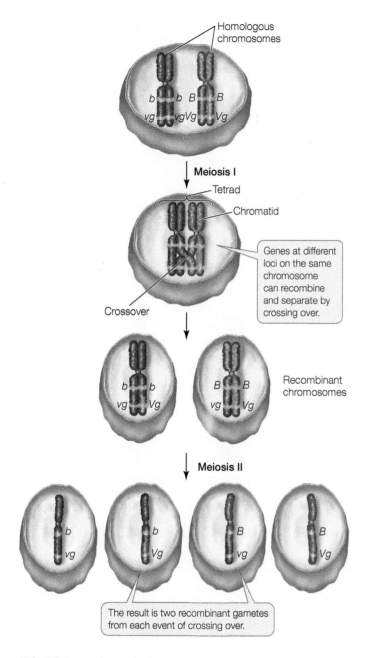

FIGURE 8.14 Crossing Over Results in Genetic Recombination
(Page 157)

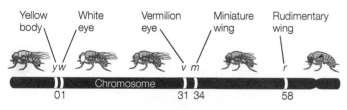

Genetic map in map units

IN-TEXT ART (Page 157)

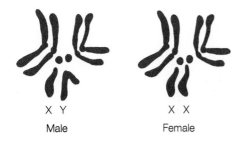

IN-TEXT ART *(Page 157)*

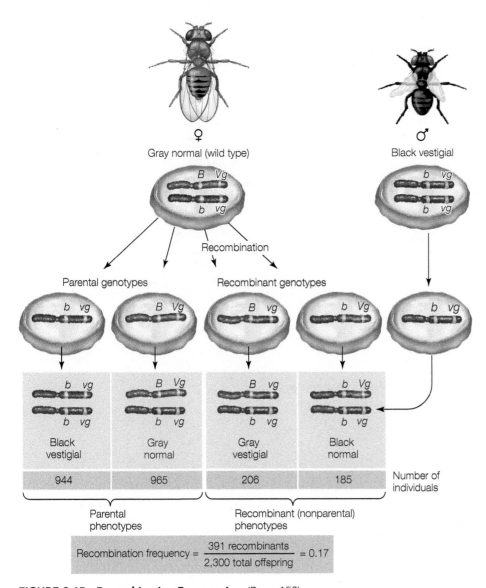

FIGURE 8.15   Recombination Frequencies *(Page 158)*

(A)

(B)

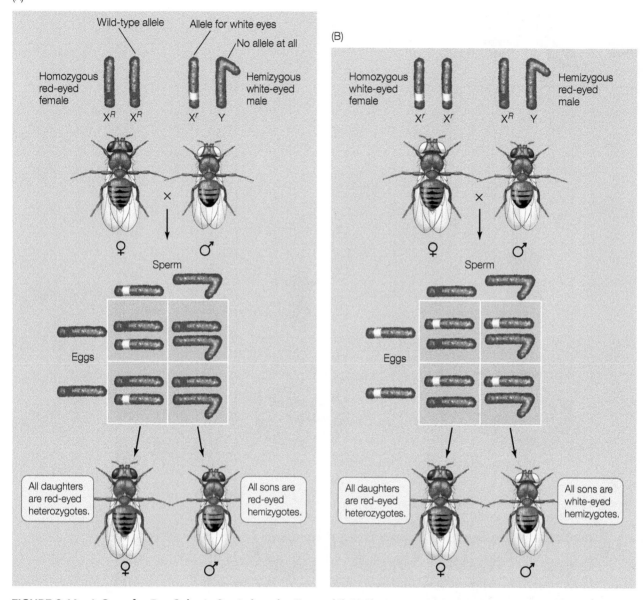

FIGURE 8.16 A Gene for Eye Color Is Carried on the *Drosophila* X Chromosome *(Page 159)*

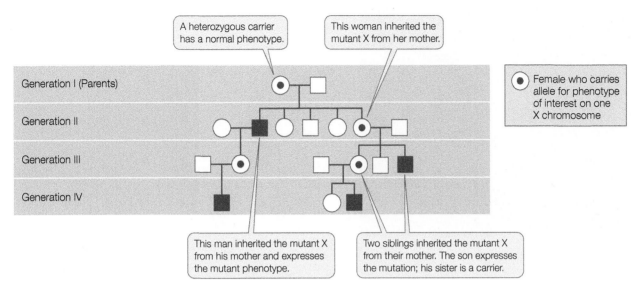

FIGURE 8.17 Red–Green Color Blindness Is Carried on the Human X Chromosome *(Page 160)*

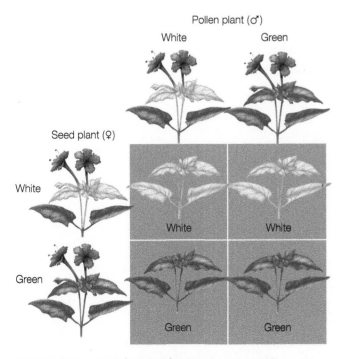

FIGURE 8.18 Cytoplasmic Inheritance *(Page 160)*

(A)

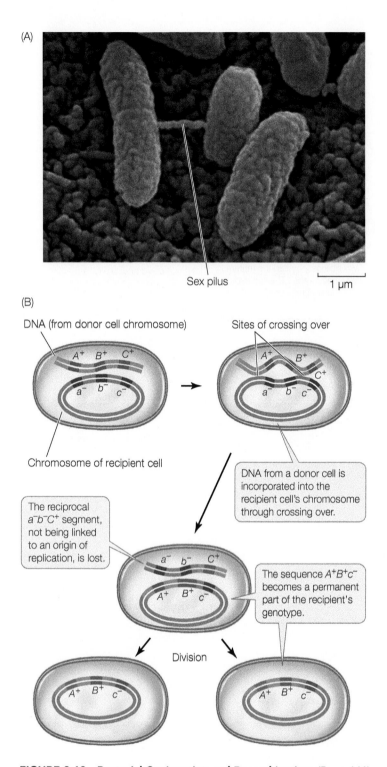

Sex pilus

1 µm

(B)

DNA (from donor cell chromosome)

Sites of crossing over

A^+ B^+ C^+

a^- b^- c^-

Chromosome of recipient cell

A^+ B^+ C^+

a^- b^- c^-

DNA from a donor cell is incorporated into the recipient cell's chromosome through crossing over.

The reciprocal $a^-b^-C^+$ segment, not being linked to an origin of replication, is lost.

a^- b^- C^+

A^+ B^+ c^-

The sequence $A^+B^+c^-$ becomes a permanent part of the recipient's genotype.

Division

A^+ B^+ c^-

A^+ B^+ c^-

FIGURE 8.19 Bacterial Conjugation and Recombination *(Page 161)*

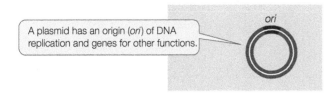

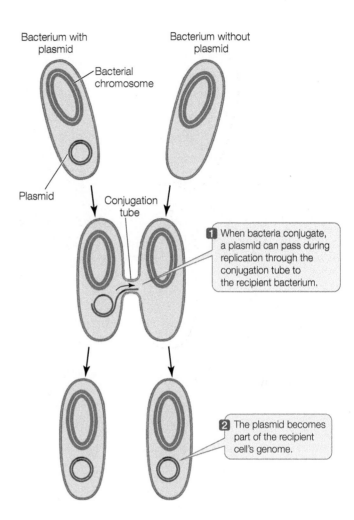

FIGURE 8.20   Gene Transfer by Plasmids *(Page 162)*

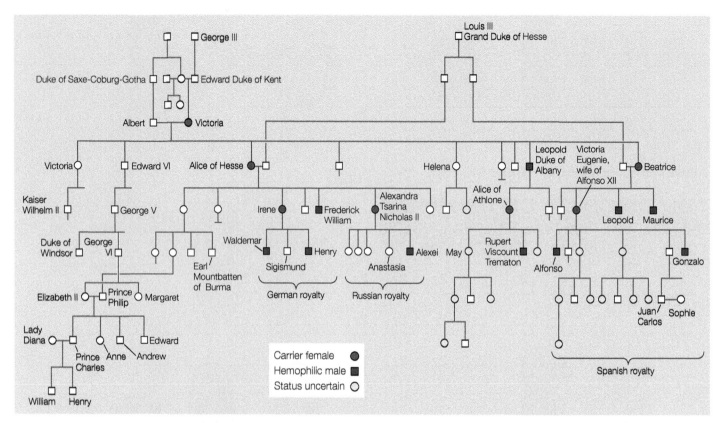

FIGURE 8.21   Sex Linkage in Royal Families of Europe (Page 163)

DNA and Its Role in Heredity

(A)

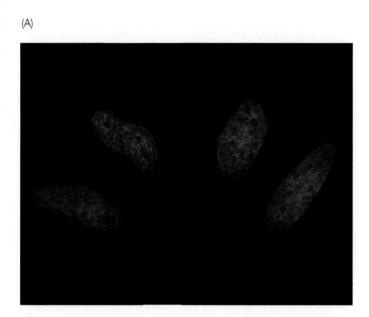

FIGURE 9.1 DNA in the Nucleus and in the Cell Cycle *(Page 166)*

(B)

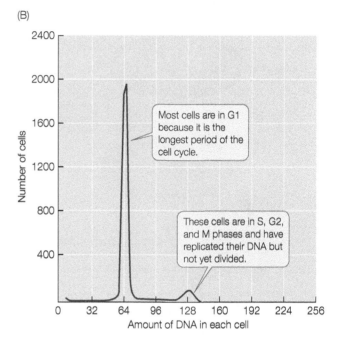

Most cells are in G1 because it is the longest period of the cell cycle.

These cells are in S, G2, and M phases and have replicated their DNA but not yet divided.

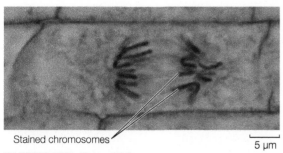

Stained chromosomes

5 μm

IN-TEXT ART *(Page 166)*

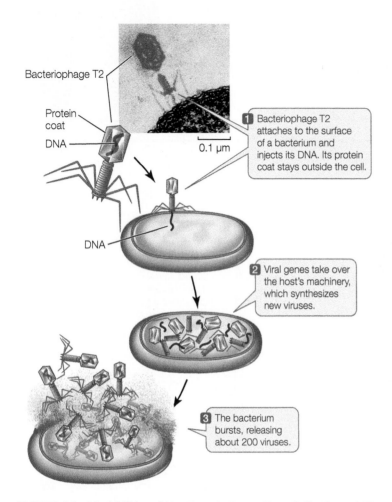

Bacteriophage T2

Protein coat

DNA

0.1 μm

1 Bacteriophage T2 attaches to the surface of a bacterium and injects its DNA. Its protein coat stays outside the cell.

DNA

2 Viral genes take over the host's machinery, which synthesizes new viruses.

3 The bacterium bursts, releasing about 200 viruses.

FIGURE 9.2 Viral DNA and Not Protein Enters Host Cells *(Page 167)*

INVESTIGATION

FIGURE 9.3   Transformation of Eukaryotic Cells   The use of a marker gene shows that mammalian cells can be genetically transformed by DNA. Usually, the marker gene is carried on a larger DNA molecule.

HYPOTHESIS

DNA can transform eukaryotic cells.

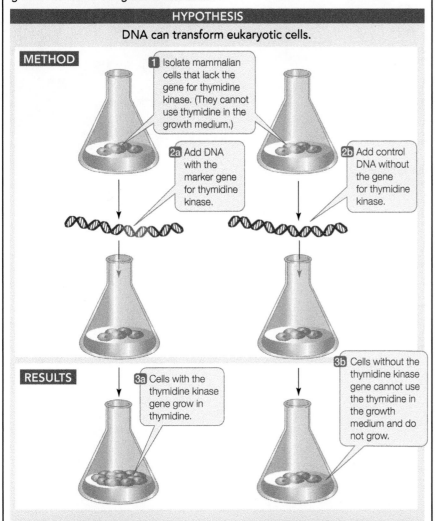

METHOD

1. Isolate mammalian cells that lack the gene for thymidine kinase. (They cannot use thymidine in the growth medium.)

2a. Add DNA with the marker gene for thymidine kinase.

2b. Add control DNA without the gene for thymidine kinase.

RESULTS

3a. Cells with the thymidine kinase gene grow in thymidine.

3b. Cells without the thymidine kinase gene cannot use the thymidine in the growth medium and do not grow.

CONCLUSION

The cells were transformed by DNA.

ANALYZE THE DATA

Transformation was achieved by adding the DNA in a solution of calcium chloride ($CaCl_2$) at pH 7. In other experiments, the type or amount of DNA, pH, or $CaCl_2$ concentration was varied. The transformation efficiency was calculated as the percentage of cells that produced colonies on a medium containing thymidine. Explain these data.

Transformation conditions	Efficiency (%)
Mammalian DNA with TK gene	
10 µg	15
20 µg	55
30 µg	10
40 µg	5
20 µg, no $CaCl_2$	10
20 µg, pH 6.5	0
20 µg, pH 7.5	0
Bacterial virus DNA with TK gene	
20 µg	0

Go to **yourBioPortal.com** for original citations, discussions, and relevant links for all INVESTIGATION figures.

(A)

(B)

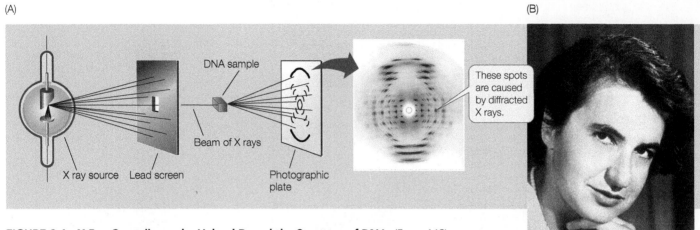

FIGURE 9.4   X-Ray Crystallography Helped Reveal the Structure of DNA *(Page 169)*

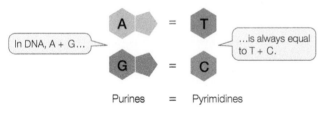

IN-TEXT ART *(Page 169)*

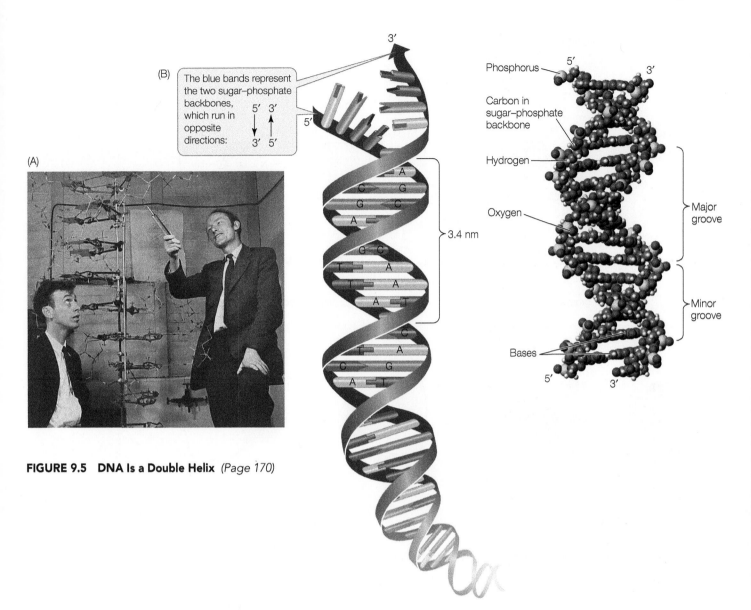

(B) The blue bands represent the two sugar–phosphate backbones, which run in opposite directions:

5′ → 3′
3′ ← 5′

(A)

3.4 nm

Phosphorus

Carbon in sugar–phosphate backbone

Hydrogen

Oxygen

Major groove

Minor groove

Bases

FIGURE 9.5 DNA Is a Double Helix *(Page 170)*

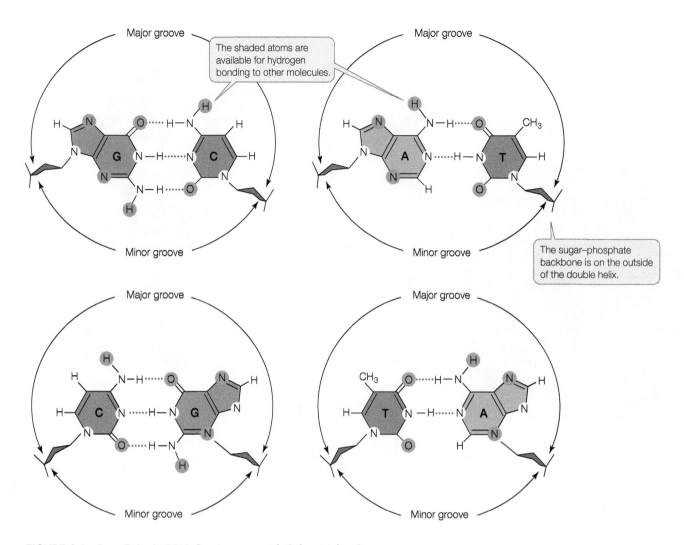

FIGURE 9.6 Base Pairs in DNA Can Interact with Other Molecules *(Page 171)*

Original DNA

After one round
of replication

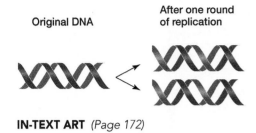

IN-TEXT ART *(Page 172)*

Growing strand

5′ end

Template strand

3′ end

OH

T ⋯ A

Phosphate

C ⋯⋯ G

Sugar

Base

A ⋯ T

C ⋯⋯ G

Nucleotides are added
to the 3′ end.

OH   3′ end

G

5′ end

C

OH

3′ end

C pairs with G.

C

5′ end

The enzyme DNA
polymerase adds the
next deoxyribonucleotide
to the —OH group at the
3′ end of the growing strand
and releases pyrophosphate.

DNA polymerase

Growing strand

5′ end

3′ end

OH

T ⋯ A

C ⋯⋯ G

A ⋯ T

C ⋯⋯ G

C ⋯⋯ G

OH   3′ end

Pyrophosphate ion

Bonds linking the
phosphate groups are
broken, releasing energy
to drive the reaction.

C

5′ end

Phosphate ions

FIGURE 9.7   Each New DNA Strand Grows by the Addition of Nucleotides to Its 3′ End *(Page 172)*

(A) Prokaryotic

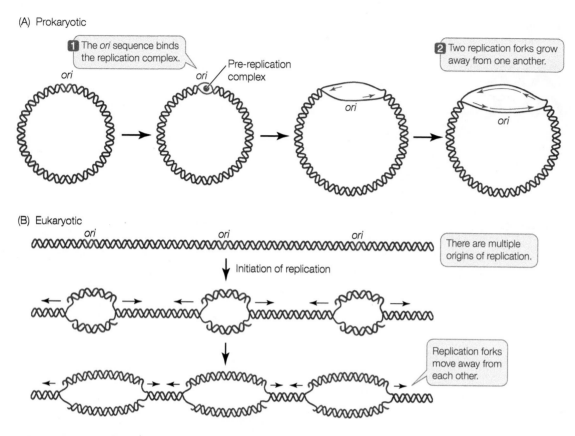

(B) Eukaryotic

FIGURE 9.8 The Origin of DNA Replication *(Page 173)*

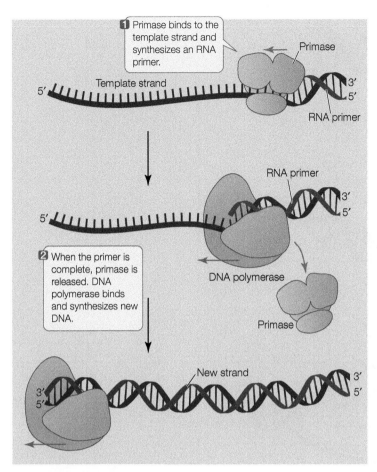

1 Primase binds to the template strand and synthesizes an RNA primer.

Primase

Template strand

3′
5′

RNA primer

5′

RNA primer

3′
5′

DNA polymerase

2 When the primer is complete, primase is released. DNA polymerase binds and synthesizes new DNA.

Primase

New strand

3′
5′

3′
5′

FIGURE 9.9   DNA Forms with a Primer *(Page 174)*

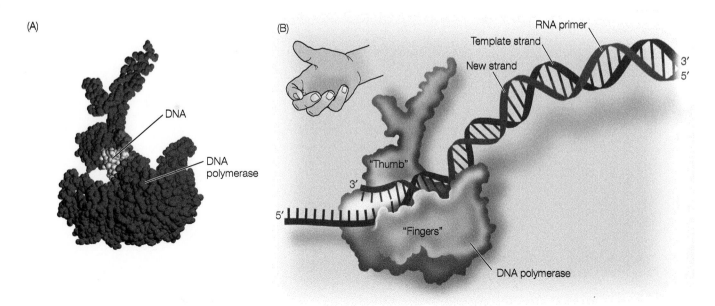

(A)

DNA

DNA polymerase

(B)

RNA primer

Template strand

New strand

3′
5′

"Thumb"

3′

5′

"Fingers"

DNA polymerase

FIGURE 9.10   DNA Polymerase Binds to the Template Strand *(Page 174)*

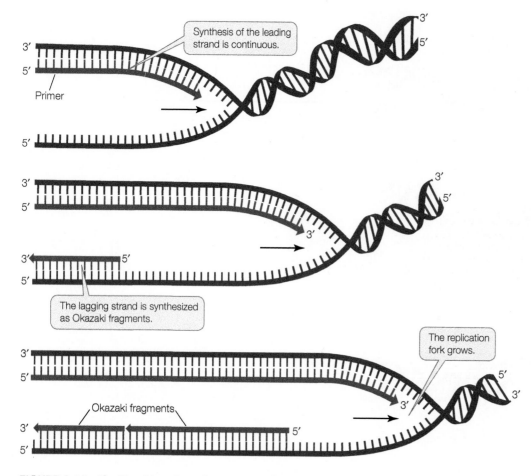

FIGURE 9.11   The Two New Strands Form in Different Ways *(Page 175)*

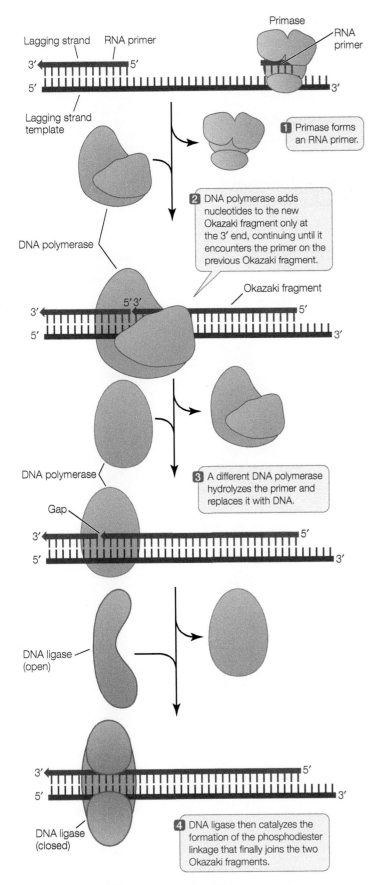

FIGURE 9.12 The Lagging Strand Story (Page 176)

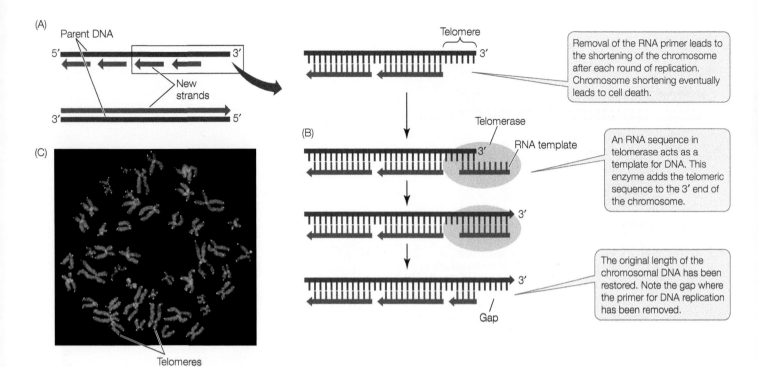

(A)
Parent DNA
New strands

(B)
Telomere
Telomerase
RNA template
Gap

Removal of the RNA primer leads to the shortening of the chromosome after each round of replication. Chromosome shortening eventually leads to cell death.

An RNA sequence in telomerase acts as a template for DNA. This enzyme adds the telomeric sequence to the 3' end of the chromosome.

The original length of the chromosomal DNA has been restored. Note the gap where the primer for DNA replication has been removed.

(C)
Telomeres

FIGURE 9.13   Telomeres and Telomerase *(Page 177)*

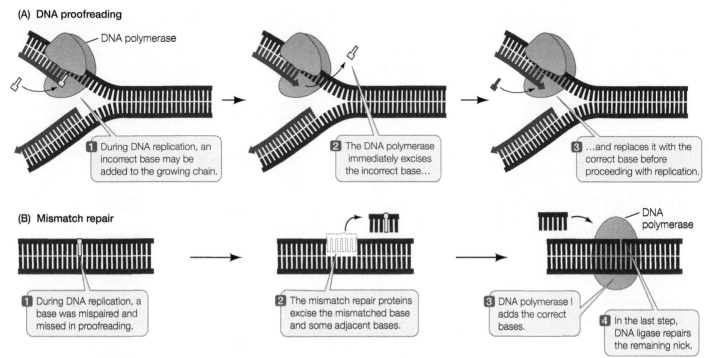

FIGURE 9.14 DNA Repair Mechanisms *(Page 178)*

RESEARCH TOOLS

FIGURE 9.15 The Polymerase Chain Reaction The steps in this cyclic process are repeated many times to produce millions of identical copies of a DNA fragment. This makes enough DNA for chemical analysis and genetic manipulations.

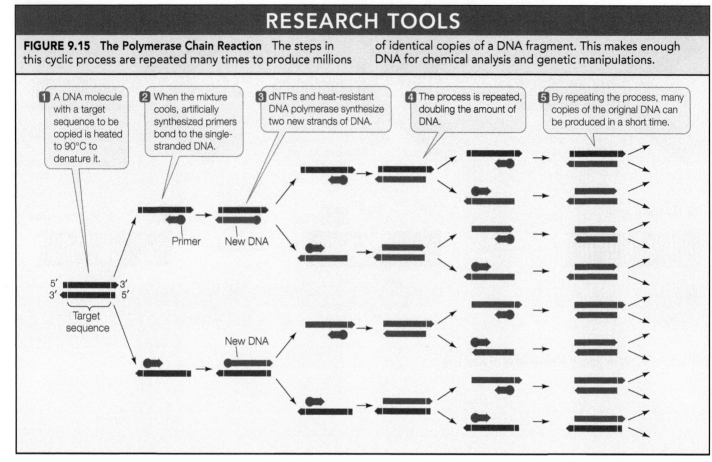

1 A DNA molecule with a target sequence to be copied is heated to 90°C to denature it.

2 When the mixture cools, artificially synthesized primers bond to the single-stranded DNA.

3 dNTPs and heat-resistant DNA polymerase synthesize two new strands of DNA.

4 The process is repeated, doubling the amount of DNA.

5 By repeating the process, many copies of the original DNA can be produced in a short time.

Primer

New DNA

5′ 3′
3′ 5′

Target sequence

New DNA

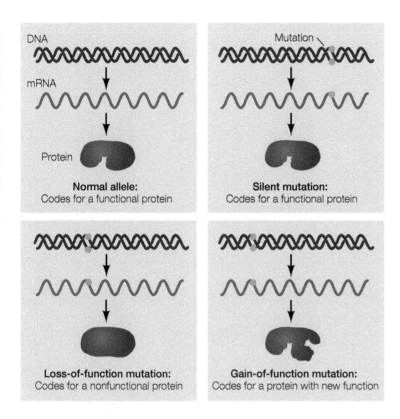

DNA

mRNA

Protein

Normal allele:
Codes for a functional protein

Mutation

Silent mutation:
Codes for a functional protein

Loss-of-function mutation:
Codes for a nonfunctional protein

Gain-of-function mutation:
Codes for a protein with new function

FIGURE 9.16 Mutation and Phenotype *(Page 180)*

IN-TEXT ART *(Page 180)*

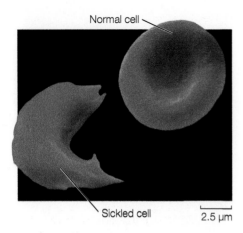

Normal cell

Sickled cell

2.5 μm

IN-TEXT ART *(Page 181)*

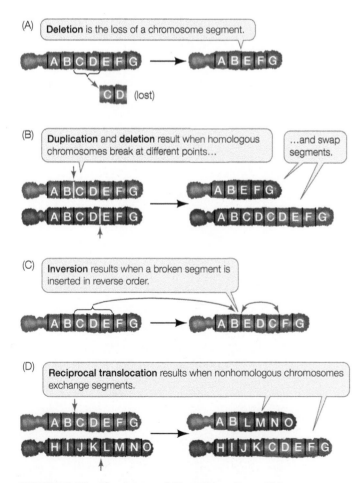

(A) **Deletion** is the loss of a chromosome segment.

A B C D E F G → A B E F G

C D (lost)

(B) **Duplication** and **deletion** result when homologous chromosomes break at different points…

…and swap segments.

A B C D E F G → A B E F G

A B C D E F G → A B C D C D E F G

(C) **Inversion** results when a broken segment is inserted in reverse order.

A B C D E F G → A B E D C F G

(D) **Reciprocal translocation** results when nonhomologous chromosomes exchange segments.

A B C D E F G → A B L M N O

H I J K L M N O → H I J K C D E F G

FIGURE 9.17 Chromosomal Mutations *(Page 181)*

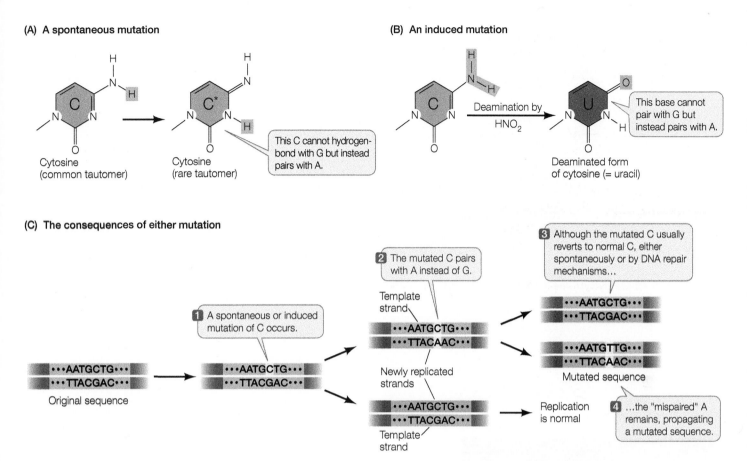

FIGURE 9.18   Spontaneous and Induced Mutations *(Page 182)*

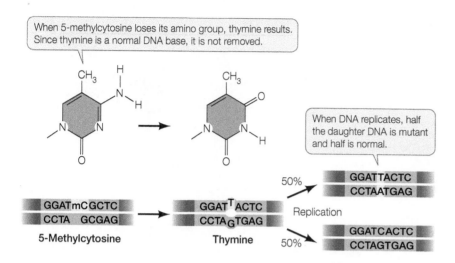

FIGURE 9.19 5-Methylcytosine in DNA Is a "Hotspot" for Mutations *(Page 183)*

FIGURE 9.20 A Neanderthal Child *(Page 185)*

From DNA to Protein: Gene Expression

10

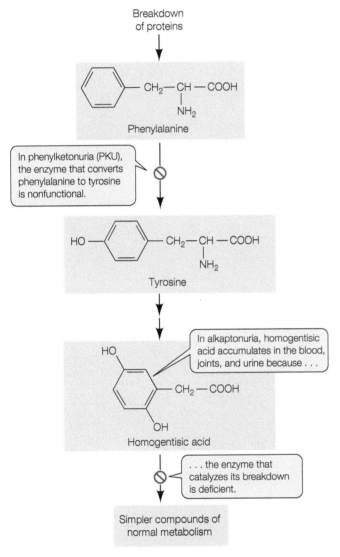

FIGURE 10.1 Metabolic Diseases and Enzymes *(Page 188)*

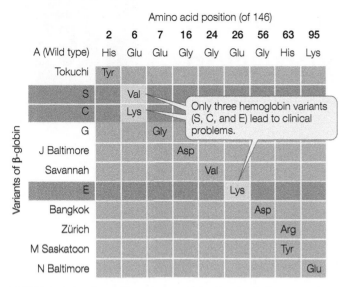

Amino acid position (of 146)

	2	6	7	16	24	26	56	63	95
A (Wild type)	His	Glu	Glu	Gly	Gly	Glu	Gly	His	Lys
Tokuchi	Tyr								
S		Val							
C		Lys							
G			Gly						
J Baltimore				Asp					
Savannah					Val				
E						Lys			
Bangkok							Asp		
Zürich								Arg	
M Saskatoon								Tyr	
N Baltimore									Glu

Variants of β-globin

Only three hemoglobin variants (S, C, and E) lead to clinical problems.

FIGURE 10.2 Gene Mutations and Amino Acid Changes *(Page 189)*

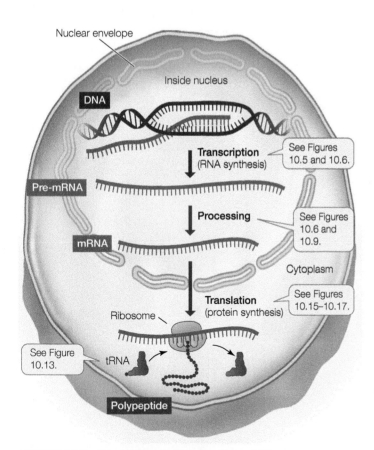

Nuclear envelope

Inside nucleus

DNA

Transcription (RNA synthesis) — See Figures 10.5 and 10.6.

Pre-mRNA

Processing — See Figures 10.6 and 10.9.

mRNA

Cytoplasm

Translation (protein synthesis) — See Figures 10.15–10.17.

Ribosome

See Figure 10.13.

tRNA

Polypeptide

FIGURE 10.3 From Gene to Protein *(Page 190)*

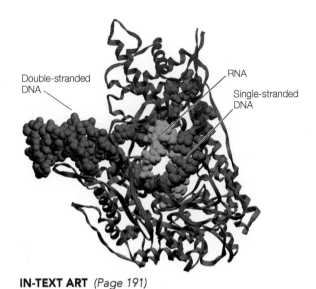

IN-TEXT ART *(Page 191)*

Double-stranded DNA

RNA

Single-stranded DNA

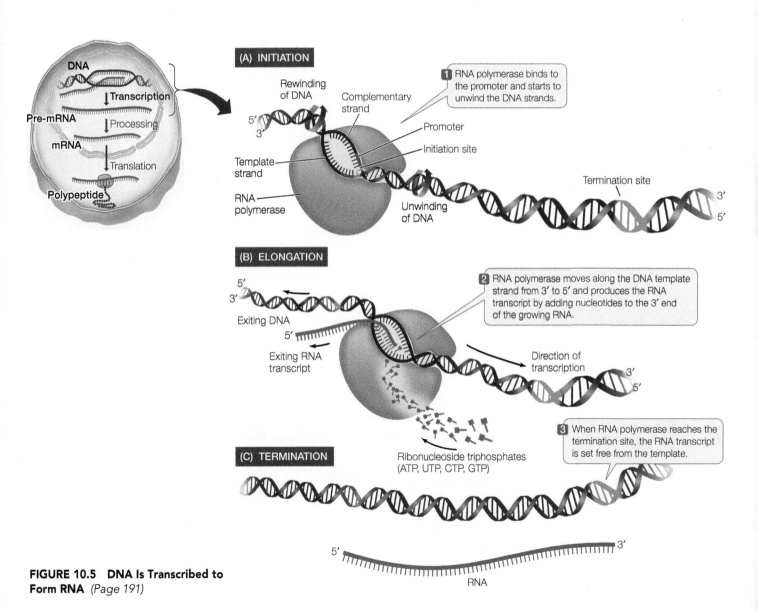

(A) INITIATION

DNA

↓ **Transcription**

Pre-mRNA

↓ Processing

mRNA

↓ Translation

Polypeptide

Rewinding of DNA

Complementary strand

5′
3′

Template strand

RNA polymerase

Unwinding of DNA

Promoter

Initiation site

Termination site

3′
5′

1 RNA polymerase binds to the promoter and starts to unwind the DNA strands.

(B) ELONGATION

5′
3′

Exiting DNA

5′

Exiting RNA transcript

Ribonucleoside triphosphates (ATP, UTP, CTP, GTP)

Direction of transcription

3′
5′

2 RNA polymerase moves along the DNA template strand from 3′ to 5′ and produces the RNA transcript by adding nucleotides to the 3′ end of the growing RNA.

3 When RNA polymerase reaches the termination site, the RNA transcript is set free from the template.

(C) TERMINATION

5′

3′

RNA

FIGURE 10.5   DNA Is Transcribed to Form RNA *(Page 191)*

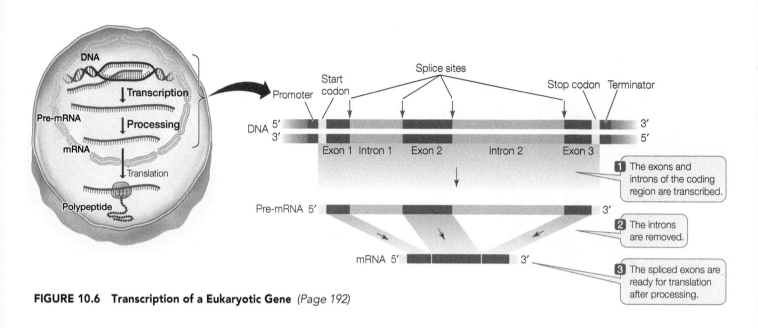

FIGURE 10.6 **Transcription of a Eukaryotic Gene** *(Page 192)*

TABLE 10.1	Differences between Prokaryotic and Eukaryotic Gene Expression	
CHARACTERISTIC	**PROKARYOTES**	**EUKARYOTES**
Transcription and translation occurrence	At the same time in the cytoplasm	Transcription in the nucleus, then translation in the cytoplasm
Gene structure	Transcribed regions not interrupted by introns	Transcribed regions often interrupted by non-coding introns
Modification of mRNA after initial transcription but before translation	None	Introns spliced out; 5′ cap and 3′ poly A added

RESEARCH TOOLS

FIGURE 10.7 Nucleic Acid Hybridization Base pairing permits the detection of a sequence that is complementary to the probe.

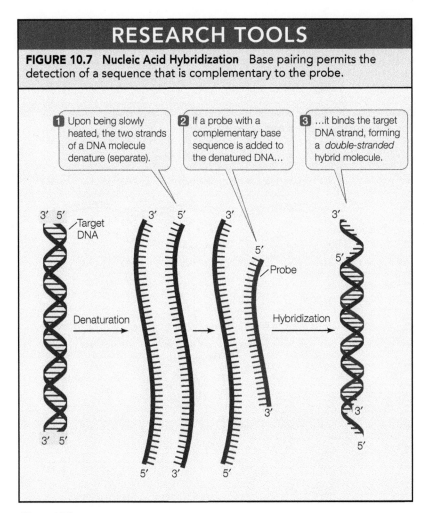

1 Upon being slowly heated, the two strands of a DNA molecule denature (separate).

2 If a probe with a complementary base sequence is added to the denatured DNA...

3 ...it binds the target DNA strand, forming a *double-stranded* hybrid molecule.

(Page 193)

INVESTIGATION

FIGURE 10.8 Demonstrating the Existence of Introns When an mRNA transcript of the β-globin gene was hybridized with the double-stranded DNA of that gene, the introns in the DNA "looped out." This demonstrated that the coding region of a eukaryotic gene can contain noncoding DNA that is not present in the mature mRNA transcript.

HYPOTHESIS

All regions within the coding sequence of a gene end up in its mRNA.

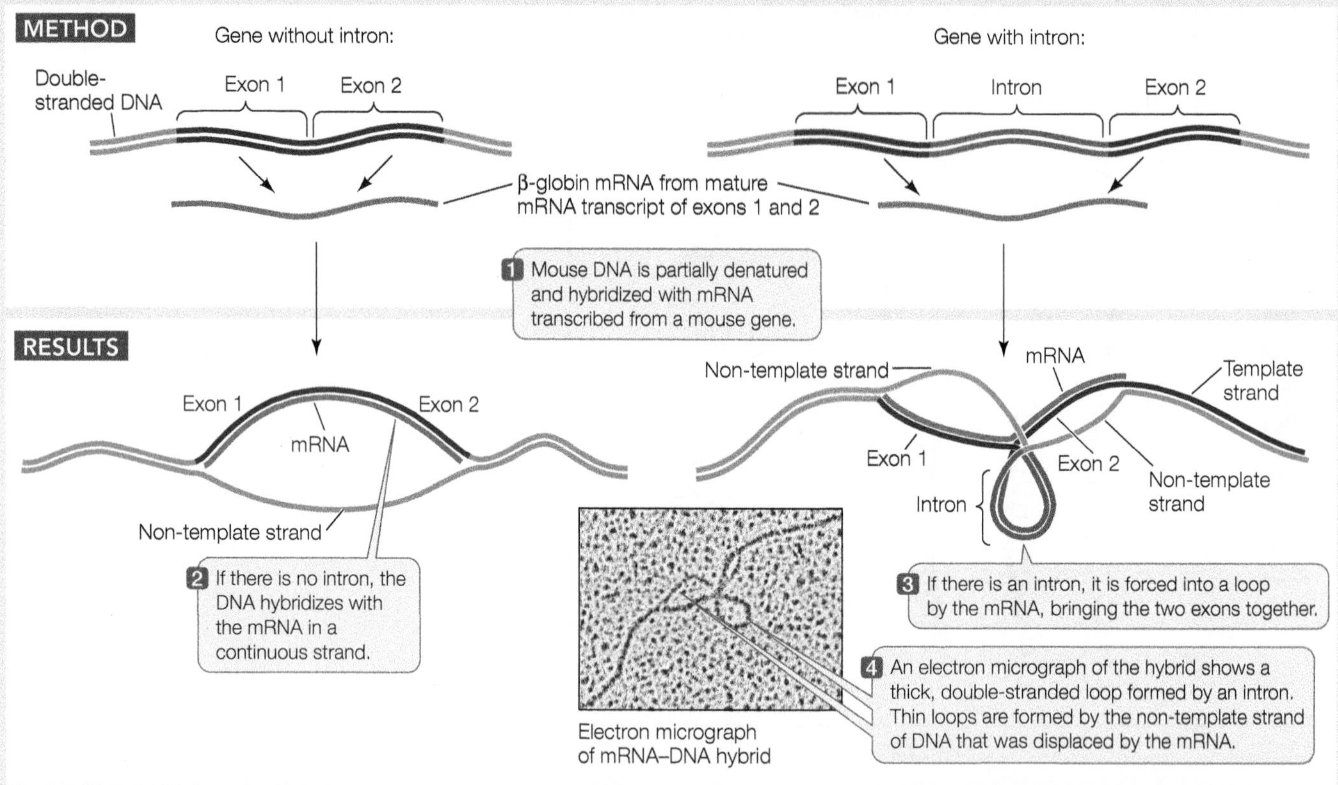

METHOD

Gene without intron:

Gene with intron:

Double-stranded DNA — Exon 1 — Exon 2

Exon 1 — Intron — Exon 2

β-globin mRNA from mature mRNA transcript of exons 1 and 2

1 Mouse DNA is partially denatured and hybridized with mRNA transcribed from a mouse gene.

RESULTS

Exon 1 — mRNA — Exon 2

Non-template strand

Non-template strand — mRNA — Template strand

Exon 1 — Exon 2 — Non-template strand

Intron

2 If there is no intron, the DNA hybridizes with the mRNA in a continuous strand.

3 If there is an intron, it is forced into a loop by the mRNA, bringing the two exons together.

Electron micrograph of mRNA–DNA hybrid

4 An electron micrograph of the hybrid shows a thick, double-stranded loop formed by an intron. Thin loops are formed by the non-template strand of DNA that was displaced by the mRNA.

CONCLUSION

The DNA contains noncoding regions within the genes that are not present in the mature mRNA.

Go to **yourBioPortal.com** for original citations, discussions, and relevant links for all INVESTIGATION figures.

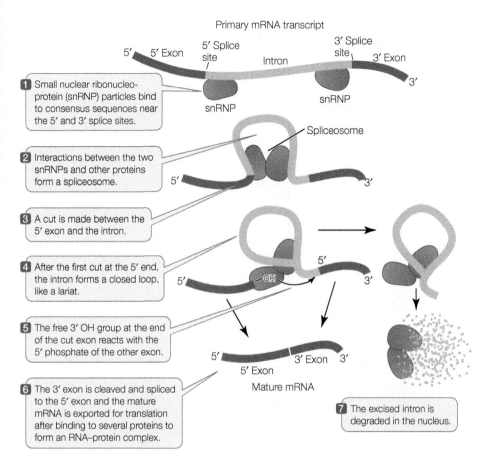

Primary mRNA transcript

1 Small nuclear ribonucleo-protein (snRNP) particles bind to consensus sequences near the 5' and 3' splice sites.

2 Interactions between the two snRNPs and other proteins form a spliceosome.

3 A cut is made between the 5' exon and the intron.

4 After the first cut at the 5' end, the intron forms a closed loop, like a lariat.

5 The free 3' OH group at the end of the cut exon reacts with the 5' phosphate of the other exon.

6 The 3' exon is cleaved and spliced to the 5' exon and the mature mRNA is exported for translation after binding to several proteins to form an RNA–protein complex.

7 The excised intron is degraded in the nucleus.

FIGURE 10.9   The Spliceosome: An RNA Splicing Machine *(Page 195)*

IN-TEXT ART *(Page 195)*

INVESTIGATION

FIGURE 10.10   Deciphering the Genetic Code   Nirenberg and Matthaei used a test-tube protein synthesis system to determine the amino acids specified by particular synthetic mRNAs.

HYPOTHESIS

A triplet codon based on three-base codons specifies amino acids.

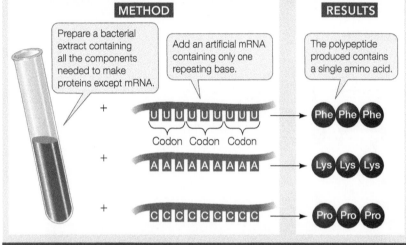

METHOD

Prepare a bacterial extract containing all the components needed to make proteins except mRNA.

Add an artificial mRNA containing only one repeating base.

Codon   Codon   Codon

RESULTS

The polypeptide produced contains a single amino acid.

Phe Phe Phe

Lys Lys Lys

Pro Pro Pro

CONCLUSION

UUU is an mRNA codon for phenylalanine.
AAA is an mRNA codon for lysine.
CCC is an mRNA codon for proline.

ANALYZE THE DATA

Poly U, an artificial mRNA, was added to a test tube with all other components for protein synthesis ("Complete system"). Other test tubes differed from the complete system as indicated in the table. Samples were tested for radioactive phenylalanine incorporation with these results:

Condition	Radioactivity in protein
Complete system	29,500
Minus poly U mRNA	70
Minus ribosomes	52
Minus ATP	83
Plus RNase (hydrolyzes RNA)	120
Plus DNase	27,600
Radioactive glycine instead of phenylalanine	33
Mixture of 19 radioactive amino acids minus phenylalanine	276

Explain the results for each of the conditions.

For more, go to Working with Data 10.1 at **yourBioPortal.com**.

Go to **yourBioPortal.com** for original citations, discussions, and relevant links for all INVESTIGATION figures.

Second letter

	U	C	A	G	
U	UUU UUC Phenyl-alanine UUA UUG Leucine	UCU UCC UCA UCG Serine	UAU UAC Tyrosine UAA Stop codon UAG Stop codon	UGU UGC Cysteine UGA Stop codon UGG Tryptophan	U C A G
C	CUU CUC CUA CUG Leucine	CCU CCC CCA CCG Proline	CAU CAC Histidine CAA CAG Glutamine	CGU CGC CGA CGG Arginine	U C A G
A	AUU AUC AUA Isoleucine AUG Methionine; start codon	ACU ACC ACA ACG Threonine	AAU AAC Asparagine AAA AAG Lysine	AGU AGC Serine AGA AGG Arginine	U C A G
G	GUU GUC GUA GUG Valine	GCU GCC GCA GCG Alanine	GAU GAC Aspartic acid GAA GAG Glutamic acid	GGU GGC GGA GGG Glycine	U C A G

First letter (left) · Third letter (right)

FIGURE 10.11 The Genetic Code *(Page 197)*

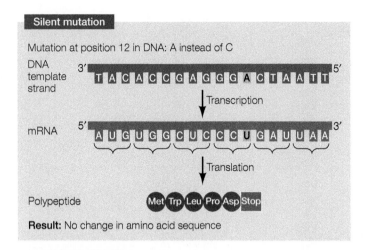

Silent mutation

Mutation at position 12 in DNA: A instead of C

Result: No change in amino acid sequence

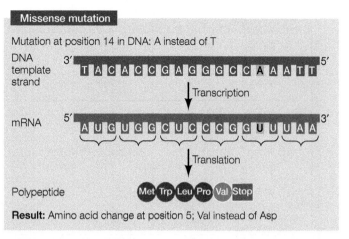

Missense mutation

Mutation at position 14 in DNA: A instead of T

Result: Amino acid change at position 5; Val instead of Asp

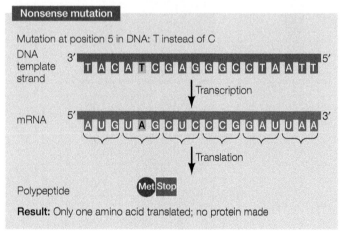

Nonsense mutation

Mutation at position 5 in DNA: T instead of C

Result: Only one amino acid translated; no protein made

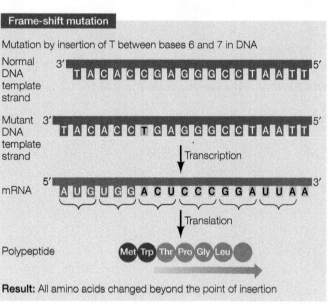

Frame-shift mutation

Mutation by insertion of T between bases 6 and 7 in DNA

Result: All amino acids changed beyond the point of insertion

FIGURE 10.12 Mutations *(Page 198)*

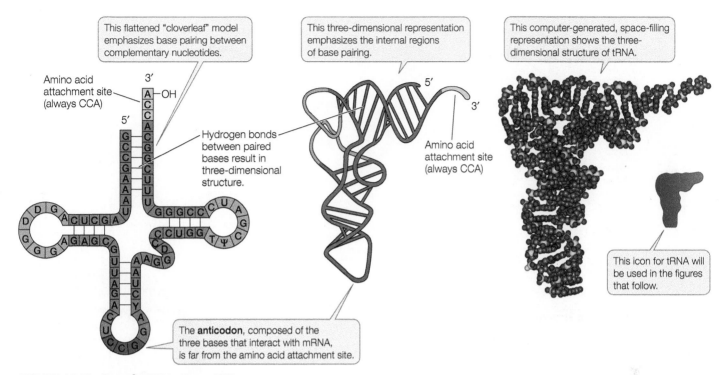

This flattened "cloverleaf" model emphasizes base pairing between complementary nucleotides.

This three-dimensional representation emphasizes the internal regions of base pairing.

This computer-generated, space-filling representation shows the three-dimensional structure of tRNA.

Amino acid attachment site (always CCA)

Hydrogen bonds between paired bases result in three-dimensional structure.

Amino acid attachment site (always CCA)

This icon for tRNA will be used in the figures that follow.

The **anticodon**, composed of the three bases that interact with mRNA, is far from the amino acid attachment site.

FIGURE 10.13 Transfer RNA (Page 199)

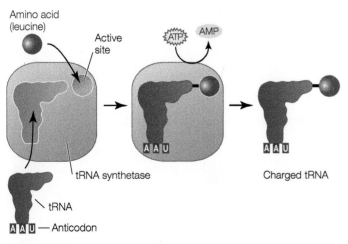

Amino acid (leucine)

Active site

ATP

AMP

tRNA synthetase

Charged tRNA

tRNA

Anticodon

IN-TEXT ART (Page 200)

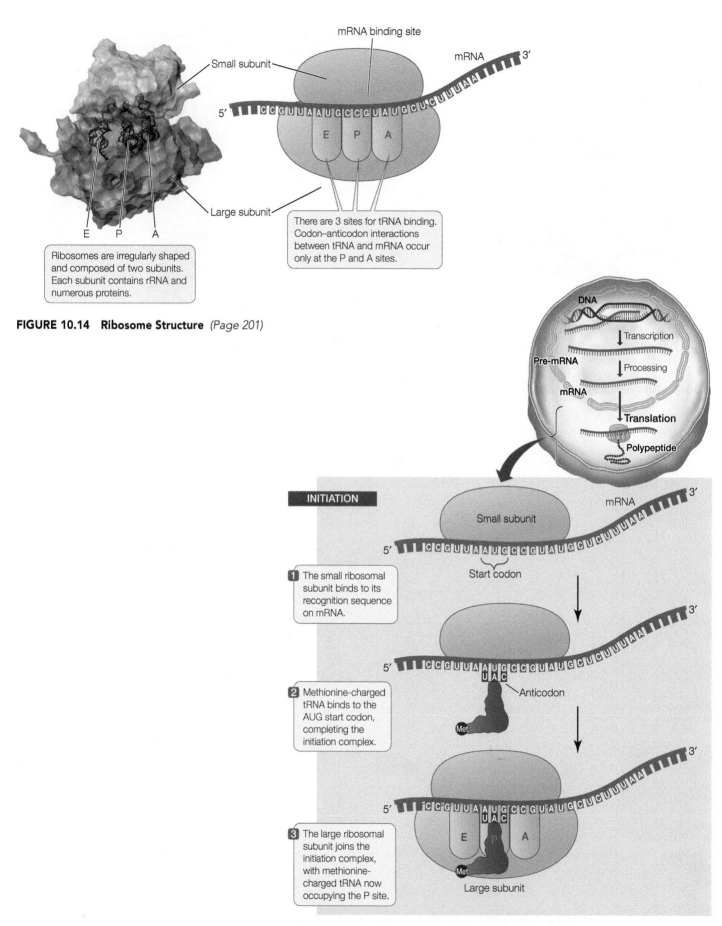

FIGURE 10.14   Ribosome Structure *(Page 201)*

FIGURE 10.15   The Initiation of Translation *(Page 201)*

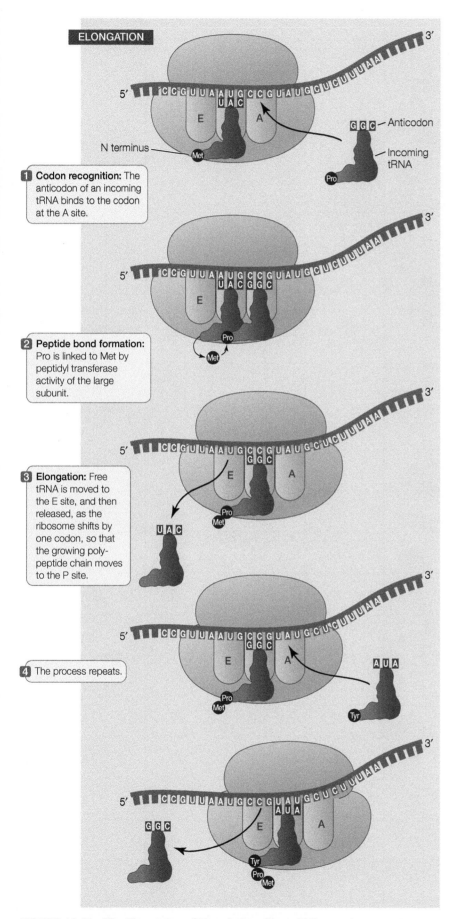

FIGURE 10.16   The Elongation of Translation *(Page 202)*

TERMINATION

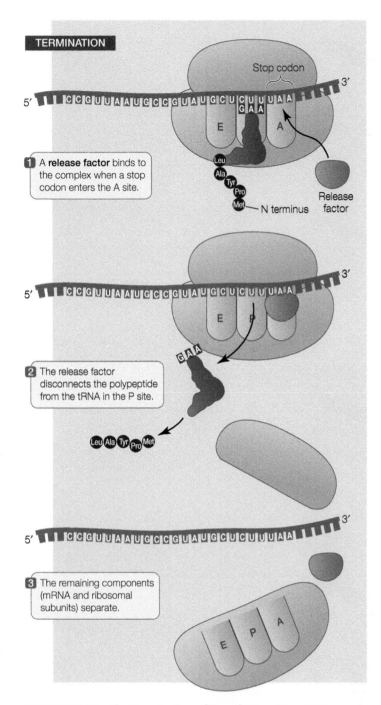

1 A **release factor** binds to the complex when a stop codon enters the A site.

2 The release factor disconnects the polypeptide from the tRNA in the P site.

3 The remaining components (mRNA and ribosomal subunits) separate.

FIGURE 10.17 The Termination of Translation *(Page 203)*

TABLE 10.2	Signals that Start and Stop Transcription and Translation	
	TRANSCRIPTION	**TRANSLATION**
Initiation	Promoter DNA	AUG start codon in the mRNA
Termination	Terminator DNA	UAA, UAG, or UGA in the mRNA

(Page 203)

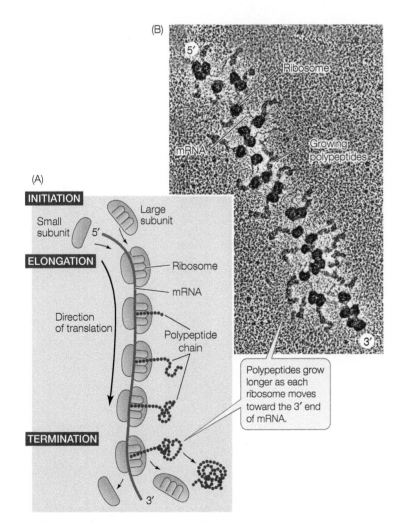

FIGURE 10.18 A Polysome *(Page 203)*

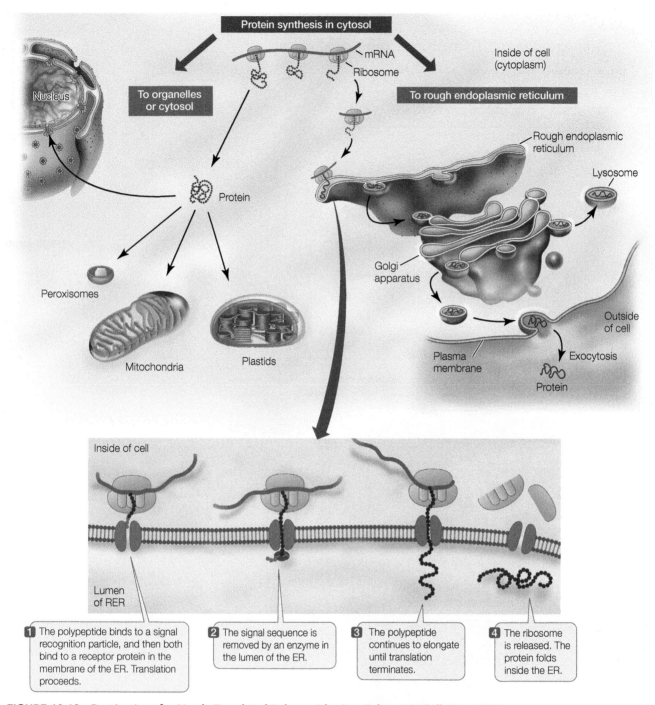

Protein synthesis in cytosol

To organelles or cytosol

To rough endoplasmic reticulum

mRNA
Ribosome

Inside of cell (cytoplasm)

Nucleus

Protein

Peroxisomes

Mitochondria

Plastids

Rough endoplasmic reticulum

Lysosome

Golgi apparatus

Plasma membrane

Outside of cell

Exocytosis

Protein

Inside of cell

Lumen of RER

1 The polypeptide binds to a signal recognition particle, and then both bind to a receptor protein in the membrane of the ER. Translation proceeds.

2 The signal sequence is removed by an enzyme in the lumen of the ER.

3 The polypeptide continues to elongate until translation terminates.

4 The ribosome is released. The protein folds inside the ER.

FIGURE 10.19 Destinations for Newly Translated Polypeptides in a Eukaryotic Cell *(Page 204)*

INVESTIGATION

FIGURE 10.20 Testing the Signal   A series of experiments were used to test whether the nuclear localization signal (NLS) sequence is all that is needed to direct a protein to the nucleus.

HYPOTHESIS

A nuclear localization signal (NLS) is necessary for import of a protein into the nucleus.

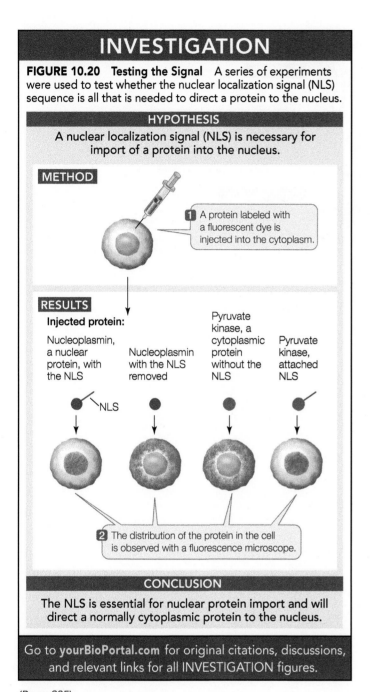

METHOD

1 A protein labeled with a fluorescent dye is injected into the cytoplasm.

RESULTS

Injected protein:

Nucleoplasmin, a nuclear protein, with the NLS

Nucleoplasmin with the NLS removed

Pyruvate kinase, a cytoplasmic protein without the NLS

Pyruvate kinase, attached NLS

NLS

2 The distribution of the protein in the cell is observed with a fluorescence microscope.

CONCLUSION

The NLS is essential for nuclear protein import and will direct a normally cytoplasmic protein to the nucleus.

Go to **yourBioPortal.com** for original citations, discussions, and relevant links for all INVESTIGATION figures.

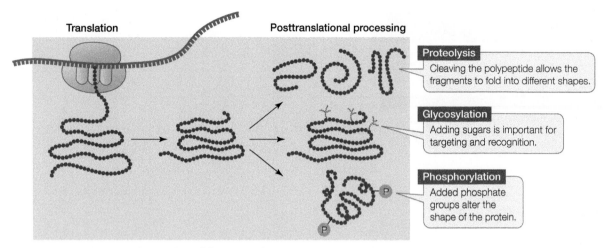

FIGURE 10.21 Posttranslational Modifications of Proteins *(Page 206)*

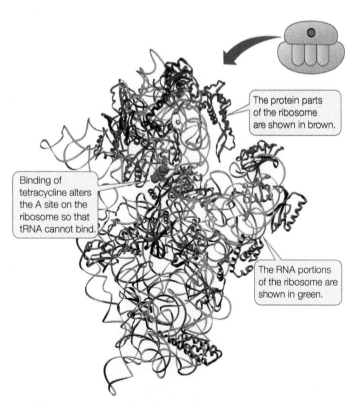

FIGURE 10.22 **An Antibiotic at the Ribosome** *(Page 206)*

Regulation of Gene Expression

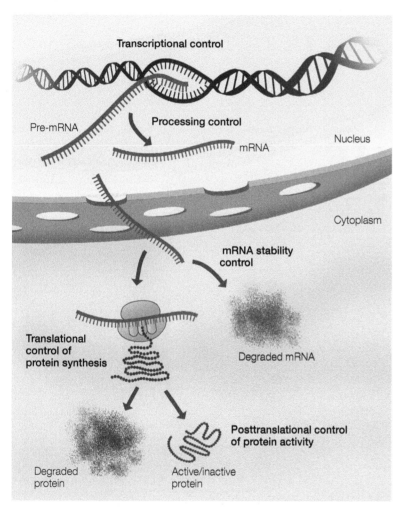

FIGURE 11.1 Potential Points for the Regulation of Gene Expression
(Page 209)

(A) Negative regulation

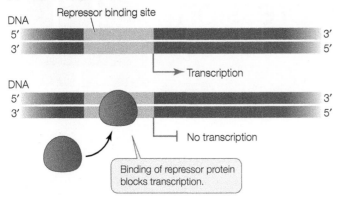

(B) Positive regulation

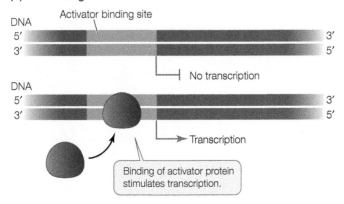

FIGURE 11.2 Positive and Negative Regulation *(Page 210)*

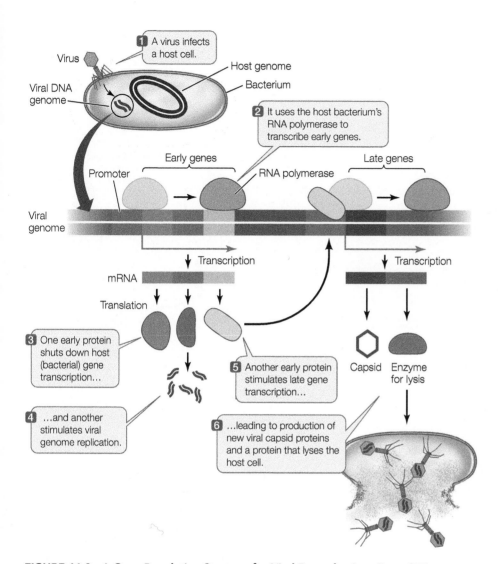

FIGURE 11.3   A Gene Regulation Strategy for Viral Reproduction *(Page 211)*

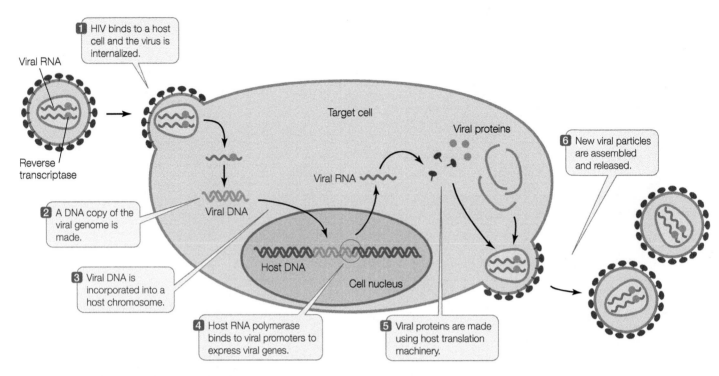

FIGURE 11.4 The Reproductive Cycle of HIV *(Page 211)*

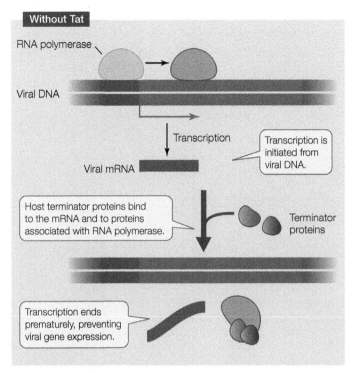

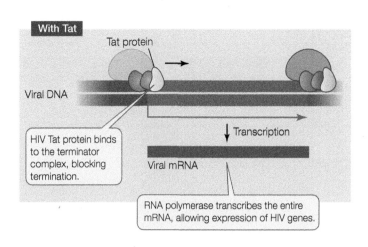

FIGURE 11.5 **Regulation of Transcription by HIV** *(Page 212)*

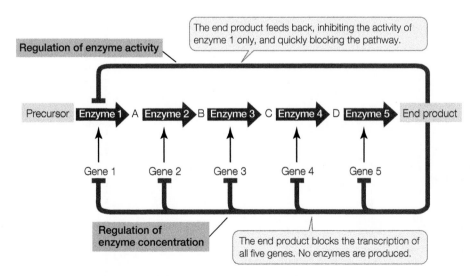

FIGURE 11.6 **Two Ways to Regulate a Metabolic Pathway** *(Page 213)*

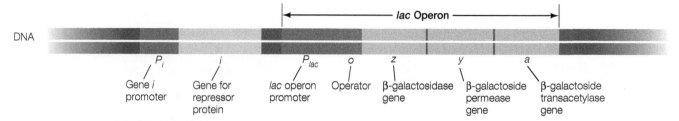

FIGURE 11.7   The *lac* Operon of *E. coli* *(Page 213)*

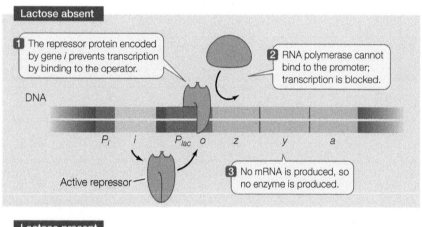

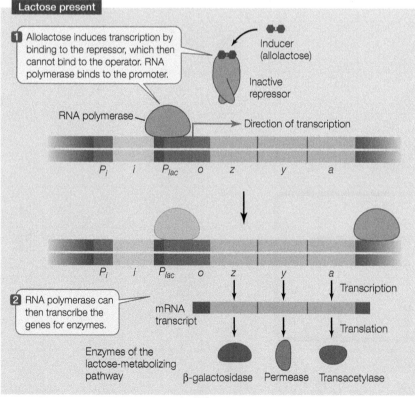

FIGURE 11.8   The *lac* Operon: An Inducible System *(Page 214)*

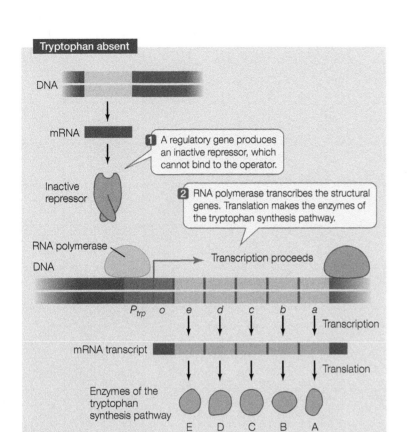

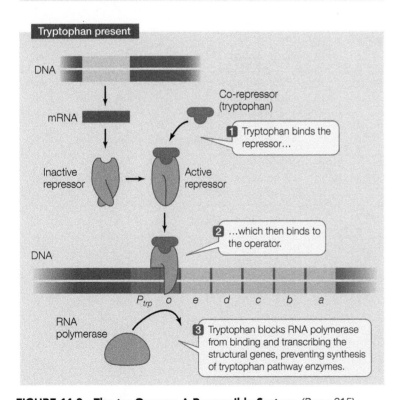

FIGURE 11.9 The *trp* Operon: A Repressible System *(Page 215)*

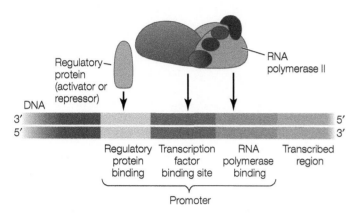

IN-TEXT ART *(Page 216)*

TABLE 11.1	Transcription in Bacteria and Eukaryotes	
CHARACTERISTIC	**BACTERIA**	**EUKARYOTES**
Locations of functionally related genes	Often clustered in operons	Often distant from one another with separate promoters
RNA polymerases	One	Three: I: transcribes rRNA II: transcribes mRNA III: transcribes tRNA and small RNAs
Promoters and other regulatory sequences	Few	Many
Initiation of transcription	Binding of RNA polymerase	Binding of many proteins, including RNA polymerase, to promoter

(Page 216)

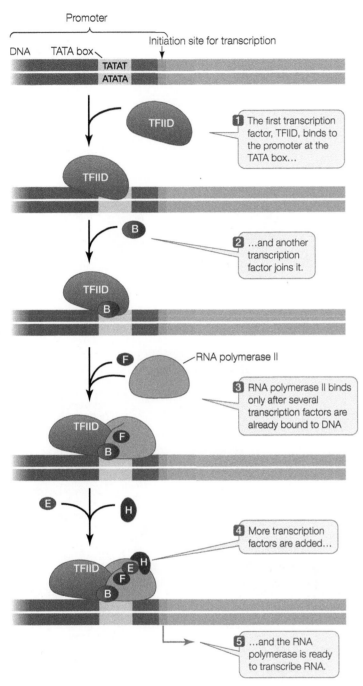

FIGURE 11.10   The Initiation of Transcription in Eukaryotes
(Page 217)

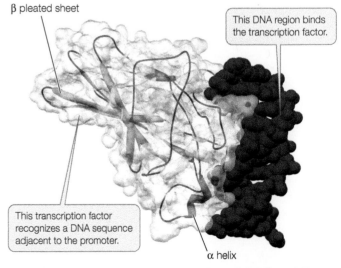

FIGURE 11.11   A Transcription Factor Protein Binds to DNA
(Page 217)

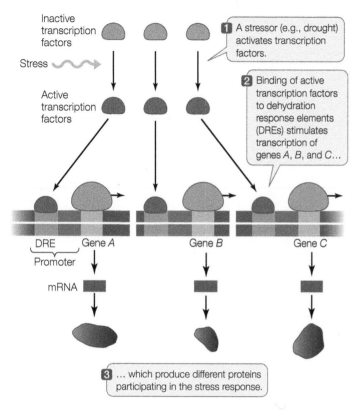

FIGURE 11.12 Coordinating Gene Expression *(Page 218)*

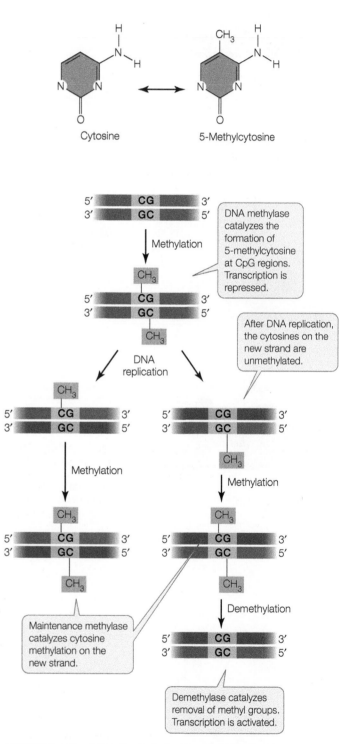

FIGURE 11.13 DNA Methylation: An Epigenetic Change *(Page 218)*

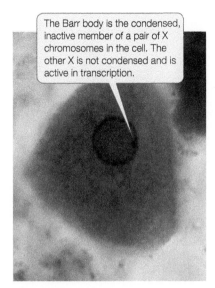

The Barr body is the condensed, inactive member of a pair of X chromosomes in the cell. The other X is not condensed and is active in transcription.

FIGURE 11.14   X Chromosome Inactivation *(Page 219)*

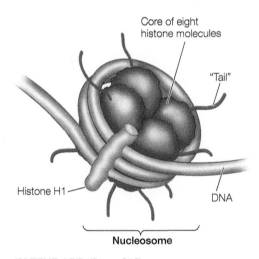

Core of eight histone molecules

"Tail"

Histone H1

DNA

Nucleosome

IN-TEXT ART *(Page 219)*

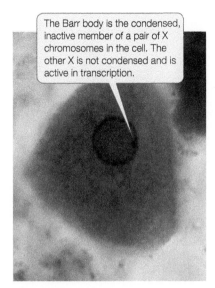

Lysine in histone

Acetyl CoA

Acetyl-lysine

IN-TEXT ART *(Page 219)*

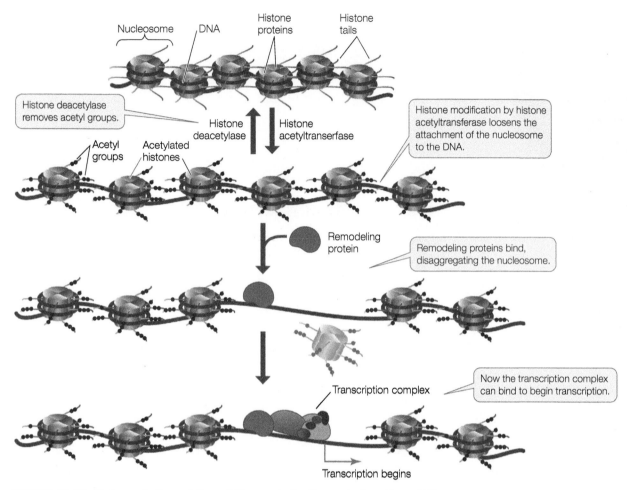

FIGURE 11.15 **Epigenetic Remodeling of Chromatin for Transcription** *(Page 220)*

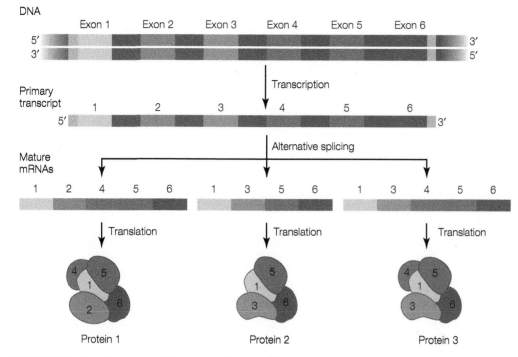

FIGURE 11.16 Alternative Splicing Results in Different Mature mRNAs and Proteins *(Page 221)*

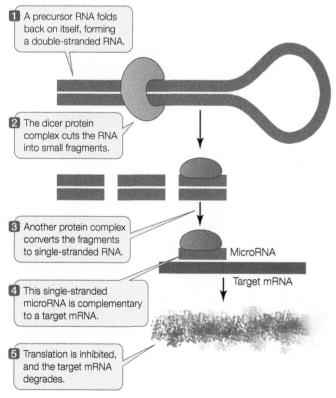

1 A precursor RNA folds back on itself, forming a double-stranded RNA.

2 The dicer protein complex cuts the RNA into small fragments.

3 Another protein complex converts the fragments to single-stranded RNA.

MicroRNA

Target mRNA

4 This single-stranded microRNA is complementary to a target mRNA.

5 Translation is inhibited, and the target mRNA degrades.

FIGURE 11.17 mRNA Degradation Caused by MicroRNAs *(Page 222)*

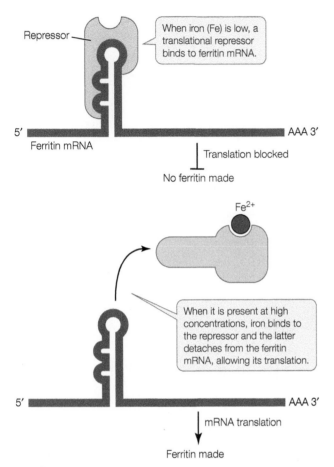

FIGURE 11.18 A Repressor of Translation *(Page 223)*

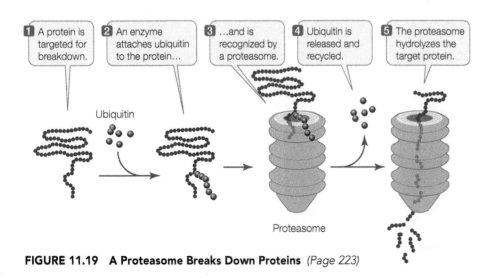

FIGURE 11.19 A Proteasome Breaks Down Proteins *(Page 223)*

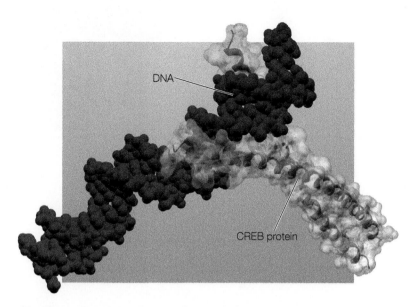

FIGURE 11.20   An Explanation for Alcoholism? *(Page 224)*

(A)

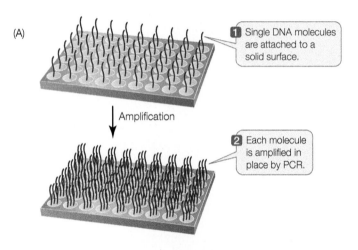

1 Single DNA molecules are attached to a solid surface.

Amplification

2 Each molecule is amplified in place by PCR.

(B)

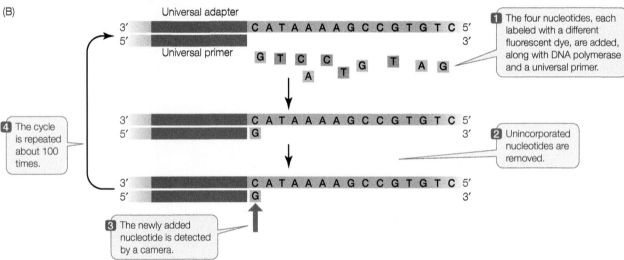

Universal adapter

1 The four nucleotides, each labeled with a different fluorescent dye, are added, along with DNA polymerase and a universal primer.

4 The cycle is repeated about 100 times.

2 Unincorporated nucleotides are removed.

3 The newly added nucleotide is detected by a camera.

FIGURE 12.1 DNA Sequencing *(Page 228)*

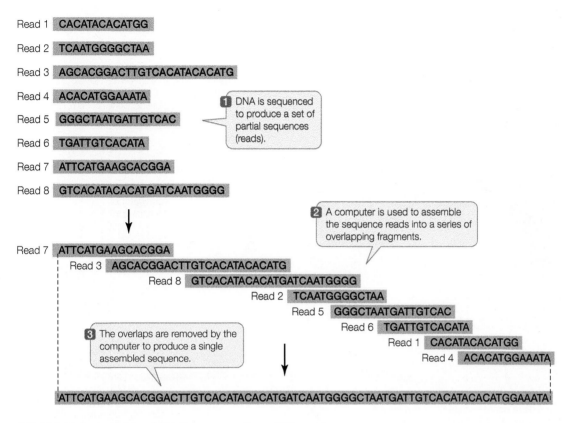

FIGURE 12.2 Arranging DNA Sequences *(Page 229)*

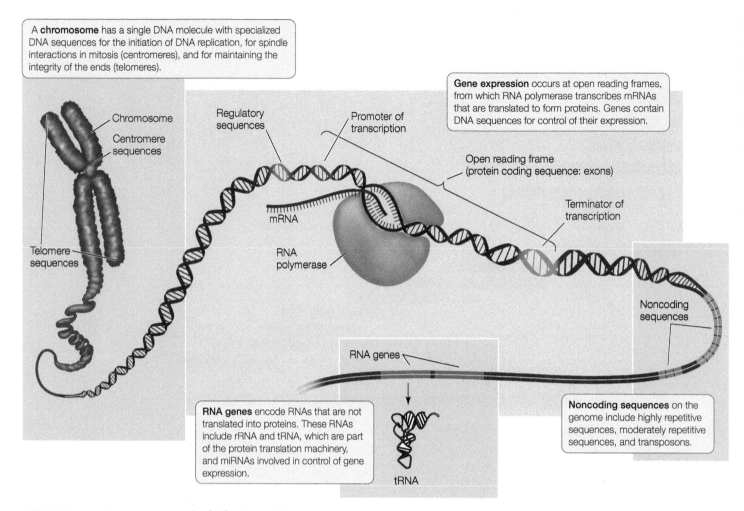

A **chromosome** has a single DNA molecule with specialized DNA sequences for the initiation of DNA replication, for spindle interactions in mitosis (centromeres), and for maintaining the integrity of the ends (telomeres).

Chromosome

Centromere sequences

Telomere sequences

Regulatory sequences

Promoter of transcription

Gene expression occurs at open reading frames, from which RNA polymerase transcribes mRNAs that are translated to form proteins. Genes contain DNA sequences for control of their expression.

Open reading frame (protein coding sequence: exons)

Terminator of transcription

mRNA

RNA polymerase

Noncoding sequences

RNA genes

Noncoding sequences on the genome include highly repetitive sequences, moderately repetitive sequences, and transposons.

RNA genes encode RNAs that are not translated into proteins. These RNAs include rRNA and tRNA, which are part of the protein translation machinery, and miRNAs involved in control of gene expression.

tRNA

FIGURE 12.3 The Genomic Book of Life *(Page 229)*

(A)

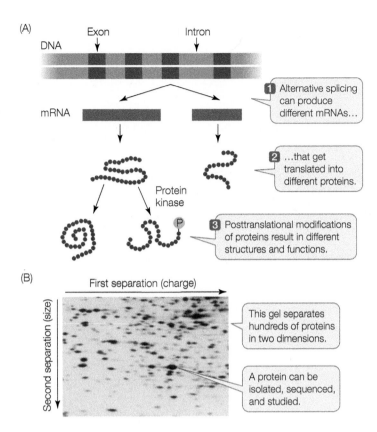

(B)

First separation (charge) →

Second separation (size) ↓

This gel separates hundreds of proteins in two dimensions.

A protein can be isolated, sequenced, and studied.

FIGURE 12.4 Proteomics *(Page 230)*

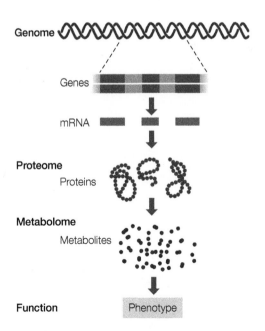

FIGURE 12.5 Genomics, Proteomics, and Metabolomics *(Page 231)*

TABLE 12.1	Gene Functions in Three Bacteria		
	NUMBER OF GENES IN:		
CATEGORY	E. coli	H. influenzae	M. genitalium
Total protein-coding genes	4,288	1,727	482
Biosynthesis of amino acids	131	68	1
Biosynthesis of cofactors	103	54	5
Biosynthesis of nucleotides	58	53	19
Cell envelope proteins	237	84	17
Energy metabolism	243	112	31
Intermediary metabolism	188	30	6
Lipid metabolism	48	25	6
DNA replication, recombination, and repair	115	87	32
Protein folding	9	6	7
Regulatory proteins	178	64	7
Transcription	55	27	12
Translation	182	141	101
Uptake of molecules from the environment	427	123	34

(Page 232)

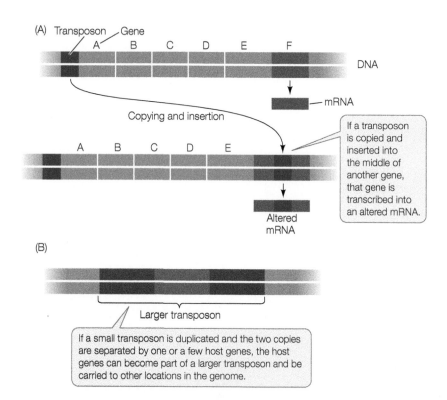

FIGURE 12.6 DNA Sequences That Move *(Page 233)*

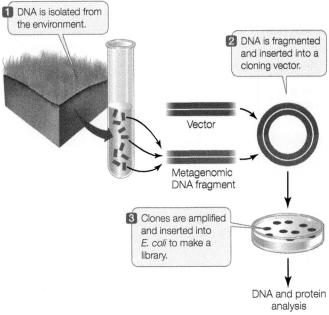

1 DNA is isolated from the environment.

2 DNA is fragmented and inserted into a cloning vector.

Vector

Metagenomic DNA fragment

3 Clones are amplified and inserted into *E. coli* to make a library.

DNA and protein analysis

FIGURE 12.7   Metagenomics *(Page 233)*

INVESTIGATION

FIGURE 12.8   Using Transposon Mutagenesis to Determine the Minimal Genome   *Mycoplasma genitalium* has one of the smallest genomes of any prokaryote. But are all of its genes essential to life? By inactivating the genes one by one, scientists determined which of them are essential for the cell's survival. This research may lead to the construction of artificial cells with customized genomes, designed to perform functions such as degrading oil and making plastics.

HYPOTHESIS

Only some of the genes in a bacterial genome are essential for cell survival.

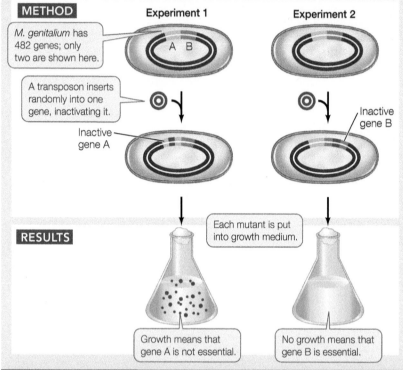

METHOD

Experiment 1

Experiment 2

M. genitalium has 482 genes; only two are shown here.

A B

A transposon inserts randomly into one gene, inactivating it.

Inactive gene A

Inactive gene B

RESULTS

Each mutant is put into growth medium.

Growth means that gene A is not essential.

No growth means that gene B is essential.

CONCLUSION

If each gene is inactivated in turn, a "minimal essential genome" can be determined.

ANALYZE THE DATA

The growth of *M. genitalium* strains with insertions in genes (intragenic regions) was compared with the growth of strains with insertions in noncoding (intergenic) regions of the genome:

Type of insertion	Number of different genes/regions	Number that grew
Intragenic	482	100
Intergenic	199	184

A. Explain these data in terms of genes essential for growth and survival. Are all of the genes in *M. genitalium* essential for growth? If not, how many are essential? Why did some of the insertions in intergenic regions prevent growth?

B. If a transposon inserts into the following regions of genes, there might be no effect on phenotoype. Explain in each case:
(i) near the 3' end of the coding region
(ii) within a gene coding for rRNA

How does this affect your answer to the first question?

Go to **yourBioPortal.com** for original citations, discussions, and relevant links for all INVESTIGATION figures.

TABLE 12.2	Representative Sequenced Genomes			
ORGANISM	HAPLOID GENOME SIZE (Mb)	NUMBER OF GENES	PROTEIN-CODING SEQUENCE	NOTABLE GENES
Bacteria				
M. genitalium	0.58	482	88%	Minimal genome
H. influenzae	1.8	1,738	89%	
E. coli	4.6	4,377	88%	
Yeasts				Targeting; cell organelles
S. cerevisiae	12.1	5,770	70%	
S. pombe	12.1	4,929	60%	
Plants				Photosynthesis; cell walls
A. thaliana	157	28,000	25%	
Rice	394	37,544	12%	Water tolerance for roots
Soybean	1,115	46,000	7%	Lipid synthesis, storage
Animals				
C. elegans	100	19,427	25%	Tissue formation
D. melanogaster	130	13,379	13%	Embryonic development
Human	3,200	24,000	1.2%	

Mb = millions of base pairs

(Page 235)

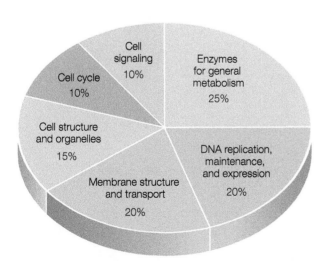

FIGURE 12.9 Functions of the Eukaryotic Genome (Page 236)

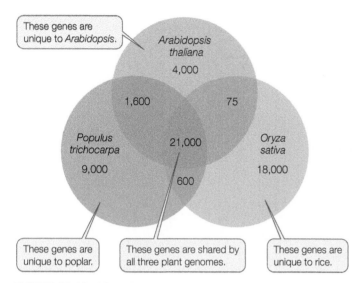

FIGURE 12.10 **Plant Genomes** *(Page 237)*

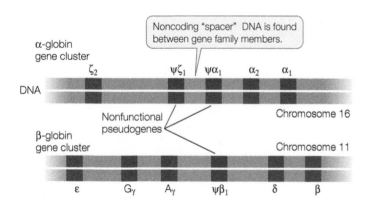

FIGURE 12.11 **The Globin Gene Family** *(Page 237)*

TABLE 12.3	Types of Sequences in Eukaryotic Genomes		
CATEGORY		**TRANSCRIBED**	**TRANSLATED**
Single-copy genes			
Promoters and expression control sequences		No	No
Introns		Yes	No
Exons		Yes	Yes
Moderately repetitive sequences			
rRNA and tRNA genes		Yes	No
Transposons			
I. Retrotransposons			
LTR retrotransposons		Yes	No
SINEs		Yes	No
LINEs		Yes	Yes
II. DNA transposons		Yes	Yes
Highly repetitive short sequences		No	No

(Page 238)

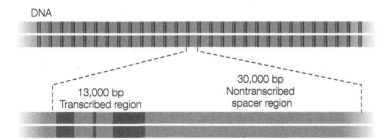

IN-TEXT ART *(Page 238)*

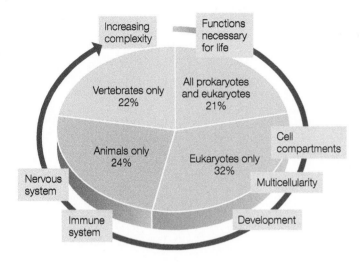

FIGURE 12.12 Evolution of the Genome *(Page 239)*

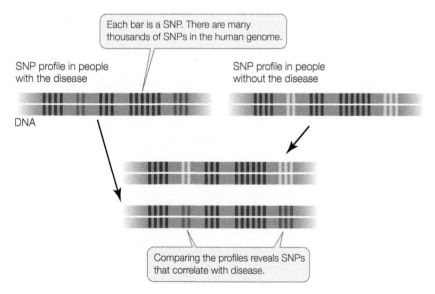

FIGURE 12.13 SNP Genotyping and Disease *(Page 240)*

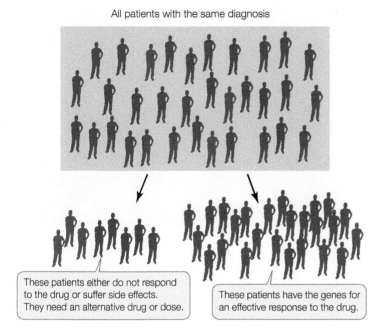

All patients with the same diagnosis

These patients either do not respond to the drug or suffer side effects. They need an alternative drug or dose.

These patients have the genes for an effective response to the drug.

FIGURE 12.14 Pharmacogenomics *(Page 241)*

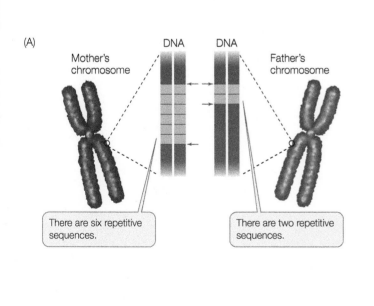

(A)

DNA   DNA

Mother's
chromosome

Father's
chromosome

There are six repetitive sequences.

There are two repetitive sequences.

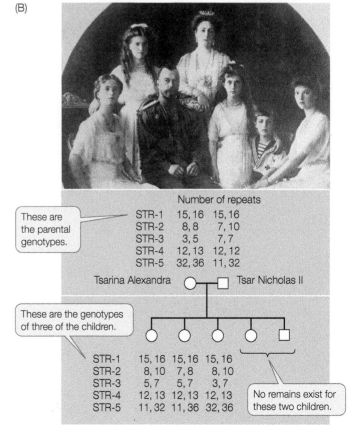

(B)

	Number of repeats	
STR-1	15, 16	15, 16
STR-2	8, 8	7, 10
STR-3	3, 5	7, 7
STR-4	12, 13	12, 12
STR-5	32, 36	11, 32

These are the parental genotypes.

Tsarina Alexandra ○——□ Tsar Nicholas II

These are the genotypes of three of the children.

STR-1	15, 16	15, 16	15, 16
STR-2	8, 10	7, 8	8, 10
STR-3	5, 7	5, 7	3, 7
STR-4	12, 13	12, 13	12, 13
STR-5	11, 32	11, 36	32, 36

No remains exist for these two children.

FIGURE 12.15 DNA Fingerprinting *(Page 242)*

(A)

(B)

FIGURE 12.16 Muscular Gene *(Page 243)*

*Bam*HI
```
5′··· G̲G A T C C ··· 3′
3′··· C C T A G̲G ··· 5′
```

*Hind*III
```
5′··· A̲A G C T T ··· 3′
3′··· T T C G A̲A ··· 5′
```

*Eco*RI
```
5′··· G̲A A T T C ··· 3′
3′··· C T T A A̲G ··· 5′
```

IN-TEXT ART *(Page 245)*

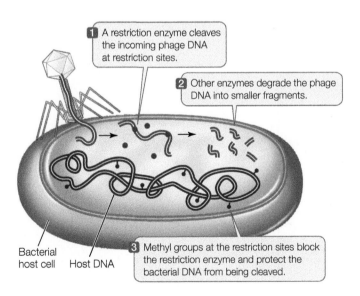

1 A restriction enzyme cleaves the incoming phage DNA at restriction sites.

2 Other enzymes degrade the phage DNA into smaller fragments.

3 Methyl groups at the restriction sites block the restriction enzyme and protect the bacterial DNA from being cleaved.

Bacterial host cell   Host DNA

FIGURE 13.1   Bacteria Fight Invading Viruses by Making Restriction Enzymes *(Page 245)*

RESEARCH TOOLS

FIGURE 13.2 Separating Fragments of DNA by Gel Electrophoresis
A mixture of DNA fragments is placed in a gel and an electric field is applied across the gel. The negatively charged DNA moves toward the positive end of the field, with smaller molecules moving faster than larger ones. After minutes to hours for separation, the electric power is shut off and the separated fragments can be analyzed.

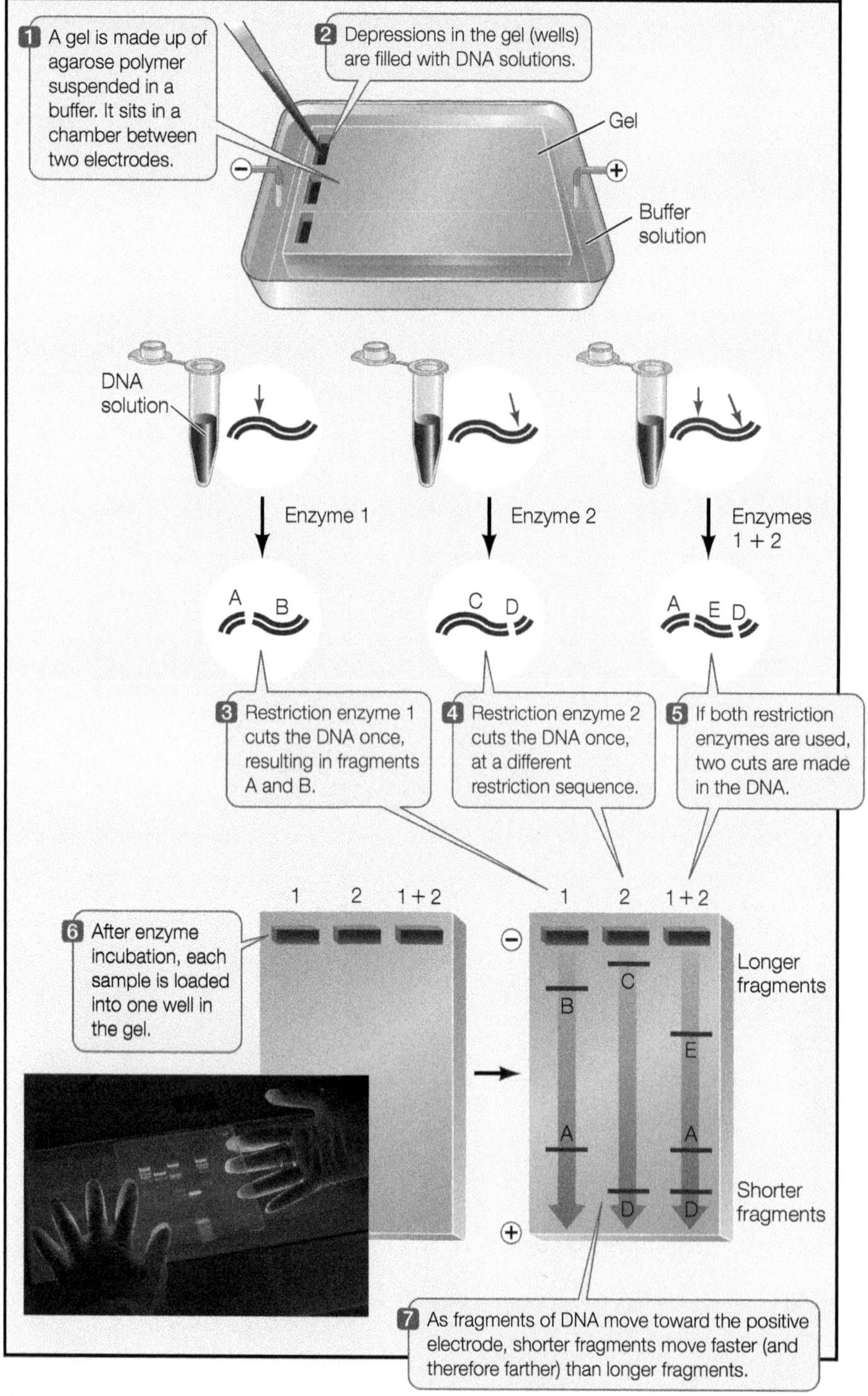
1 A gel is made up of agarose polymer suspended in a buffer. It sits in a chamber between two electrodes.
2 Depressions in the gel (wells) are filled with DNA solutions.
Gel
Buffer solution
DNA solution
Enzyme 1
Enzyme 2
Enzymes 1 + 2
A B
C D
A E D
3 Restriction enzyme 1 cuts the DNA once, resulting in fragments A and B.
4 Restriction enzyme 2 cuts the DNA once, at a different restriction sequence.
5 If both restriction enzymes are used, two cuts are made in the DNA.
1 2 1+2
6 After enzyme incubation, each sample is loaded into one well in the gel.
Longer fragments
Shorter fragments
B C E A A D D
7 As fragments of DNA move toward the positive electrode, shorter fragments move faster (and therefore farther) than longer fragments.

(Page 246)

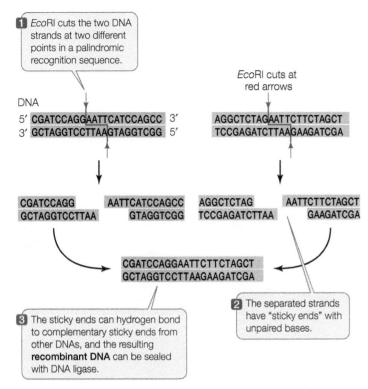

FIGURE 13.3   Cutting, Splicing, and Joining DNA *(Page 247)*

INVESTIGATION

FIGURE 13.4 Recombinant DNA With the discovery of restriction enzymes and DNA ligase, it became possible to combine DNA fragments from different sources in the laboratory. But would such "recombinant DNA" be functional when inserted into a living cell? The results of this experiment completely changed the scope of genetic research, increasing our knowledge of gene structure and function, and ushering in the new field of biotechnology.

HYPOTHESIS

Biologically functional recombinant chromosomes can be made in the laboratory.

METHOD *E. coli* plasmids carrying a gene for resistance to either the antibiotic kanamycin (kan^r) or tetracycline (tet^r) are cut with a restriction enzyme.

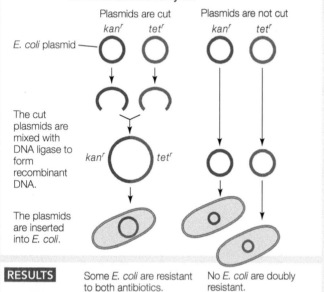

E. coli plasmid

The cut plasmids are mixed with DNA ligase to form recombinant DNA.

The plasmids are inserted into *E. coli*.

RESULTS Some *E. coli* are resistant to both antibiotics. No *E. coli* are doubly resistant.

CONCLUSION

Two DNA fragments with different genes can be joined to make a recombinant DNA molecule, and the resulting DNA is functional.

ANALYZE THE DATA

Two plasmids were used in this study: pSC101 had a gene for resistance to tetracycline and pSC102 had a gene for resistance to kanamycin. Equal quantities of the plasmids—either intact, cut with *Eco*RI, or cut with *Eco*RI and then sealed with DNA ligase—were mixed and incubated with antibiotic-sensitive *E. coli*. The *E. coli* were then grown on various combinations of the antibiotics. Here are the results:

DNA treatment	Number of resistant colonies		
	Tetracycline only	Kanamycin only	Both antibiotics
None	200,000	100,000	200
*Eco*RI cut	10,000	1,100	70
*Eco*RI, then ligase	12,000	1,300	570

A. Did treatment with *Eco*RI affect the transformation efficiency? Explain.
B. Did treatment with DNA ligase affect the transformation efficiency of each cut plasmid? Which quantitative data support your answer?
C. How did doubly antibiotic-resistant bacteria arise in the "none" treatment? (Hint: see Concept 9.3.)
D. Did the *Eco*RI followed by ligase treatment increase the appearance of doubly antibiotic-resistant bacteria? What data support your answer?

For more, go to Working with Data 13.1 at **yourBioPortal.com**.

Go to **yourBioPortal.com** for original citations, discussions, and relevant links for all INVESTIGATION figures.

Plasmid pBR322
Host: *E. coli*

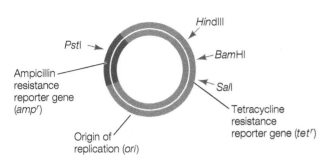

*Pst*I

*Hin*dIII

*Bam*HI

*Sal*I

Ampicillin
resistance
reporter gene
(*amp^r*)

Origin of
replication (*ori*)

Tetracycline
resistance
reporter gene (*tet^r*)

↓ Recognition sites for restriction enzymes

IN-TEXT ART *(Page 249)*

Ti plasmid
Hosts: *Agrobacterium tumefaciens* (plasmid)
and infected plants (T DNA)

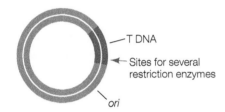

T DNA

Sites for several
restriction enzymes

ori

IN-TEXT ART *(Page 250)*

RESEARCH TOOLS

FIGURE 13.5 Marking Recombinant DNA by Inactivating a Gene Selectable marker (reporter) genes are used by scientists to select for bacteria that have taken up a plasmid. A second reporter gene allows for the identification of bacteria harboring the recombinant plasmid. The host bacteria in this experiment could display any of the three phenotypes indicated in the table.

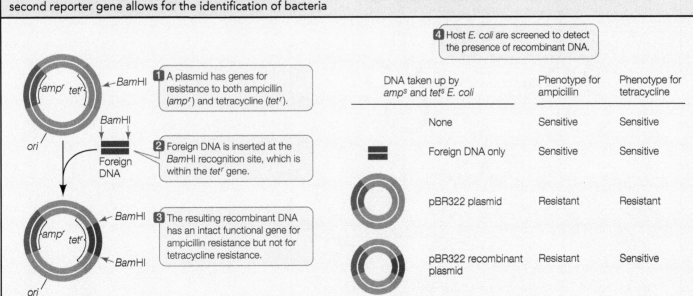

1 A plasmid has genes for resistance to both ampicillin (*amp^r*) and tetracycline (*tet^r*).

2 Foreign DNA is inserted at the *Bam*HI recognition site, which is within the *tet^r* gene.

3 The resulting recombinant DNA has an intact functional gene for ampicillin resistance but not for tetracycline resistance.

4 Host *E. coli* are screened to detect the presence of recombinant DNA.

DNA taken up by *amp^s* and *tet^s E. coli*	Phenotype for ampicillin	Phenotype for tetracycline
None	Sensitive	Sensitive
Foreign DNA only	Sensitive	Sensitive
pBR322 plasmid	Resistant	Resistant
pBR322 recombinant plasmid	Resistant	Sensitive

(Page 250)

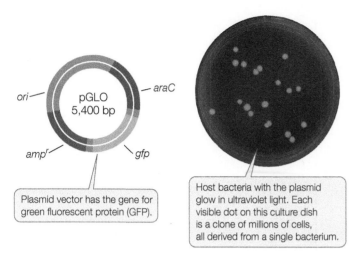

Plasmid vector has the gene for green fluorescent protein (GFP).

Host bacteria with the plasmid glow in ultraviolet light. Each visible dot on this culture dish is a clone of millions of cells, all derived from a single bacterium.

FIGURE 13.6   Green Fluorescent Protein as a Reporter
(Page 251)

RESEARCH TOOLS

FIGURE 13.7   Constructing Libraries   Intact genomic DNA is too large to be introduced into host cells. A genomic library can be made by breaking the DNA into small fragments, incorporating the fragments into a vector, and then transforming host cells with the recombinant vectors. Each colony of cells contains many copies of a small part of the genome. Similarly, there are many mRNAs in a cell. These can be copied into cDNAs and a library made from them. The DNA in these colonies can then be isolated for analysis.

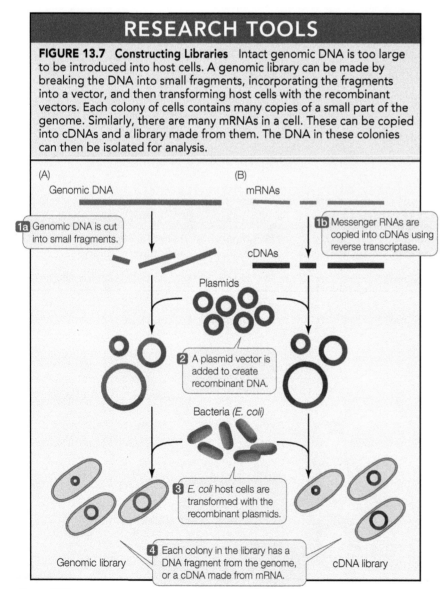

(A) Genomic DNA

(B) mRNAs

1a Genomic DNA is cut into small fragments.

1b Messenger RNAs are copied into cDNAs using reverse transcriptase.

cDNAs

Plasmids

2 A plasmid vector is added to create recombinant DNA.

Bacteria (E. coli)

3 E. coli host cells are transformed with the recombinant plasmids.

Genomic library

cDNA library

4 Each colony in the library has a DNA fragment from the genome, or a cDNA made from mRNA.

RESEARCH TOOLS

FIGURE 13.8 Making a Knockout Mouse Animals carrying mutations are rare. Homologous recombination is used to replace a normal mouse gene with an inactivated copy of that gene, thus "knocking out" the gene. Discovering what happens to a mouse with an inactive gene tells us much about the normal role of that gene.

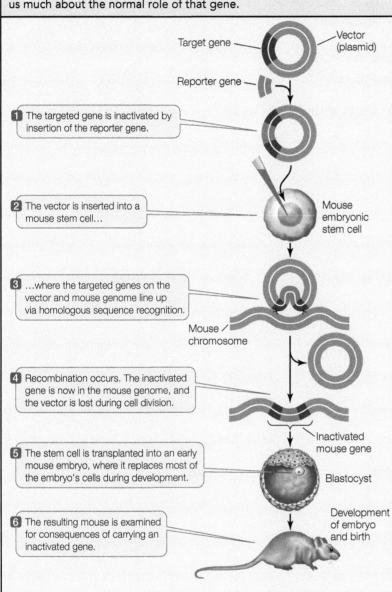

Target gene
Vector (plasmid)

Reporter gene

1 The targeted gene is inactivated by insertion of the reporter gene.

2 The vector is inserted into a mouse stem cell...

Mouse embryonic stem cell

3 ...where the targeted genes on the vector and mouse genome line up via homologous sequence recognition.

Mouse chromosome

4 Recombination occurs. The inactivated gene is now in the mouse genome, and the vector is lost during cell division.

Inactivated mouse gene

5 The stem cell is transplanted into an early mouse embryo, where it replaces most of the embryo's cells during development.

Blastocyst

Development of embryo and birth

6 The resulting mouse is examined for consequences of carrying an inactivated gene.

(Page 253)

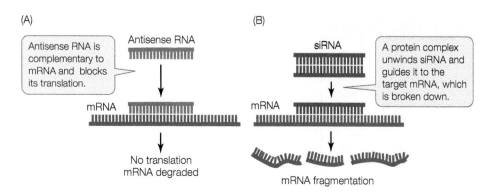

(A)

Antisense RNA is complementary to mRNA and blocks its translation.

Antisense RNA

mRNA

No translation
mRNA degraded

(B)

siRNA

A protein complex unwinds siRNA and guides it to the target mRNA, which is broken down.

mRNA

mRNA fragmentation

FIGURE 13.9   Using Antisense RNA and siRNA to Block the Translation of mRNA
(Page 254)

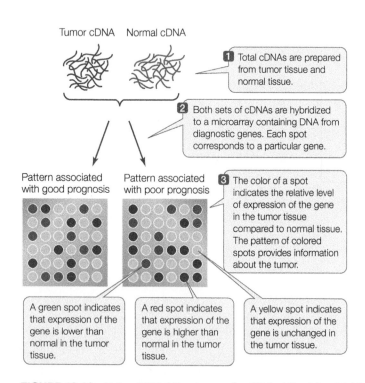

Tumor cDNA   Normal cDNA

1 Total cDNAs are prepared from tumor tissue and normal tissue.

2 Both sets of cDNAs are hybridized to a microarray containing DNA from diagnostic genes. Each spot corresponds to a particular gene.

Pattern associated with good prognosis

Pattern associated with poor prognosis

3 The color of a spot indicates the relative level of expression of the gene in the tumor tissue compared to normal tissue. The pattern of colored spots provides information about the tumor.

A green spot indicates that expression of the gene is lower than normal in the tumor tissue.

A red spot indicates that expression of the gene is higher than normal in the tumor tissue.

A yellow spot indicates that expression of the gene is unchanged in the tumor tissue.

FIGURE 13.10   Using DNA Microarrays for Clinical Decision-Making
(Page 255)

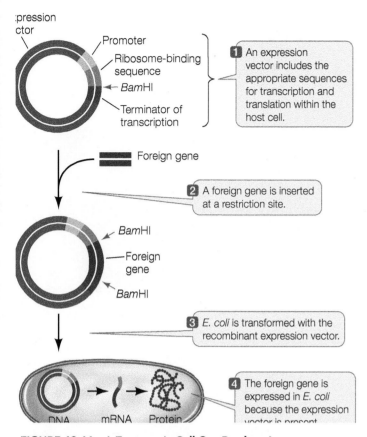

FIGURE 13.11   A Transgenic Cell Can Produce Large Amounts of the Transgene's Protein Product *(Page 256)*

TABLE 13.1	Some Medically Useful Products of Biotechnology
PRODUCT	**USE**
Erythropoietin	Prevents anemia in patients undergoing kidney dialysis and cancer therapy
Colony-stimulating factor	Stimulates production of white blood cells in patients with cancer and AIDS
Bovine/porcine somatotropin	Stimulates growth and milk production in animals
Tissue plasminogen activator	Dissolves blood clots after heart attacks and strokes
Human growth hormone	Replaces missing hormone in people of short stature
Human insulin	Stimulates glucose uptake from blood in patients with type I diabetes mellitus
Factor VIII	Replaces clotting factor missing in patients with hemophilia A
Platelet-derived growth factor	Stimulates wound healing

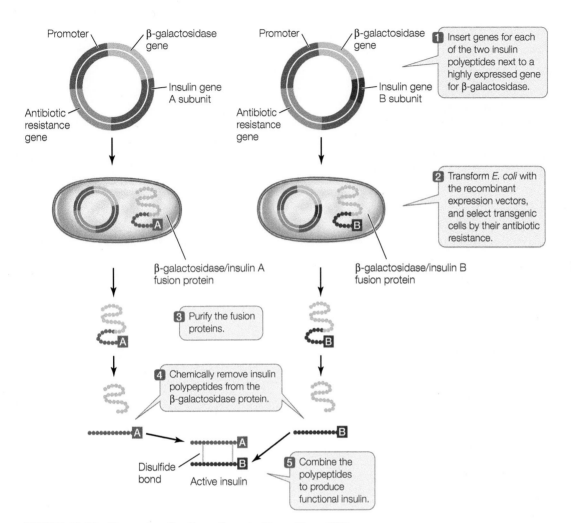

Promoter

β-galactosidase gene

Insulin gene A subunit

Antibiotic resistance gene

Promoter

β-galactosidase gene

Insulin gene B subunit

Antibiotic resistance gene

1 Insert genes for each of the two insulin polyeptides next to a highly expressed gene for β-galactosidase.

2 Transform *E. coli* with the recombinant expression vectors, and select transgenic cells by their antibiotic resistance.

β-galactosidase/insulin A fusion protein

β-galactosidase/insulin B fusion protein

3 Purify the fusion proteins.

4 Chemically remove insulin polypeptides from the β-galactosidase protein.

Disulfide bond

Active insulin

5 Combine the polypeptides to produce functional insulin.

FIGURE 13.12 Human Insulin: From Gene to Drug *(Page 257)*

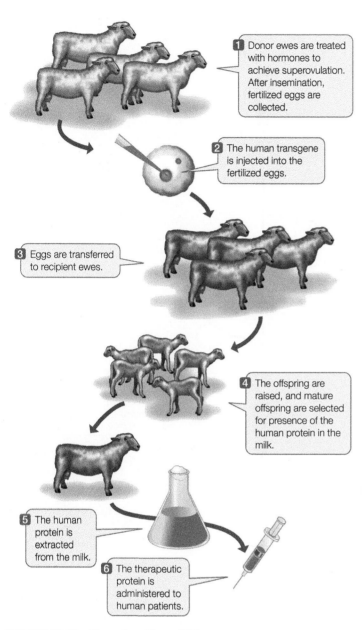

FIGURE 13.13 Pharming *(Page 258)*

TABLE 13.2	Potential Agricultural Applications of Biotechnology
PROBLEM	**TECHNOLOGY/GENES**
Improving the environmental adaptations of plants	Genes for drought tolerance, salt tolerance
Improving nutritional traits	High-lysine seeds; β-carotene in rice
Improving crops after harvest	Delay of fruit ripening; sweeter vegetables
Using plants as bioreactors	Plastics, oils, and drugs produced in plants

(Page 258)

Conventional breeding
Many generations; only gene(s) from same species can be used

Biotechnology
One generation; gene(s) from any organism can be used

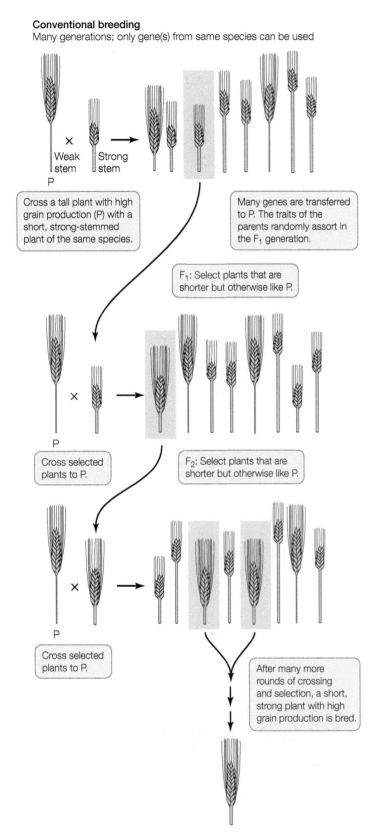

×
Weak stem   Strong stem
P

Cross a tall plant with high grain production (P) with a short, strong-stemmed plant of the same species.

Many genes are transferred to P. The traits of the parents randomly assort in the F_1 generation.

F_1: Select plants that are shorter but otherwise like P.

×
P

Cross selected plants to P.

F_2: Select plants that are shorter but otherwise like P.

×
P

Cross selected plants to P.

After many more rounds of crossing and selection, a short, strong plant with high grain production is bred.

P

Isolate somatic cells from tall plant with high grain production (P).

Construct recombinant DNA with genes for short, strong stems; can be from any organism.

Transform cells of P and produce transgenic plants with short, strong stems and high grain production.

FIGURE 13.14   Genetic Modification of Plants versus Conventional Plant Breeding *(Page 259)*

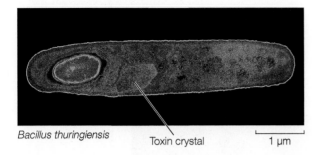

Bacillus thuringiensis   Toxin crystal   1 μm

IN-TEXT ART *(Page 259)*

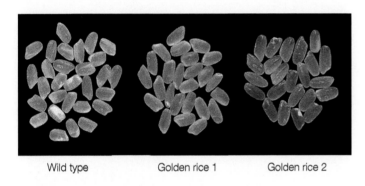

Wild type   Golden rice 1   Golden rice 2

FIGURE 13.15   Transgenic Rice Rich in β-Carotene *(Page 260)*

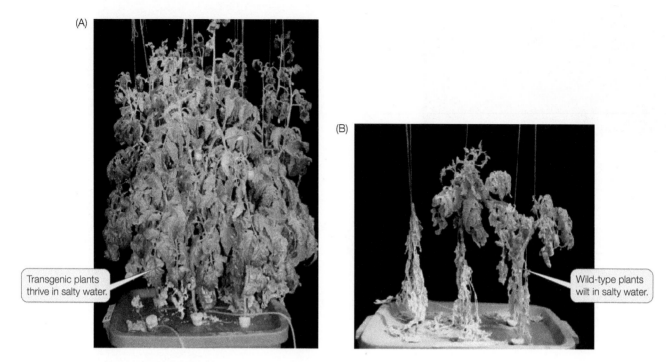

FIGURE 13.16   Salt-tolerant Tomato Plants *(Page 261)*

FIGURE 13.17   The Spoils of War *(Page 262)*

Genes, Development, and Evolution

14

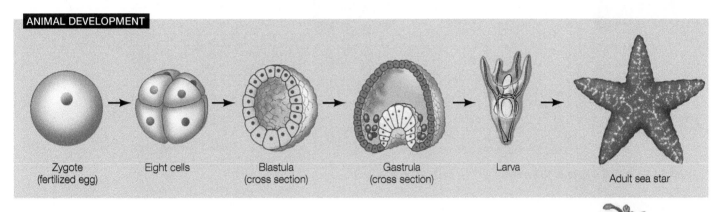

ANIMAL DEVELOPMENT

Zygote (fertilized egg) → Eight cells → Blastula (cross section) → Gastrula (cross section) → Larva → Adult sea star

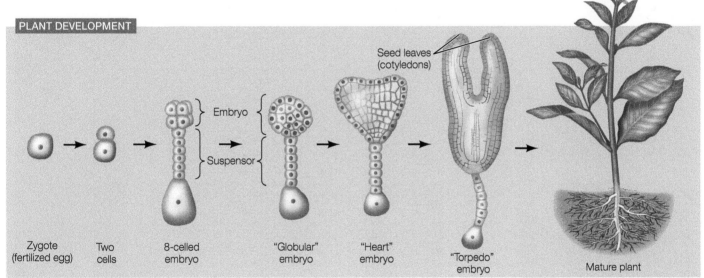

PLANT DEVELOPMENT

Seed leaves (cotyledons)

Embryo

Suspensor

Zygote (fertilized egg) → Two cells → 8-celled embryo → "Globular" embryo → "Heart" embryo → "Torpedo" embryo → Mature plant

FIGURE 14.1   Development *(Page 264)*

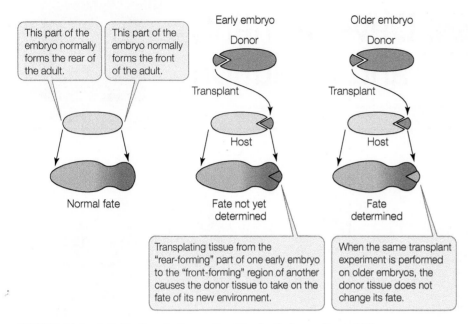

FIGURE 14.2   A Cell's Fate Is Determined in the Embryo *(Page 265)*

INVESTIGATION

FIGURE 14.3 Cloning a Plant   When cells were removed from a plant and put into a medium with nutrients and hormones, they lost many of their specialized features—in other words, they dedifferentiated and became totipotent.

HYPOTHESIS

Differentiated plant cells can be totipotent and can be induced to generate all types of the plant's cells.

METHOD

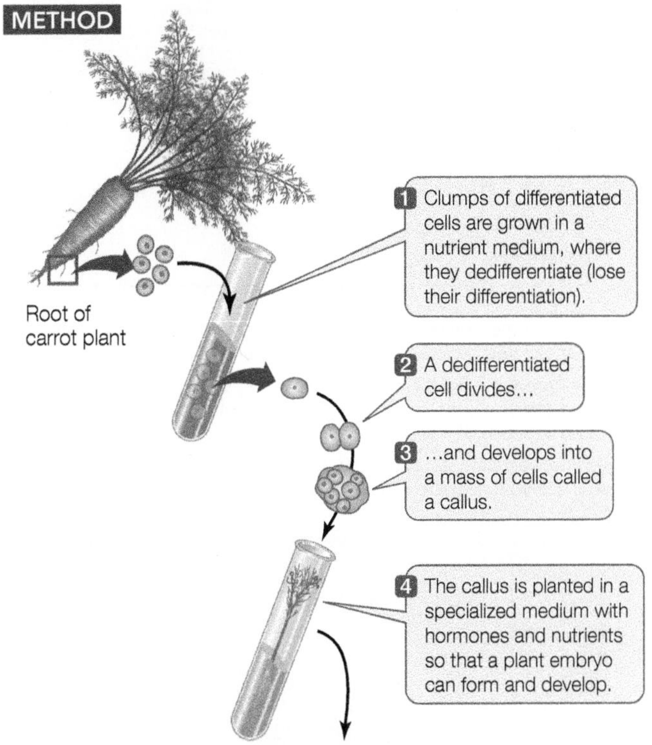

Root of carrot plant

1 Clumps of differentiated cells are grown in a nutrient medium, where they dedifferentiate (lose their differentiation).

2 A dedifferentiated cell divides...

3 ...and develops into a mass of cells called a callus.

4 The callus is planted in a specialized medium with hormones and nutrients so that a plant embryo can form and develop.

RESULTS

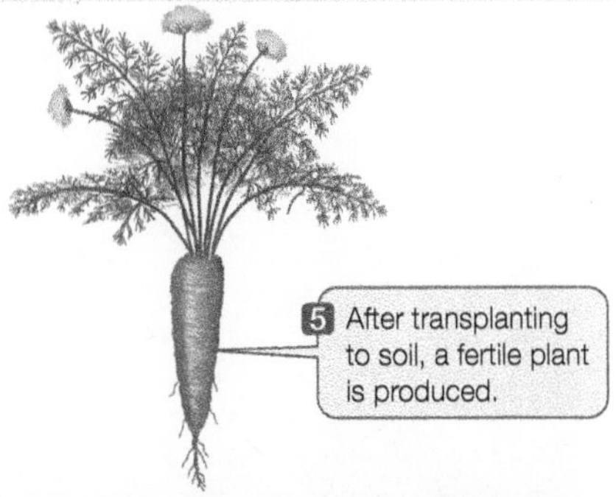

5 After transplanting to soil, a fertile plant is produced.

CONCLUSION

Differentiated plant cells can be totipotent.

Go to **yourBioPortal.com** for original citations, discussions, and relevant links for all INVESTIGATION figures.

INVESTIGATION

FIGURE 14.4 Cloning a Mammal The experimental procedure described here produced the first cloned mammal, a Dorset sheep named Dolly (shown on the left in the photo). As an adult, Dolly mated and subsequently gave birth to a normal offspring (the lamb on the right), thus proving the genetic viability of cloned mammals.

HYPOTHESIS

Differentiated animal cells are totipotent.

METHOD

1. Cells are removed from the udder of a Dorset ewe.

2. An egg is removed from a Scottish blackface ewe.

Dorset sheep (#1)

Scottish blackface sheep (#2)

Nucleus

Micropipette

3. Udder cells are deprived of nutrients in culture to halt the cell cycle prior to DNA replication.

4. The nucleus is removed from the egg.

Donor nucleus (from sheep #1)

Enucleated egg (from sheep #2)

5. The udder cell (donor) and enucleated egg are fused.

6. Mitosis-stimulating inducers cause the cell to divide.

7. An early embryo develops and is transplanted into a receptive ewe.

Scottish blackface sheep (#3)

RESULTS

8. The embryo develops and a Dorset sheep, genetically identical to #1, is born.

CONCLUSION

Differentiated animal cells are totipotent in nuclear transplant experiments.

ANALYZE THE DATA

The team that cloned Dolly the sheep used a nucleus from a mammary epithelium (ME) cell. They also tried cloning by transplanting nuclei from fetal fibroblasts (FB) and embryos (EC), with these results:

Stage	Number of attempts that progressed to each stage		
	ME	FB	EC
Egg fusions	277	172	385
Embryos transferred to recipients	29	34	72
Pregnancies	1	4	14
Live lambs	1	2	4

A. Calculate the percentage survival of eggs from fusion to birth. What can you conclude about the efficiency of cloning?

B. Compare the efficiencies of cloning using different nuclear donors. What can you conclude about the ability of nuclei at different stages to be totipotent?

C. What statistical test would you use to show whether the differences in A and B were significant (see Appendix B)?

For more, go to Working with Data 14.1 at **yourBioPortal.com**.

Go to **yourBioPortal.com** for original citations, discussions, and relevant links for all INVESTIGATION figures.

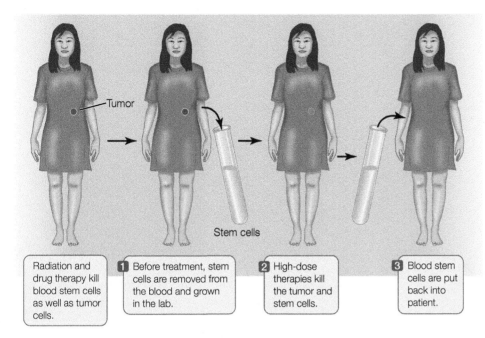

FIGURE 14.5 **Multipotent Stem Cells** *(Page 268)*

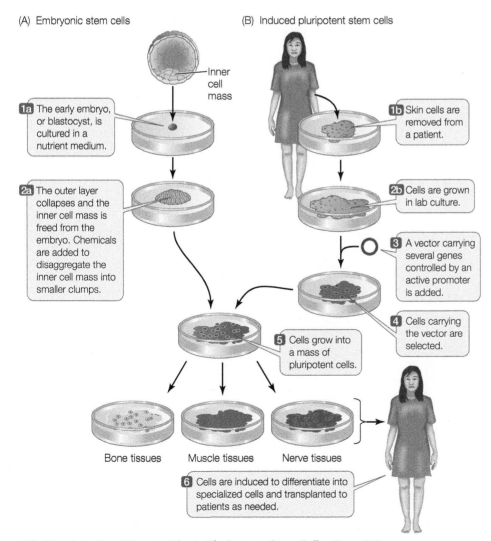

FIGURE 14.6 **Two Ways to Obtain Pluripotent Stem Cells** *(Page 268)*

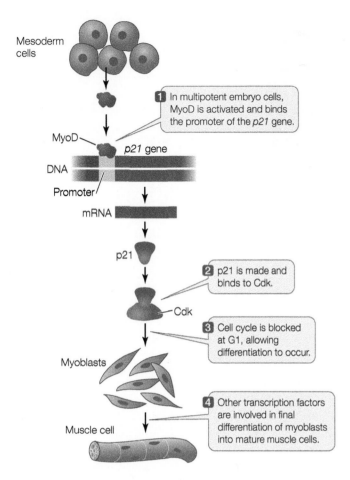

Mesoderm
cells

1 In multipotent embryo cells, MyoD is activated and binds the promoter of the *p21* gene.

MyoD

p21 gene

DNA

Promoter

mRNA

p21

2 p21 is made and binds to Cdk.

Cdk

3 Cell cycle is blocked at G1, allowing differentiation to occur.

Myoblasts

4 Other transcription factors are involved in final differentiation of myoblasts into mature muscle cells.

Muscle cell

FIGURE 14.7   Transcription and Differentiation in the Formation of Muscle Cells *(Page 270)*

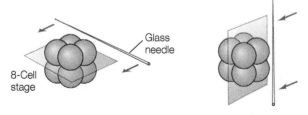

Glass
needle

8-Cell
stage

IN-TEXT ART *(Page 270)*

(A)

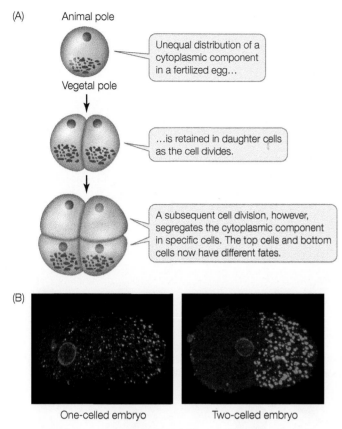

Animal pole

Unequal distribution of a cytoplasmic component in a fertilized egg…

Vegetal pole

…is retained in daughter cells as the cell divides.

A subsequent cell division, however, segregates the cytoplasmic component in specific cells. The top cells and bottom cells now have different fates.

(B)

One-celled embryo　　　Two-celled embryo

FIGURE 14.8　The Concept of Cytoplasmic Segregation *(Page 270)*

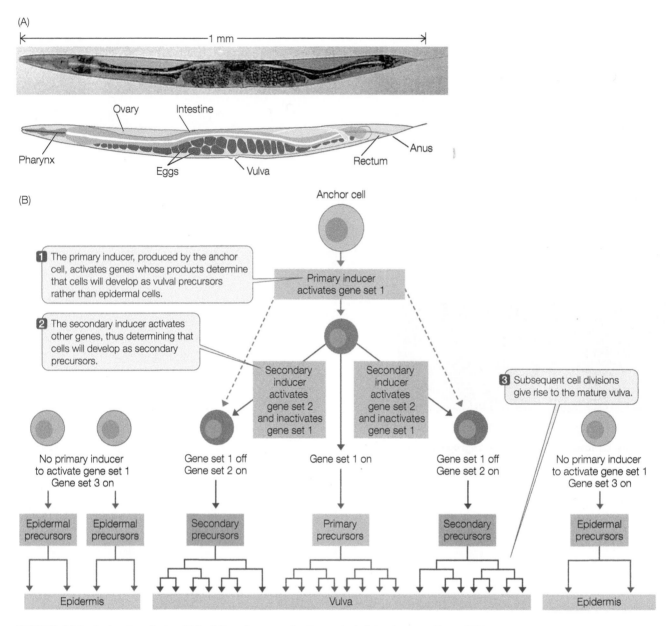

(A)

1 mm

Ovary   Intestine

Pharynx

Eggs   Vulva   Rectum   Anus

(B)

Anchor cell

1 The primary inducer, produced by the anchor cell, activates genes whose products determine that cells will develop as vulval precursors rather than epidermal cells.

Primary inducer activates gene set 1

2 The secondary inducer activates other genes, thus determining that cells will develop as secondary precursors.

Secondary inducer activates gene set 2 and inactivates gene set 1

Secondary inducer activates gene set 2 and inactivates gene set 1

3 Subsequent cell divisions give rise to the mature vulva.

No primary inducer to activate gene set 1
Gene set 3 on

Gene set 1 off
Gene set 2 on

Gene set 1 on

Gene set 1 off
Gene set 2 on

No primary inducer to activate gene set 1
Gene set 3 on

Epidermal precursors

Epidermal precursors

Secondary precursors

Primary precursors

Secondary precursors

Epidermal precursors

Epidermis

Vulva

Epidermis

FIGURE 14.9 Induction during Vulval Development in *Caenorhabditis elegans* *(Page 271)*

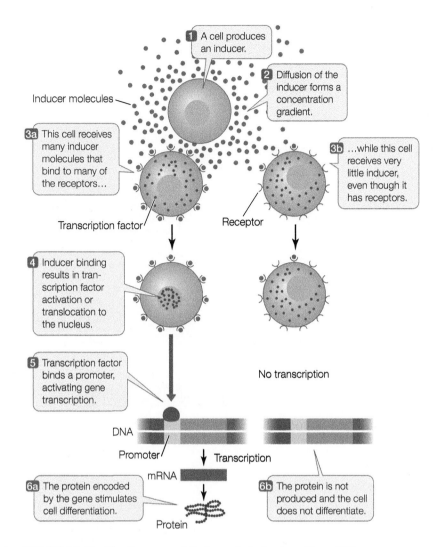

FIGURE 14.10 The Concept of Embryonic Induction (Page 272)

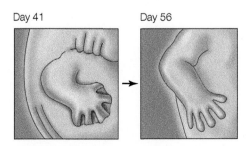

Day 41   Day 56

IN-TEXT ART (Page 273)

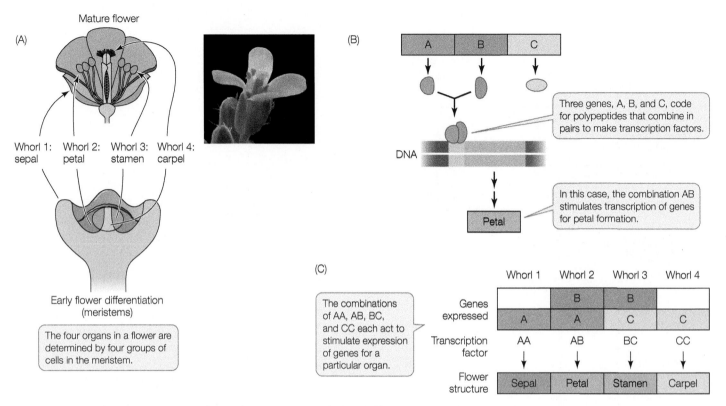

FIGURE 14.11   **Gene Expression and Morphogenesis in *Arabidopsis* Flowers** *(Page 274)*

(A)

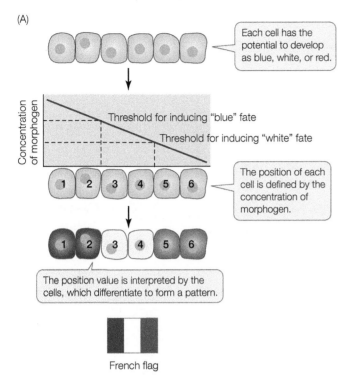

Each cell has the potential to develop as blue, white, or red.

Threshold for inducing "blue" fate

Threshold for inducing "white" fate

The position of each cell is defined by the concentration of morphogen.

The position value is interpreted by the cells, which differentiate to form a pattern.

French flag

FIGURE 14.12   The French Flag Model *(Page 275)*

(B)

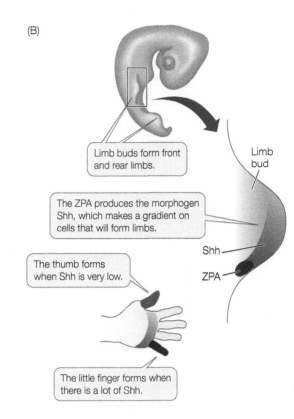

Limb buds form front and rear limbs.

The ZPA produces the morphogen Shh, which makes a gradient on cells that will form limbs.

The thumb forms when Shh is very low.

Limb bud

Shh

ZPA

The little finger forms when there is a lot of Shh.

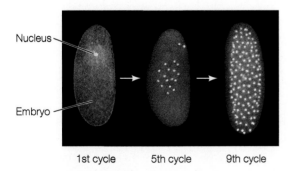

Nucleus

Embryo

1st cycle   5th cycle   9th cycle

IN-TEXT ART *(Page 276)*

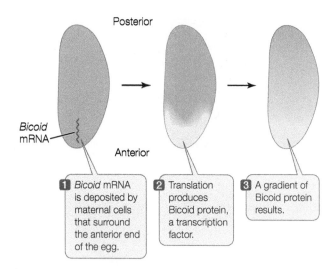

1 *Bicoid* mRNA is deposited by maternal cells that surround the anterior end of the egg.

2 Translation produces Bicoid protein, a transcription factor.

3 A gradient of Bicoid protein results.

IN-TEXT ART *(Page 276)*

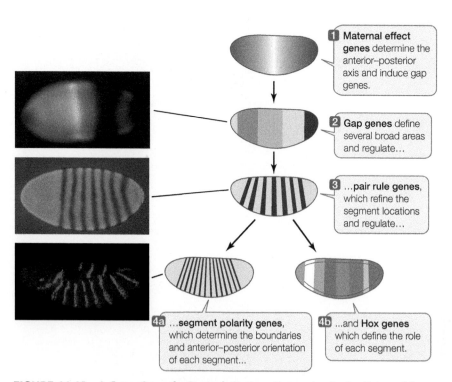

1 **Maternal effect genes** determine the anterior–posterior axis and induce gap genes.

2 **Gap genes** define several broad areas and regulate…

3 …**pair rule genes**, which refine the segment locations and regulate…

4a …**segment polarity genes**, which determine the boundaries and anterior–posterior orientation of each segment…

4b …and **Hox genes** which define the role of each segment.

FIGURE 14.13   A Gene Cascade Controls Pattern Formation in the *Drosophila* Embryo *(Page 277)*

(A)

Antenna

(B)

Leg where
antenna
should be

FIGURE 14.14 A Homeotic Mutation in *Drosophila* *(Page 277)*

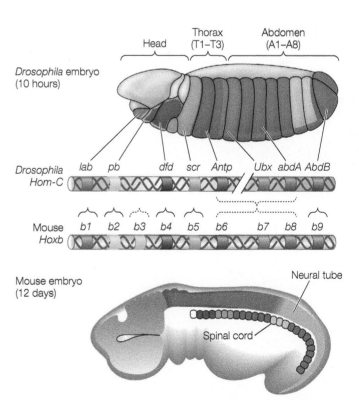

**FIGURE 14.15 Regulatory Genes Show Similar Expression
Patterns** *(Page 279)*

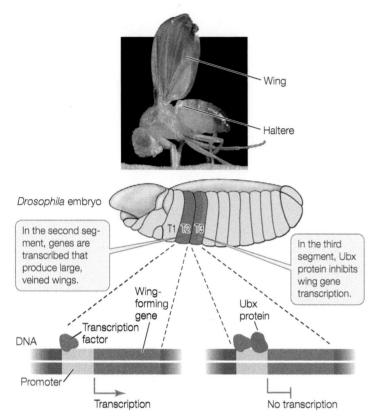

Wing

Haltere

Drosophila embryo

T1 T2 T3

In the second segment, genes are transcribed that produce large, veined wings.

In the third segment, Ubx protein inhibits wing gene transcription.

Wing-forming gene

Ubx protein

DNA

Transcription factor

Promoter

Transcription

No transcription

FIGURE 14.16 Segments Differentiate under Control of Genetic Switches *(Page 280)*

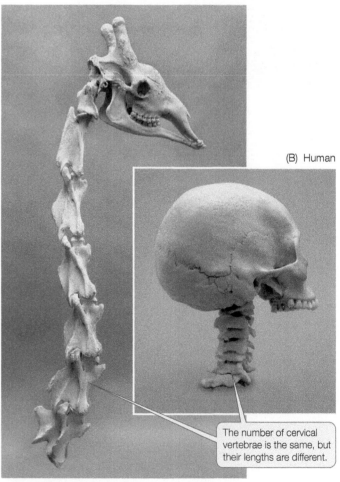

(A) Giraffe

(B) Human

The number of cervical vertebrae is the same, but their lengths are different.

FIGURE 14.17 Heterochrony in the Development of a Longer Neck *(Page 280)*

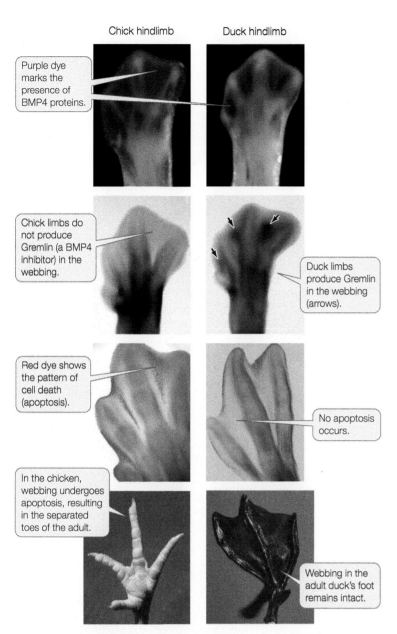

FIGURE 14.18   Changes in Gremlin Expression Correlate with Changes in Hindlimb Structure *(Page 281)*

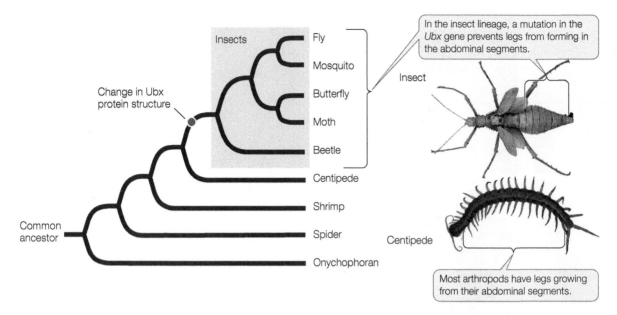

FIGURE 14.19 **A Mutation in a Hox Gene Changed the Number of Legs in Insects** *(Page 282)*

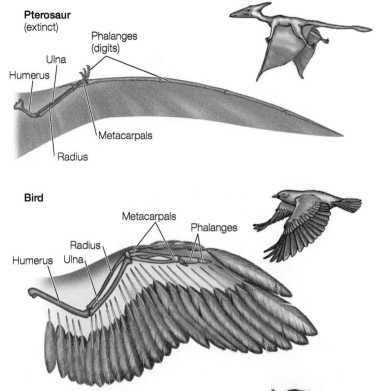

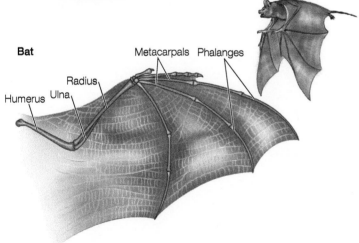

FIGURE 14.20 Wings Evolved Three Times in Vertebrates *(Page 283)*

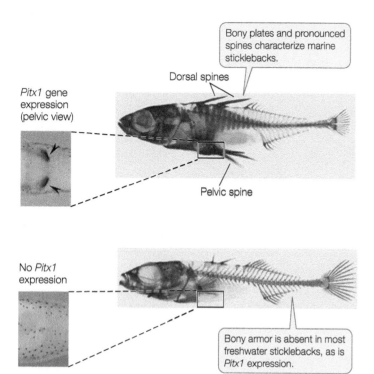

Pitx1 gene expression (pelvic view)

No *Pitx1* expression

Dorsal spines

Bony plates and pronounced spines characterize marine sticklebacks.

Pelvic spine

Bony armor is absent in most freshwater sticklebacks, as is *Pitx1* expression.

FIGURE 14.21   Parallel Phenotypic Evolution in Sticklebacks
(Page 283)

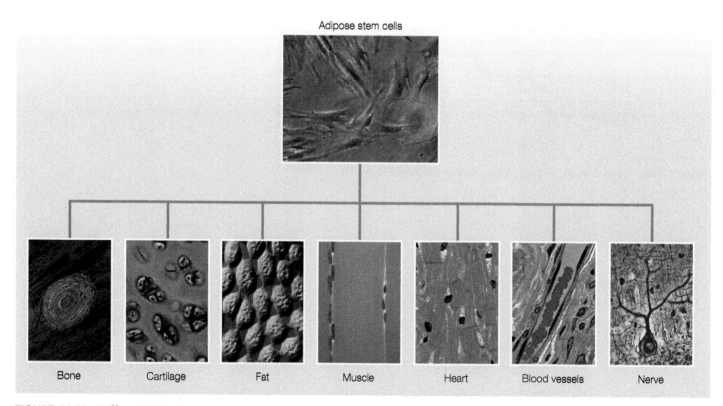

Adipose stem cells

Bone   Cartilage   Fat   Muscle   Heart   Blood vessels   Nerve

FIGURE 14.22   Differentiation Potential of Stem Cells from Fat *(Page 284)*

Mechanisms of Evolution  15

Charles Robert Darwin

IN-TEXT ART *(Page 289)*

HMS *Beagle*

IN-TEXT ART *(Page 289)*

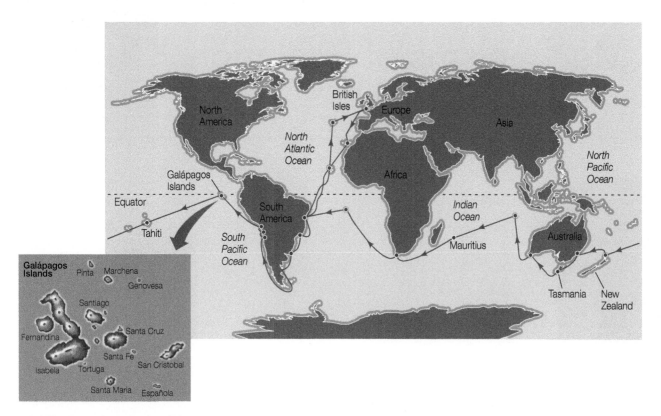

FIGURE 15.1 The Voyage of the _Beagle_ (Page 290)

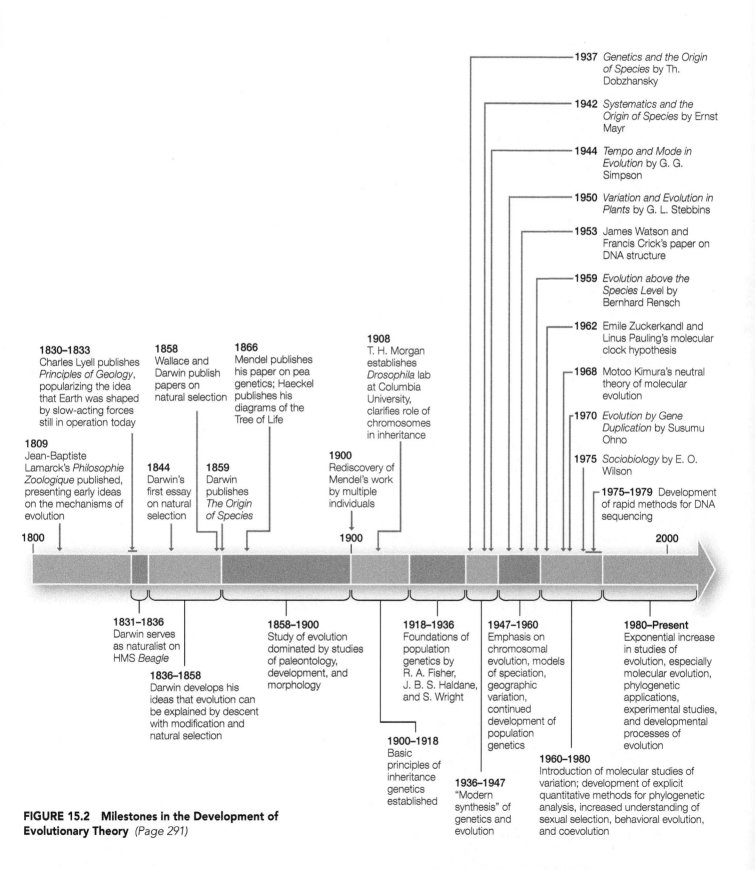

1937 *Genetics and the Origin of Species* by Th. Dobzhansky

1942 *Systematics and the Origin of Species* by Ernst Mayr

1944 *Tempo and Mode in Evolution* by G. G. Simpson

1950 *Variation and Evolution in Plants* by G. L. Stebbins

1953 James Watson and Francis Crick's paper on DNA structure

1959 *Evolution above the Species Level* by Bernhard Rensch

1962 Emile Zuckerkandl and Linus Pauling's molecular clock hypothesis

1968 Motoo Kimura's neutral theory of molecular evolution

1970 *Evolution by Gene Duplication* by Susumu Ohno

1975 *Sociobiology* by E. O. Wilson

1975–1979 Development of rapid methods for DNA sequencing

1830–1833 Charles Lyell publishes *Principles of Geology*, popularizing the idea that Earth was shaped by slow-acting forces still in operation today

1809 Jean-Baptiste Lamarck's *Philosophie Zoologique* published, presenting early ideas on the mechanisms of evolution

1858 Wallace and Darwin publish papers on natural selection

1844 Darwin's first essay on natural selection

1866 Mendel publishes his paper on pea genetics; Haeckel publishes his diagrams of the Tree of Life

1859 Darwin publishes *The Origin of Species*

1908 T. H. Morgan establishes *Drosophila* lab at Columbia University, clarifies role of chromosomes in inheritance

1900 Rediscovery of Mendel's work by multiple individuals

1800

1900

2000

1831–1836 Darwin serves as naturalist on HMS *Beagle*

1836–1858 Darwin develops his ideas that evolution can be explained by descent with modification and natural selection

1858–1900 Study of evolution dominated by studies of paleontology, development, and morphology

1918–1936 Foundations of population genetics by R. A. Fisher, J. B. S. Haldane, and S. Wright

1900–1918 Basic principles of inheritance genetics established

1936–1947 "Modern synthesis" of genetics and evolution

1947–1960 Emphasis on chromosomal evolution, models of speciation, geographic variation, continued development of population genetics

1960–1980 Introduction of molecular studies of variation; development of explicit quantitative methods for phylogenetic analysis, increased understanding of sexual selection, behavioral evolution, and coevolution

1980–Present Exponential increase in studies of evolution, especially molecular evolution, phylogenetic applications, experimental studies, and developmental processes of evolution

FIGURE 15.2   Milestones in the Development of Evolutionary Theory *(Page 291)*

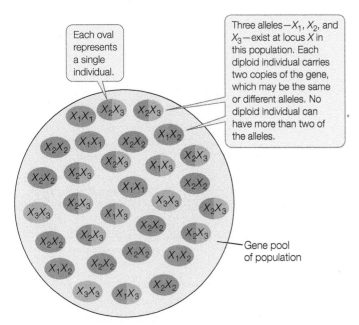

Each oval represents a single individual.

Three alleles—X_1, X_2, and X_3—exist at locus X in this population. Each diploid individual carries two copies of the gene, which may be the same or different alleles. No diploid individual can have more than two of the alleles.

Gene pool of population

FIGURE 15.3   A Gene Pool *(Page 292)*

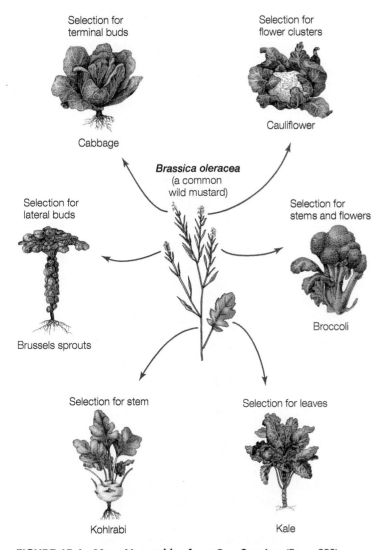

Selection for terminal buds

Cabbage

Selection for flower clusters

Cauliflower

Brassica oleracea (a common wild mustard)

Selection for lateral buds

Brussels sprouts

Selection for stems and flowers

Broccoli

Selection for stem

Kohlrabi

Selection for leaves

Kale

FIGURE 15.4   Many Vegetables from One Species *(Page 293)*

FIGURE 15.5 Artificial Selection *(Page 294)*

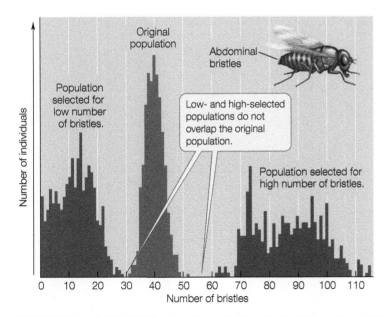

FIGURE 15.6 Artificial Selection Reveals Genetic Variation *(Page 294)*

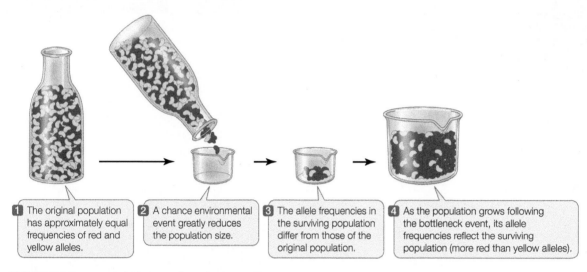

1 The original population has approximately equal frequencies of red and yellow alleles.

2 A chance environmental event greatly reduces the population size.

3 The allele frequencies in the surviving population differ from those of the original population.

4 As the population grows following the bottleneck event, its allele frequencies reflect the surviving population (more red than yellow alleles).

FIGURE 15.7   A Population Bottleneck *(Page 295)*

Euplectes progne

FIGURE 15.8   What Is the Advantage? *(Page 296)*

INVESTIGATION

FIGURE 15.9   Sexual Selection in Action   Behavioral ecologist Malte Andersson tested Darwin's hypothesis that excessively long tails evolved in male widowbirds because female preference for longer-tailed males increased their mating and reproductive success.

HYPOTHESIS

Female widowbirds prefer to mate with the male that displays the longest tail; longer-tailed males thus are favored by sexual selection because they will father more offspring.

METHOD

1. Capture males and artificially lengthen or shorten tails by cutting or gluing on feathers. In a control group, cut and replace tails to their normal length (to control for the effects of tail-cutting).
2. Release the males to establish their territories and mate.
3. Count the nests with eggs or young on each male's territory.

RESULTS

Male widowbirds with artificially shortened tails established and defended display sites sucessfully but fathered fewer offspring than did control or unmanipulated males. Males with artificially lengthened tales fathered the most offspring.

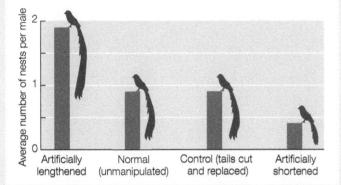

CONCLUSION

Sexual selection in *Euplectes progne* has favored the evolution of long tails in the male.

ANALYZE THE DATA

Are the differences plotted above significantly different?
See Working with Data 15.1 at **yourBioPortal.com**
for a simple method to test the statistical significance
of the differences using the following data.

| Group | Number of nests per male | | |
	Shortened tail	Control	Elongated tail
1	0	0	2
2	0	0	2
3	2	3	5
4	1	2	4
5	0	1	2
6	0	1	2
7	0	1	0
8	0	0	0
9	1	0	0

Go to **yourBioPortal.com** for original citations, discussions, and relevant links for all INVESTIGATION figures.

RESEARCH TOOLS

FIGURE 15.10 Calculating Allele and Genotype Frequencies
Allele and genotype frequencies for a gene locus with two alleles in the population can be calculated using the equations in panel 1. When the equations are applied to two populations (panel 2), we find that the *frequencies of alleles A and a in the two populations are the same*, but the alleles are distributed differently between heterozygous and homozygous genotypes.

1 In any population, where N is the total number of individuals in the population:

$$\frac{\text{Frequency}}{\text{of allele } A} = p = \frac{2N_{AA} + N_{Aa}}{2N} \qquad \frac{\text{Frequency}}{\text{of allele } a} = q = \frac{2N_{aa} + N_{Aa}}{2N}$$

Frequency of genotype $AA = N_{AA}/N$
Frequency of genotype $Aa = N_{Aa}/N$
Frequency of genotype $aa = N_{aa}/N$

2 Compute the allele and genotype frequencies for two separate populations of $N = 200$:

Population 1 (mostly homozygotes)	Population 2 (mostly heterozygotes)
$N_{AA} = 90$, $N_{Aa} = 40$, and $N_{aa} = 70$	$N_{AA} = 45$, $N_{Aa} = 130$, and $N_{aa} = 25$
$p = \dfrac{180 + 40}{400} = 0.55$	$p = \dfrac{90 + 130}{400} = 0.55$
$q = \dfrac{140 + 40}{400} = 0.45$	$q = \dfrac{50 + 130}{400} = 0.45$

Population 1:
Freq. $AA = 90/200 = 0.45$
Freq. $Aa = 40/200 = 0.20$
Freq. $aa = 70/200 = 0.35$

Population 2:
Freq. $AA = 45/200 = 0.225$
Freq. $Aa = 130/200 = 0.65$
Freq. $aa = 25/200 = 0.125$

Generation I (Founder population)

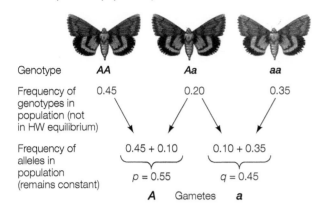

Genotype   **AA**   **Aa**   **aa**

Frequency of genotypes in population (not in HW equilibrium)   0.45   0.20   0.35

Frequency of alleles in population (remains constant)

0.45 + 0.10   0.10 + 0.35

$p = 0.55$ $q = 0.45$

A   Gametes   **a**

Generation II (Hardy–Weinberg equilibrium restored)

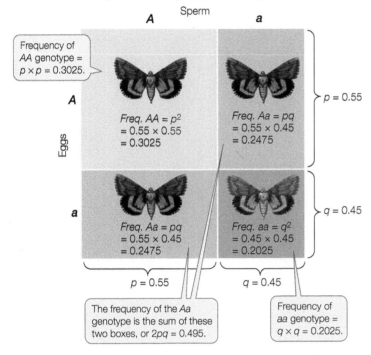

Sperm

A   **a**

Eggs

Frequency of *AA* genotype = $p \times p = 0.3025$.

A

Freq. AA $= p^2$
$= 0.55 \times 0.55$
$= 0.3025$

Freq. Aa $= pq$
$= 0.55 \times 0.45$
$= 0.2475$

$p = 0.55$

a

Freq. Aa $= pq$
$= 0.55 \times 0.45$
$= 0.2475$

Freq. aa $= q^2$
$= 0.45 \times 0.45$
$= 0.2025$

$q = 0.45$

$p = 0.55$ $q = 0.45$

The frequency of the *Aa* genotype is the sum of these two boxes, or $2pq = 0.495$.

Frequency of *aa* genotype = $q \times q = 0.2025$.

FIGURE 15.11   One Generation of Random Mating Restores Hardy–Weinberg Equilibrium *(Page 298)*

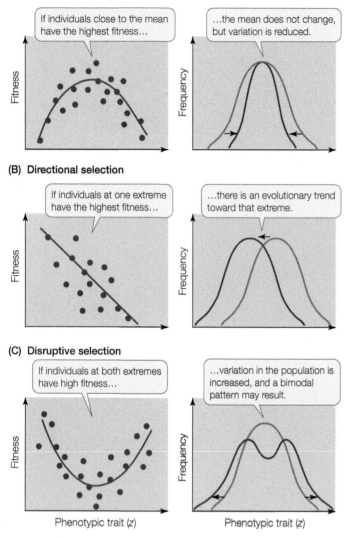

(A) Stabilizing selection

If individuals close to the mean have the highest fitness...

...the mean does not change, but variation is reduced.

Fitness

Frequency

(B) Directional selection

If individuals at one extreme have the highest fitness...

...there is an evolutionary trend toward that extreme.

Fitness

Frequency

(C) Disruptive selection

If individuals at both extremes have high fitness...

...variation in the population is increased, and a bimodal pattern may result.

Fitness

Frequency

Phenotypic trait (z)

Phenotypic trait (z)

FIGURE 15.12   Natural Selection Can Operate in Several Ways
(Page 300)

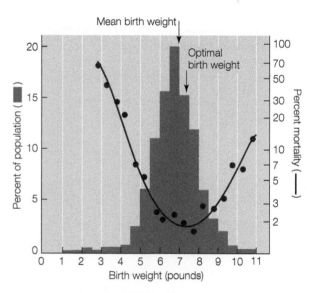

FIGURE 15.13   Human Birth Weight Is Influenced by Stabilizing Selection *(Page 301)*

FIGURE 15.14 Long Horns Are the Result of Directional Selection
(Page 301)

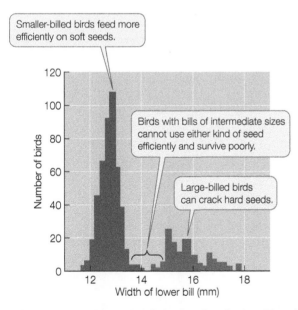

FIGURE 15.15 Disruptive Selection Results in a Bimodal Character Distribution *(Page 302)*

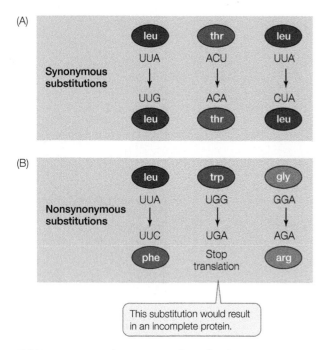

FIGURE 15.16 **When One Nucleotide Changes** *(Page 303)*

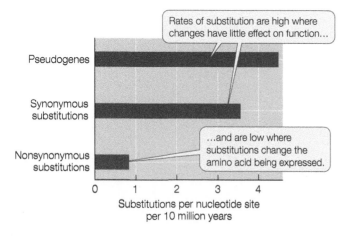

FIGURE 15.17 **Rates of Substitution Differ** *(Page 303)*

(A) *Semnopithecus* sp.   *Bos taurus*

(B) *Opisthocomus hoazin*

The lysozymes of langurs and cattle are convergent for 5 amino acid residues, indicative of the independent evolution of foregut fermentation in these two species.

	Langur	Baboon	Human	Rat	Cattle	Horse
Langur		14	18	38	32	65
Baboon	0		14	33	39	65
Human	0	1		37	41	64
Rat	0	0	0		55	64
Cattle	5	0	0	0		71
Horse	0	0	0	0	1	

FIGURE 15.18   Convergent Molecular Evolution of Lysozyme *(Page 305)*

INVESTIGATION

FIGURE 15.19   A Heterozygote Mating Advantage   Among butterflies of the genus *Colias*, males that are heterozygous for two alleles of the PGI enzyme can fly farther under a broader range of temperatures than males that are homozygous for either allele. Does this ability give heterozygous males a mating advantage?

HYPOTHESIS

Heterozygous male *Colias* will have proportionally greater mating success than homozygous males.

METHOD

1. For each of two *Colias* species, capture butterflies in the field. In the laboratory, determine their genotypes and allow them to mate.
2. Determine the genotypes of the offspring, thus revealing paternity and mating success of the males.

RESULTS

For both species, the proportion of heterozygous males that mated successfully was higher than the proportion of all males seeking females ("flying").

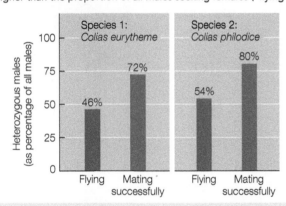

CONCLUSION

Heterozygous *Colias* males have a mating advantage over homozygous males.

ANALYZE THE DATA

Analyze these sampling data collected during the experiment (only one of several samples is shown for each species).

Species	All viable males*		Mating males	
	Heterozygous/ total	% heterozygous	Heterozygous/ total	% heterozygous
C. philodice	32/74	43.2	31/50	62.0
C. eurytheme	44/92	47.8	45/59	76.3

*"Viable males" are all males captured flying with females (hence with the potential to mate)

A. Under the assumption that the proportions of each genotype (heterozygotes and homozygotes) of mating males are the same as the proportions seen among all viable males, calculate the number of *mating males* expected to be heterozygous and the number expected to be homozygous.

B. Use a chi-square test (see Appendix B) to evaluate the significance of the difference in your expected numbers in (A) and the observed percentages of heterozygous mating males. The critical value ($P = 0.05$) of the chi-square distribution with one degree of freedom is 3.841. Are the observed and expected numbers of heterozygotes and homozygotes among mating males significantly different in these samples?

For more, go to Working with Data 15.2 at **yourBioPortal.com**.

Go to **yourBioPortal.com** for original citations, discussions, and relevant links for all INVESTIGATION figures.

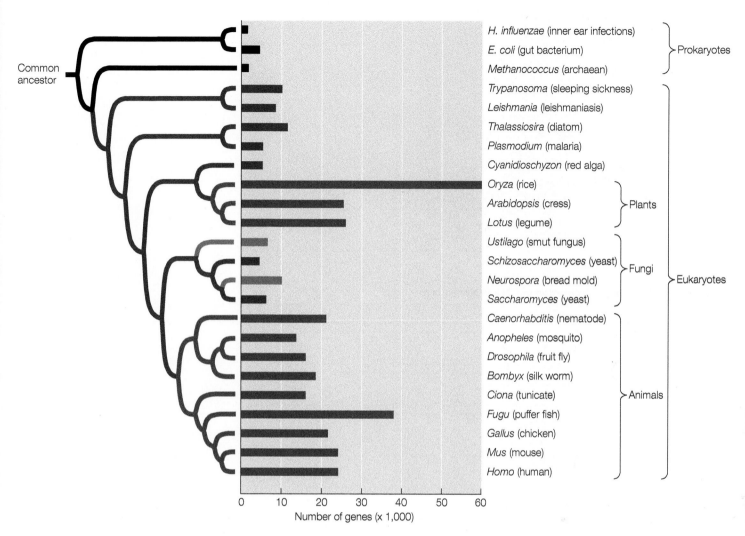

FIGURE 15.20 Genome Size Varies Widely *(Page 307)*

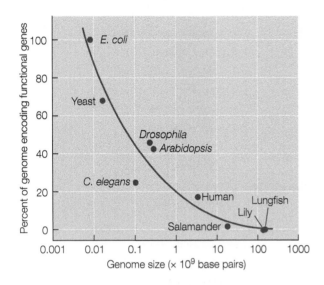

FIGURE 15.21   A Large Proportion of DNA Is Noncoding
(Page 308)

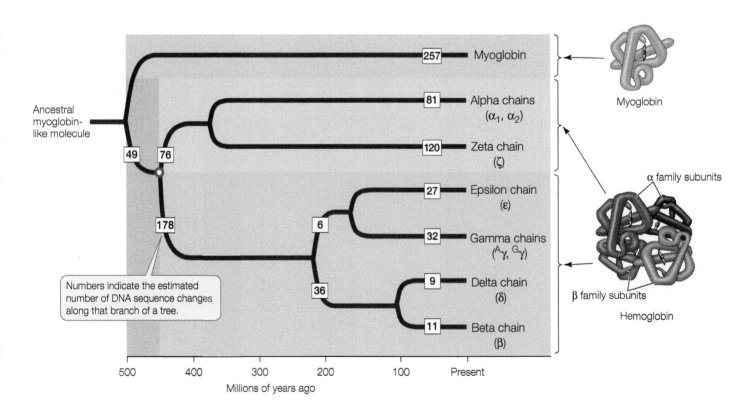

FIGURE 15.22   A Globin Family Gene Tree (Page 310)

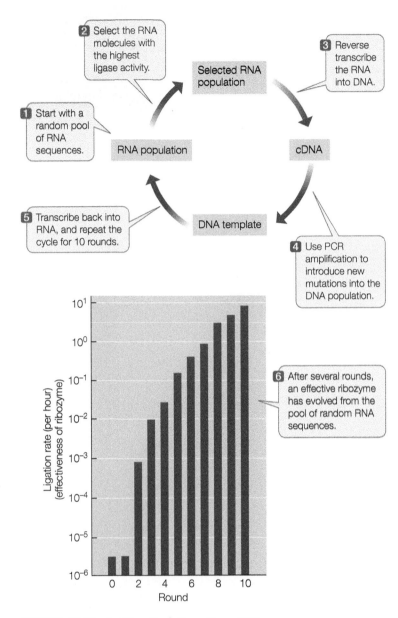

FIGURE 15.23   **In Vitro Evolution** *(Page 311)*

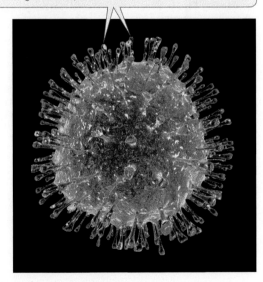

FIGURE 15.24   **Evolutionary Analysis of Surface Proteins Leads to Improved Flu Vaccines** *(Page 313)*

Reconstructing and Using Phylogenies

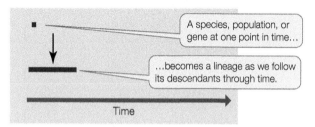

IN-TEXT ART *(Page 316)*

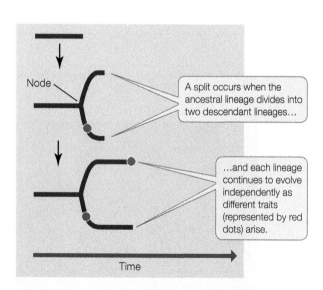

IN-TEXT ART *(Page 316)*

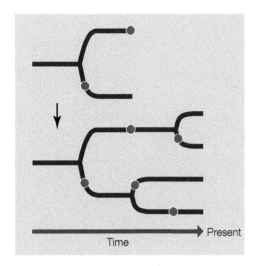

IN-TEXT ART *(Page 316)*

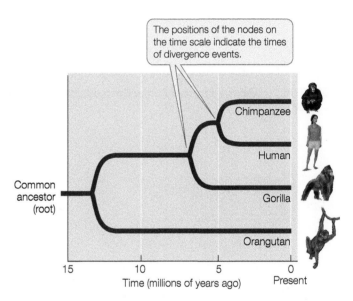

The positions of the nodes on the time scale indicate the times of divergence events.

Chimpanzee

Human

Common ancestor (root)

Gorilla

Orangutan

15   10   5   0

Time (millions of years ago)   Present

IN-TEXT ART *(Page 316)*

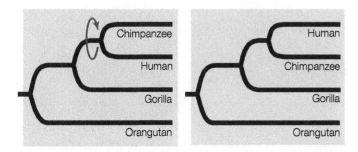

Chimpanzee

Human

Gorilla

Orangutan

Human

Chimpanzee

Gorilla

Orangutan

IN-TEXT ART *(Page 317)*

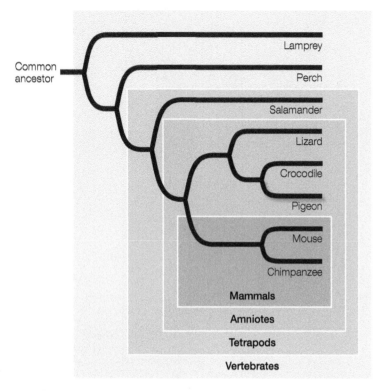

FIGURE 16.1   Clades Represent All the Descendants of a Common Ancestor *(Page 317)*

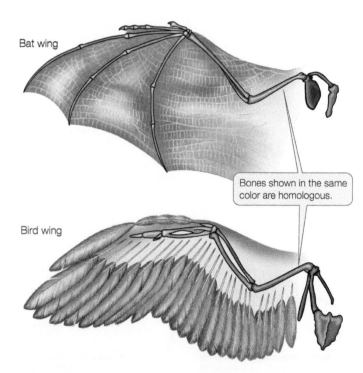

FIGURE 16.2   The Bones Are Homologous, the Wings Are Not *(Page 318)*

TABLE 16.1 Eight Vertebrates and the Presence or Absence of Some Shared Derived Traits

TAXON	JAWS	LUNGS	CLAWS OR NAILS	GIZZARD	FEATHERS	FUR	MAMMARY GLANDS	KERATINOUS SCALES
Lamprey (outgroup)	–	–	–	–	–	–	–	–
Perch	+	–	–	–	–	–	–	–
Salamander	+	+	–	–	–	–	–	–
Lizard	+	+	+	–	–	–	–	+
Crocodile	+	+	+	+	–	–	–	+
Pigeon	+	+	+	+	+	–	–	+
Mouse	+	+	+	–	–	+	+	–
Chimpanzee	+	+	+	–	–	+	+	–

(Page 319)

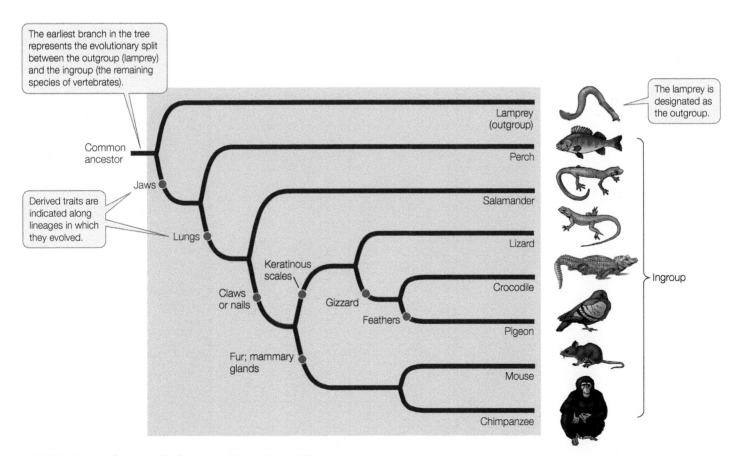

The earliest branch in the tree represents the evolutionary split between the outgroup (lamprey) and the ingroup (the remaining species of vertebrates).

The lamprey is designated as the outgroup.

Common ancestor

Jaws

Derived traits are indicated along lineages in which they evolved.

Lungs

Keratinous scales

Claws or nails

Gizzard

Feathers

Fur; mammary glands

Lamprey (outgroup)

Perch

Salamander

Lizard

Crocodile

Pigeon

Mouse

Chimpanzee

Ingroup

FIGURE 16.3 Inferring a Phylogenetic Tree *(Page 319)*

Sea squirt larva

Adult

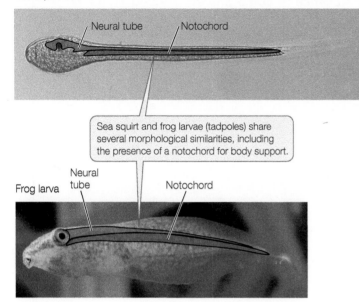

Neural tube   Notochord

Sea squirt and frog larvae (tadpoles) share several morphological similarities, including the presence of a notochord for body support.

Neural
tube

Frog larva   Notochord

Adult

Despite the similarity of their larvae, the morphology of adult frogs and sea squirts provides little evidence of the common ancestry of these two groups.

FIGURE 16.4   The Chordate Connection *(Page 322)*

INVESTIGATION

FIGURE 16.5 The Accuracy of Phylogenetic Analysis
To test whether analysis of gene sequences can accurately reconstruct evolutionary phylogeny, we must have an unambiguously known phylogeny to compare against the reconstruction. Will the observed phylogeny match the reconstruction?

HYPOTHESIS

A phylogeny reconstructed from analysis of the DNA sequences of living organisms can accurately match the known evolutionary history of the organisms.

METHOD

In the laboratory, one group of investigators produced an unambiguous phylogeny of 9 viral lineages, enhancing the mutation rate to increase variation among the lineages.

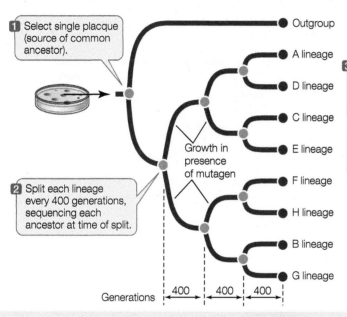

1 Select single placque (source of common ancestor).

2 Split each lineage every 400 generations, sequencing each ancestor at time of split.

Growth in presence of mutagen

Outgroup
A lineage
D lineage
C lineage
E lineage
F lineage
H lineage
B lineage
G lineage

Generations | 400 | 400 | 400

3 Present final genes (blue dots) to a second group of investigators who are unaware of the history of the lineages or the gene sequences of the ancestral viruses. These "blind" investigators then determine the sequences of the descendant genes and use these sequences to reconstruct the evolution of these lineages in the form of a phylogenetic tree.

RESULTS

The true phylogeny and ancestral DNA sequences were accurately reconstructed solely from the DNA sequences of the viruses at the tips of the tree.

CONCLUSION

Phylogenetic analysis of DNA sequences can accurately reconstruct evolutionary history.

ANALYZE THE DATA

The full DNA sequences for the T7 strains in this experiment are thousands of nucleotides long. The nucleotides ("characters") at 23 DNA positions are given in the table.

	Character at position																						
	1	2	3	4	5	6	7	8	9	10	11	12	13	14	15	16	17	18	19	20	21	22	23
Outgroup	C	C	G	G	G	C	C	T	C	C	T	C	G	A	C	C	G	G	C	A	C	G	G
A	T	C	G	G	G	C	C	C	C	C	C	C	A	A	C	C	G	A	T	A	C	A	A
B	C	C	G	G	G	T	C	C	C	T	C	C	G	A	T	T	A	G	C	G	T	G	G
C	C	C	G	G	G	C	C	C	T	C	C	T	A	A	C	C	G	G	T	A	C	A	A
D	T	C	A	G	G	C	C	C	C	C	C	C	A	A	C	C	G	A	T	A	C	A	A
E	C	T	G	G	G	C	C	C	C	C	C	T	A	A	C	C	G	G	T	A	C	A	A
F	C	T	G	A	A	C	C	C	C	C	C	C	G	A	C	T	G	G	C	G	C	G	G
G	C	C	G	G	G	T	T	C	C	T	C	C	G	A	T	T	A	G	C	G	C	G	G
H	C	C	G	G	A	C	C	C	C	C	C	C	G	C	C	T	G	G	C	G	C	G	G

A. Construct a phylogenetic tree from these DNA positions using the parsimony method. Use the outgroup to root your tree. Assume that all changes among nucleotides are equally likely.

B. Using your tree, reconstruct the DNA sequences of the ancestral lineages.

For more, go to Working with Data 16.1 at **yourBioPortal.com**.

Go to **yourBioPortal.com** for original citations, discussions, and relevant links for all INVESTIGATION figures.

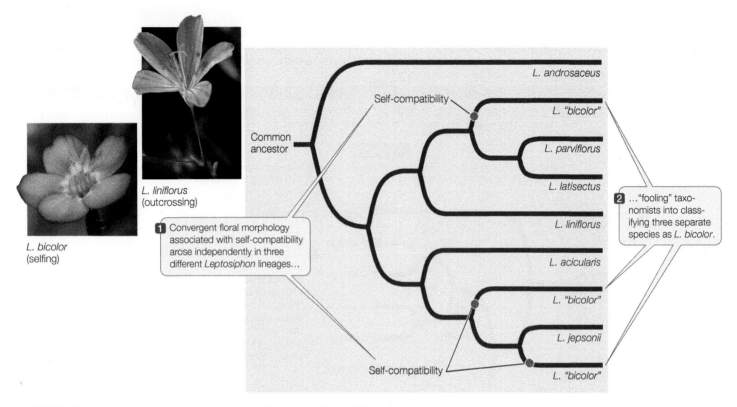

L. bicolor
(selfing)

L. liniflorus
(outcrossing)

1 Convergent floral morphology associated with self-compatibility arose independently in three different *Leptosiphon* lineages…

2 …"fooling" taxonomists into classifying three separate species as *L. bicolor*.

Common ancestor

Self-compatibility

Self-compatibility

L. androsaceus

L. "bicolor"

L. parviflorus

L. latisectus

L. liniflorus

L. acicularis

L. "bicolor"

L. jepsonii

L. "bicolor"

FIGURE 16.6   A Portion of the *Leptosiphon* Phylogeny *(Page 325)*

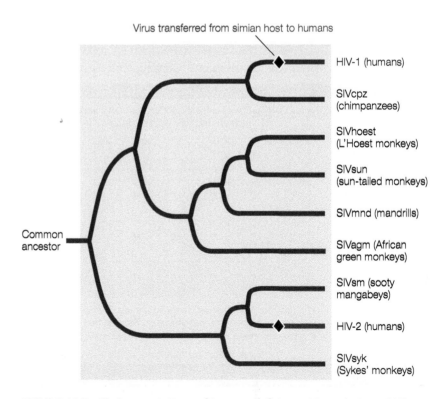

Virus transferred from simian host to humans

Common ancestor

HIV-1 (humans)

SIVcpz (chimpanzees)

SIVhoest (L'Hoest monkeys)

SIVsun (sun-tailed monkeys)

SIVmnd (mandrills)

SIVagm (African green monkeys)

SIVsm (sooty mangabeys)

HIV-2 (humans)

SIVsyk (Sykes' monkeys)

FIGURE 16.7   Phylogenetic Tree of Immunodeficiency Viruses *(Page 325)*

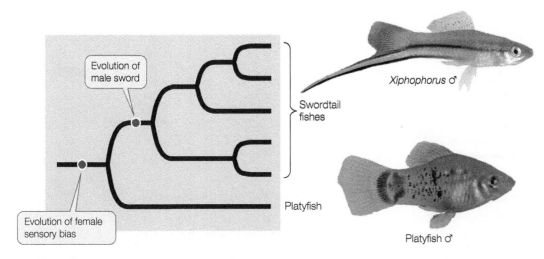

FIGURE 16.8   The Origin of a Sexually Selected Trait *(Page 326)*

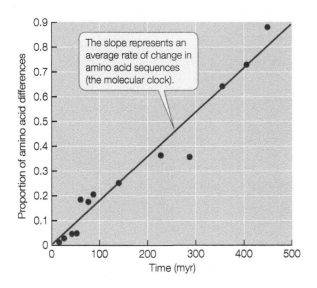

FIGURE 16.9   A Molecular Clock of the Protein Hemoglobin
(Page 327)

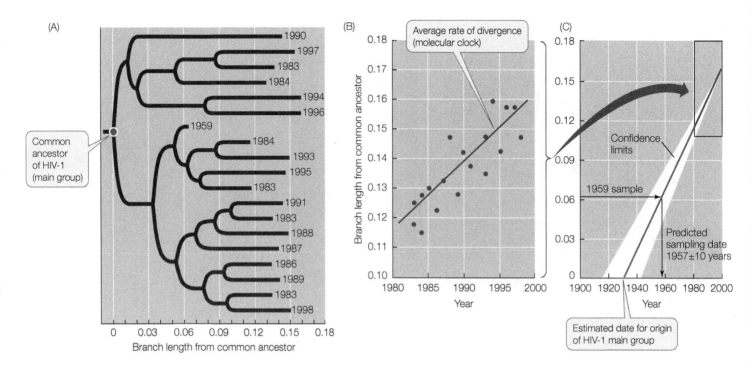

FIGURE 16.10   **Dating the Origin of HIV-1 in Human Populations** *(Page 327)*

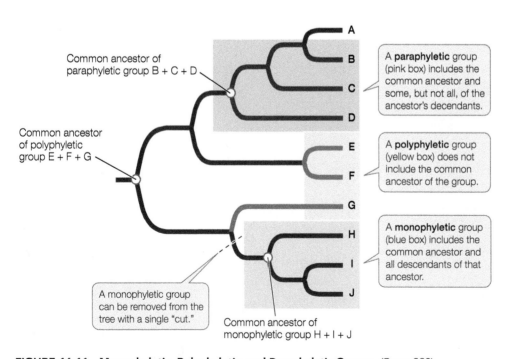

FIGURE 16.11   **Monophyletic, Polyphyletic, and Paraphyletic Groups** *(Page 328)*

(A) *Asclepias tuberosa*

(B) *Castilleja coccinea*

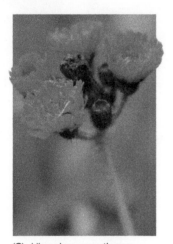

(C) *Hieracium aurantiacum*

FIGURE 16.12   Same Common Name, Not the Same Species
(Page 329)

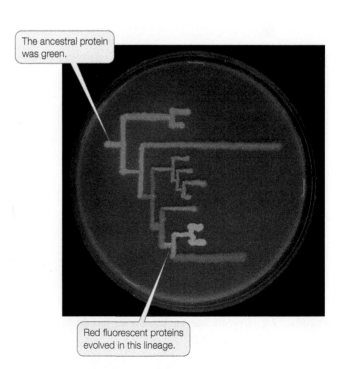

The ancestral protein was green.

Red fluorescent proteins evolved in this lineage.

FIGURE 16.13   Evolution of Fluorescent Proteins of Corals
(Page 331)

Speciation  17

(A)

Aix sponsa
Male, Florida

Aix sponsa
Male, California

(B)

Aix sponsa
Female

FIGURE 17.1 Members of the Same Species Look Alike—or Not *(Page 333)*

(A)

Hyla versicolor

(B)

Hyla chrysoscelis

FIGURE 17.2 Cryptic Species Look Alike but Do Not Interbreed *(Page 334)*

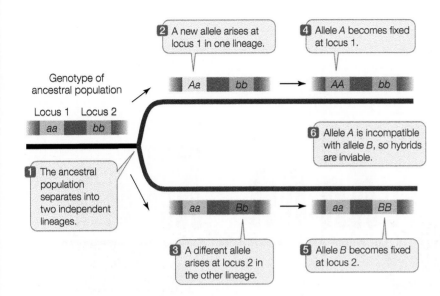

FIGURE 17.3   The Dobzhansky–Muller Model *(Page 335)*

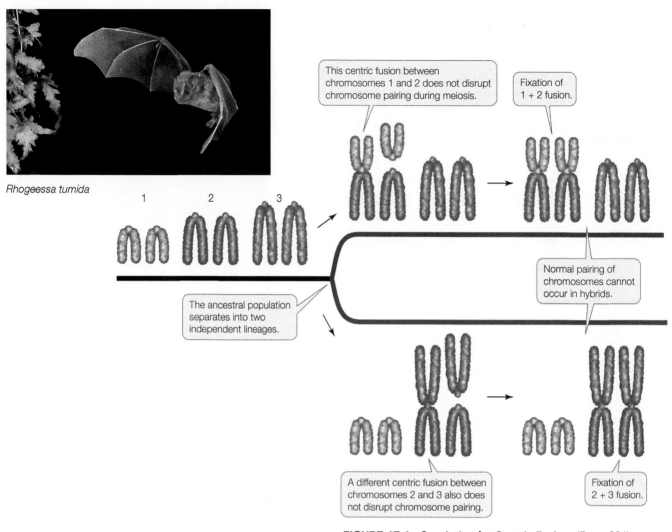

Rhogeessa tumida

FIGURE 17.4 **Speciation by Centric Fusion** *(Page 336)*

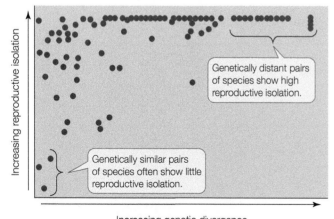

FIGURE 17.5 **Reproductive Isolation Increases with Genetic Divergence** *(Page 336)*

(A) Pliocene

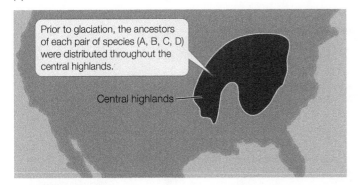

Prior to glaciation, the ancestors of each pair of species (A, B, C, D) were distributed throughout the central highlands.

Central highlands

(B) Pleistocene

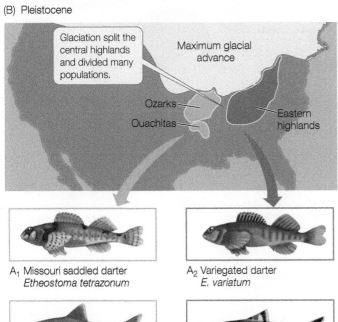

Glaciation split the central highlands and divided many populations.

Maximum glacial advance

Ozarks
Ouachitas
Eastern highlands

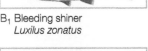

A₁ Missouri saddled darter
    Etheostoma tetrazonum

A₂ Variegated darter
    E. variatum

B₁ Bleeding shiner
    Luxilus zonatus

B₂ Warpaint shiner
    L. coccogenis

C₁ Ozark minnow
    Notropis nubilus

C₂ Tennessee shiner
    N. leuciodus

D₁ Ozark madtom
    Noturus albater

D₂ Elegant madtom
    N. elegans

FIGURE 17.6 Allopatric Speciation *(Page 337)*

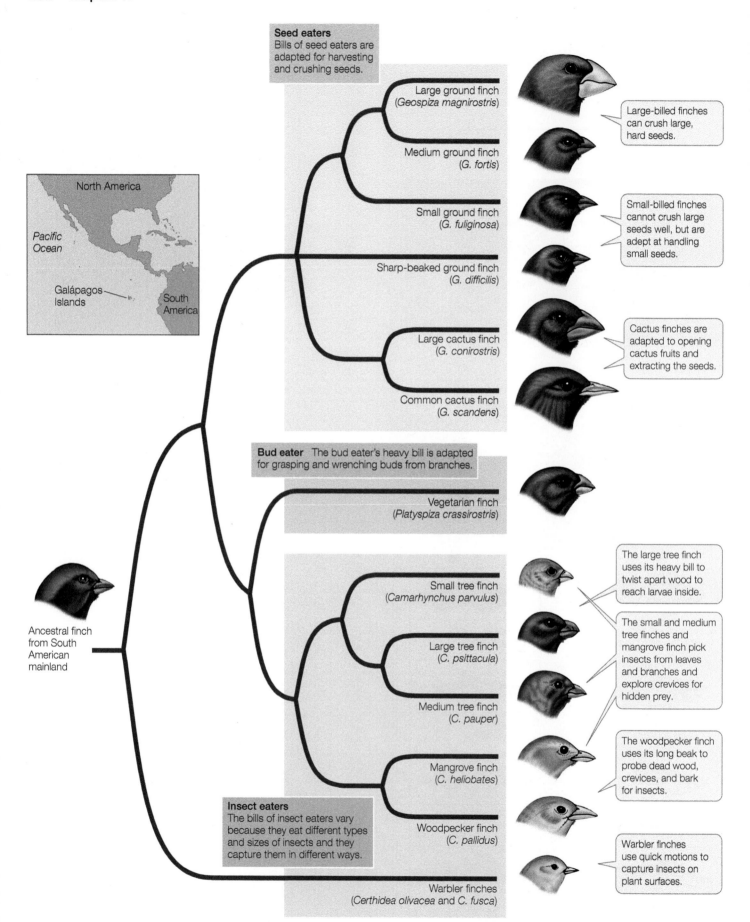

FIGURE 17.7 **Allopatric Speciation among Darwin's Finches** *(Page 339)*

FIGURE 17.8   Mechanical Isolation through Mimicry
(Page 340)

(A) Allopatric populations

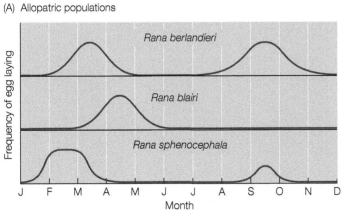

(B) Sympatric populations

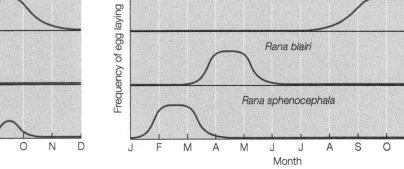

FIGURE 17.9   Temporal Isolation of Breeding Seasons *(Page 341)*

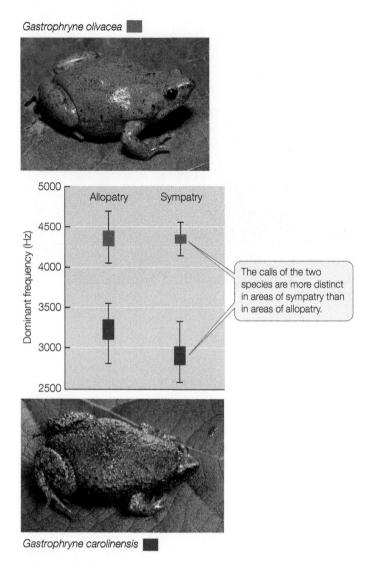

Gastrophryne olivacea

The calls of the two species are more distinct in areas of sympatry than in areas of allopatry.

Gastrophryne carolinensis

FIGURE 17.10 Behavioral Isolation in Mating Calls
(Page 341)

(A)

(B)

(C) *Aquilegia formosa*

(D) *A. pubescens*

FIGURE 17.11 Floral Morphology Is Associated with Pollinator Morphology *(Page 342)*

INVESTIGATION

FIGURE 17.12   Flower Color and Reproductive Isolation   Most *Phlox drummondii* individuals have pink flowers, but in regions where the species is sympatric with *P. cuspidata*—which is always pink—most *P. drummondii* individuals have red flowers. Most pollinators preferentially visit flowers of one color or the other. In this experiment, Donald Levin explored whether flower color acts as a prezygotic isolating mechanism that lessens the chances of hybridization between the two species.

HYPOTHESIS

Red-flowered *P. drummondii* are less likely to hybridize with *P. cuspidata* than are pink-flowered *P. drummondii*.

METHOD   1. Introduce equal numbers of red-flowered and pink-flowered *P. drummondii* individuals into an area where many pink-flowered *P. cuspidata* are growing.

P. cuspidata

P. drummondii

2. After the flowering season ends, measure hybridization by assessing the genetic composition of the seeds produced by *P. drummondii* plants of both colors.

RESULTS

Of the seeds produced by pink-flowered *P. drummondii*, 38% were hybrids with *P. cuspidata*. Only 13% of the seeds produced by red-flowered *P. drummondii* were hybrids with *P. cuspidata*

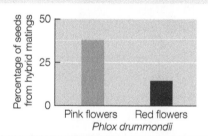

CONCLUSION

P. drummondii and *P. cuspidata* are less likely to hybridize if the flowers of the two species differ in color.

ANALYZE THE DATA

Data from Levin's experiment show that the frequency of hybridization between *Phlox drummondii* and *P. cuspidata* was strongly dependent on the former's flower color.

P. drummondii flower color	Number of progeny (seeds)		
	P. drummondii	Hybrid	Total
Red	181 (87%)	27 (13%)	208
Pink	86 (62%)	53 (38%)	139

A. The data reveal that red-flowered *P. drummondii* produced more seeds (208) than pink-flowered plants did (139), even though equal numbers of individuals of the two flower types were used. Does this difference influence your interpretation of Levin's results? Why or why not?

B. How would you improve the **experimental design** of this study? Should replicate or control sites be added? What kinds of additional test sites and conditions would you add?

For more, go to Working with Data 17.1 at **yourBioPortal.com**.

Go to **yourBioPortal.com** for original citations, discussions, and relevant links for all INVESTIGATION figures.

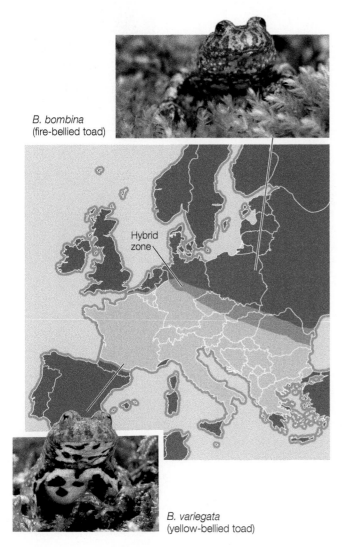

B. bombina
(fire-bellied toad)

Hybrid zone

B. variegata
(yellow-bellied toad)

FIGURE 17.13   A Hybrid Zone *(Page 345)*

FIGURE 17.14   Evolution in the Laboratory *(Page 345)*

The History of Life on Earth

18

TABLE 18.1 Earth's Geological History

RELATIVE TIME SPAN	ERA	PERIOD	ONSET	MAJOR PHYSICAL CHANGES ON EARTH
	Cenozoic	Quaternary	2.6 mya	Cold/dry climate; repeated glaciations
	Cenozoic	Tertiary	65 mya	Continents near current positions; climate cools
	Mesozoic	Cretaceous	145 mya	Northern continents attached; Gondwana begins to drift apart; meteorite strikes near present Yucatán Peninsula
	Mesozoic	Jurassic	200 mya	Two large continents form: Laurasia (north) and Gondwana (south); climate warm
	Mesozoic	Triassic	251 mya	Pangaea begins to slowly drift apart; hot/humid climate
	Paleozoic	Permian	297 mya	Extensive lowland swamps; O_2 levels 50% higher than present; by end of period continents aggregate to form Pangaea, and O_2 levels begin to drop rapidly
	Paleozoic	Carboniferous	359 mya	Climate cools; marked latitudinal climate gradients
	Paleozoic	Devonian	416 mya	Continents collide at end of period; meteorite probably strikes Earth
	Paleozoic	Silurian	444 mya	Sea levels rise; two large land masses emerge; hot/humid climate
	Paleozoic	Ordovician	488 mya	Massive glaciation, sea level drops 50 meters
	Paleozoic	Cambrian	542 mya	O_2 levels approach current levels
Precambrian	Precambrian		900 mya	O_2 level at ≈5% of current level
			1.5 bya	O_2 level at ≈1% of current level
			3.8 bya	O_2 first appears in atmosphere
			4.5 bya	

Note: mya, million years ago; bya, billion years ago.

(Page 348 and 349)

MAJOR EVENTS IN THE HISTORY OF LIFE

Humans evolve; many large mammals become extinct

Diversification of birds, mammals, flowering plants, and insects

Dinosaurs continue to diversify; mass extinction at end of period (≈76% of species disappear)

Diverse dinosaurs; radiation of ray-finned fishes; first fossils of flowering plants

Early dinosaurs; first mammals; marine invertebrates diversify; mass extinction at end of period (≈65% of species disappear)

Reptiles diversify; giant amphibians and flying insects present; mass extinction at end of period (≈96% of species disappear)

Extensive "fern" forests; first reptiles; insects diversify

Fishes diversify; first insects and amphibians; mass extinction at end of period (≈75% of marine species disappear)

Jawless fishes diversify; first ray-finned fishes; plants and animals colonize land

Mass extinction at end of period (≈75% of species disappear)

Rapid diversification of multicellular animals; diverse photosynthetic protists

Earliest fossils of multicellular animals

Eukaryotes evolve

Origin of life; prokaryotes flourish

(continued)

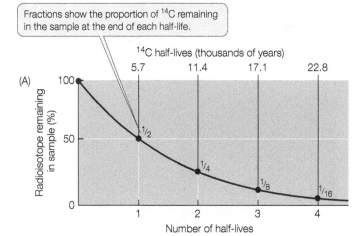

Fractions show the proportion of ^{14}C remaining in the sample at the end of each half-life.

FIGURE 18.1 Radioactive Isotopes Allow Us to Date Ancient Rocks *(Page 349)*

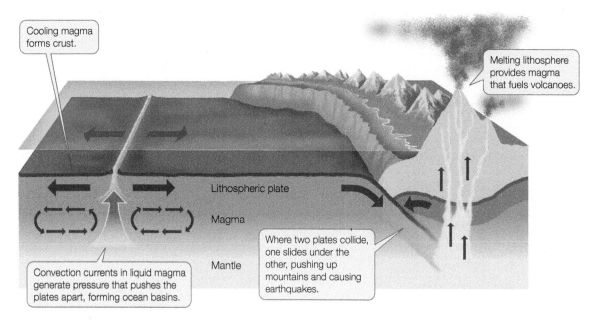

FIGURE 18.2 Plate Tectonics and Continental Drift *(Page 351)*

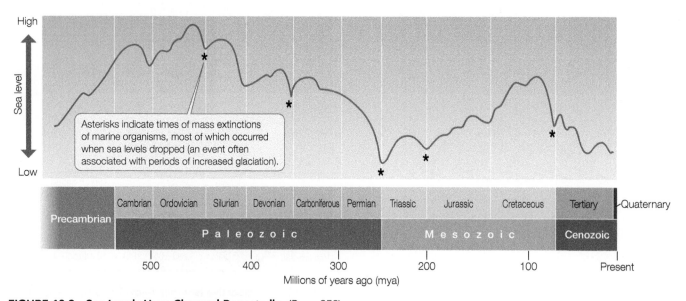

FIGURE 18.3 Sea Levels Have Changed Repeatedly *(Page 352)*

FIGURE 18.4   Volcanic Eruptions Can Cool Global Temperatures
(Page 353)

Iridium-rich layer at the Cretaceous-Tertiary (K/T) boundary

FIGURE 18.5   Evidence of a Meteorite Impact *(Page 353)*

(A)

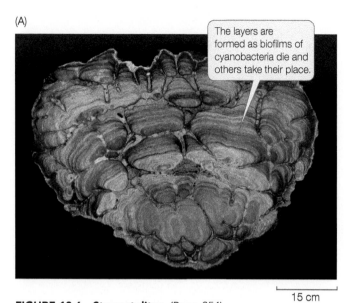

The layers are formed as biofilms of cyanobacteria die and others take their place.

15 cm

(B)

Living cyanobacteria are found in the upper parts of these stromatolites.

30 cm

FIGURE 18.6 Stromatolites *(Page 354)*

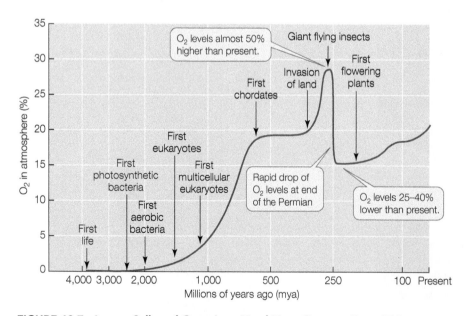

FIGURE 18.7 Larger Cells and Organisms Need More Oxygen *(Page 354)*

INVESTIGATION

FIGURE 18.8 Atmospheric Oxygen Concentrations and Body Size in Insects   C. Jaco Klok and his colleagues asked whether insects raised in hyperoxic conditions would evolve to be larger than their counterparts raised under today's atmospheric conditions. They raised strains of fruit flies (*Drosophila melanogaster*) under both conditions to test the effects of increased O_2 concentrations on the evolution of body size.

HYPOTHESIS

In hyperoxic conditions, increased partial pressure of oxygen results in evolution of increased body size in flying insects.

METHOD

1. Separate a population of fruit flies into multiple lines.
2. Raise half the lines in current atmospheric (control) conditions; raise the other lines in hyperoxic (experimental) conditions. Continue all lines for seven generations.
3. Raise the F_8 individuals of all lines under identical (current) atmospheric conditions.
4. Weigh 50 flies from each of the replicate lines and test for statistical differences in body weight.

RESULTS

The average body mass of F_8 individuals of both sexes raised under hyperoxic conditions was significantly (p < 0.001) greater than that of individuals in the control lines:

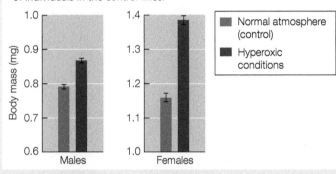

CONCLUSION

Increased O_2 concentrations led to evolution of larger body size in fruit flies, consistent with the trends seen among other flying insects in the fossil record.

ANALYZE THE DATA

The table shows the average body masses of the flies raised in hyperoxic conditions in the F_0 (i.e, before the first generation in hyperoxia), F_1, F_2, and F_8 generations.

Generation	Average body mass (mg)	
	Males	Females
F_0	0.732	1.179
F_1	0.847	1.189
F_2	0.848	1.254
F_8	0.878	1.392

A. Graph body mass versus generation for males and females.
B. Do the rates of evolution of larger body size appear to be constant throughout the experiment?
C. If you doubled the number of generations in the experiment, would you expect the increase in body mass seen under the hyperoxic conditions to double? Why or why not?

Go to **yourBioPortal.com** for original citations, discussions, and relevant links for all INVESTIGATION figures.

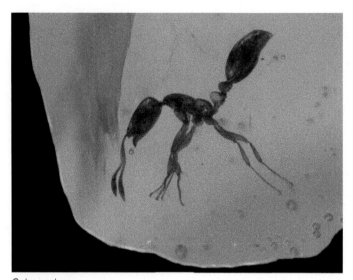

Solenopsis sp.

FIGURE 18.9 **Insect Fossils** *(Page 356)*

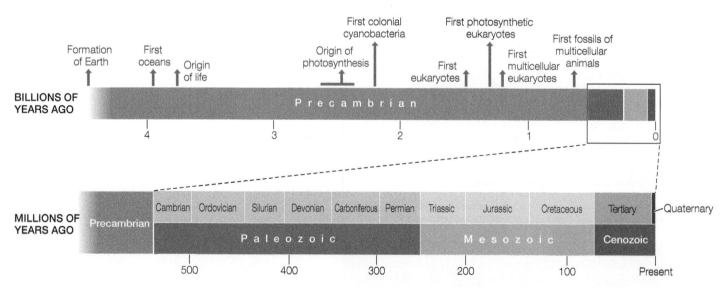

FIGURE 18.10 **A Sense of Life's Time** *(Page 357)*

Chamiodiscus arboreus

Tribrachidium heraldicum

Dickinsonia costata

FIGURE 18.11 Precambrian Life *(Page 357)*

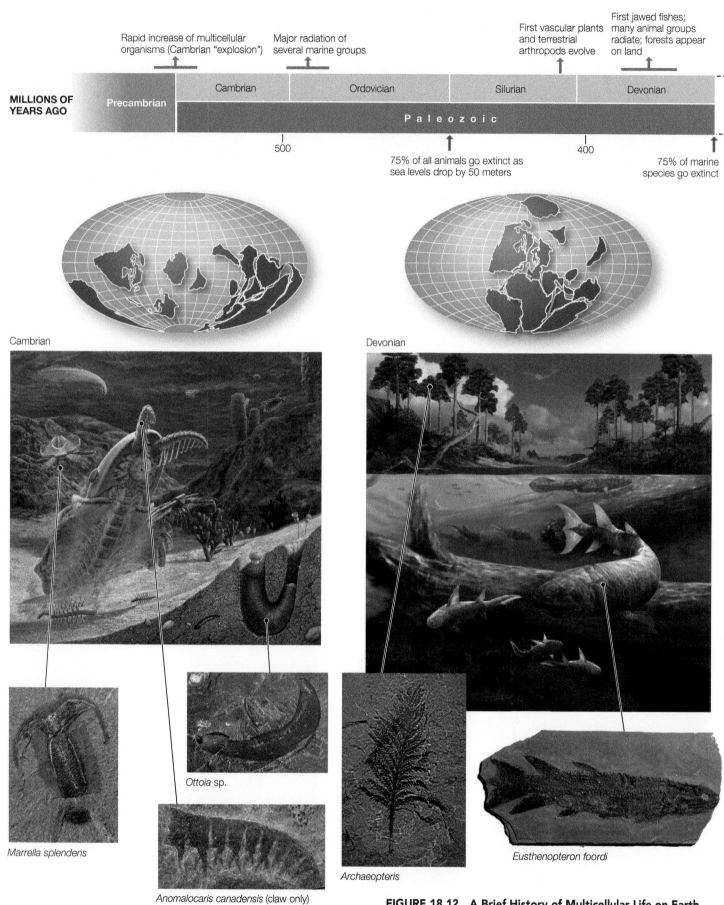

MILLIONS OF YEARS AGO

Rapid increase of multicellular organisms (Cambrian "explosion")

Major radiation of several marine groups

First vascular plants and terrestrial arthropods evolve

First jawed fishes; many animal groups radiate; forests appear on land

Precambrian

Cambrian

Ordovician

Silurian

Devonian

P a l e o z o i c

500

75% of all animals go extinct as sea levels drop by 50 meters

400

75% of marine species go extinct

Cambrian

Devonian

Marrella splendens

Ottoia sp.

Anomalocaris canadensis (claw only)

Archaeopteris

Eusthenopteron foordi

FIGURE 18.12   A Brief History of Multicellular Life on Earth
(Pages 359, 360, and 361)

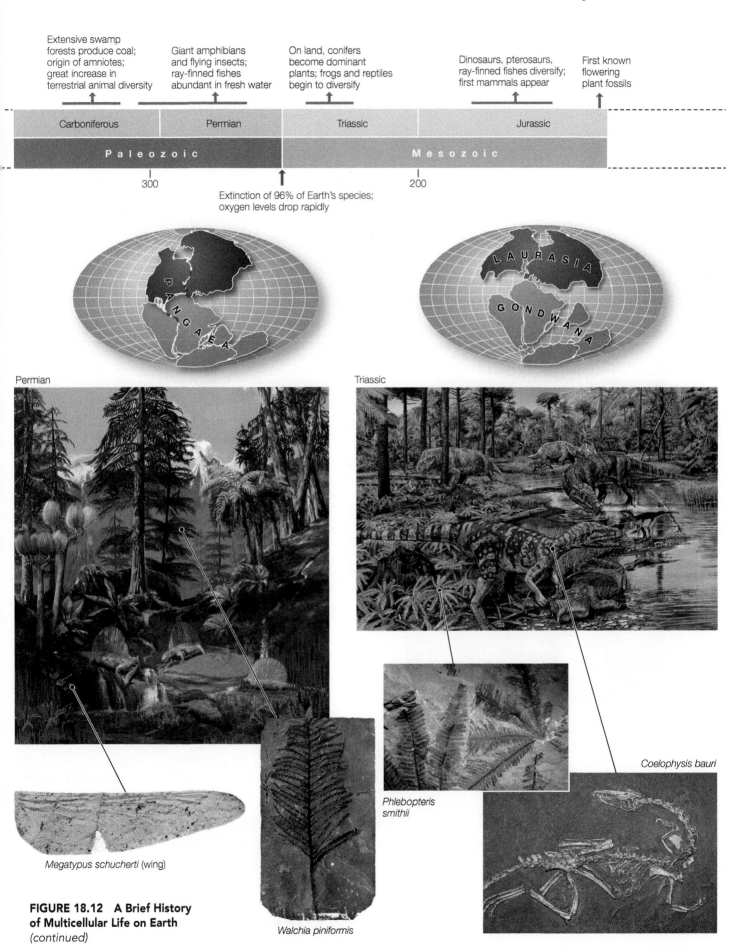

Extensive swamp forests produce coal; origin of amniotes; great increase in terrestrial animal diversity

Giant amphibians and flying insects; ray-finned fishes abundant in fresh water

On land, conifers become dominant plants; frogs and reptiles begin to diversify

Dinosaurs, pterosaurs, ray-finned fishes diversify; first mammals appear

First known flowering plant fossils

Carboniferous	Permian	Triassic	Jurassic

Paleozoic

Mesozoic

300

Extinction of 96% of Earth's species; oxygen levels drop rapidly

200

PANGAEA

LAURASIA

GONDWANA

Permian

Triassic

Megatypus schucherti (wing)

Walchia piniformis

Phlebopteris smithii

Coelophysis bauri

FIGURE 18.12 A Brief History of Multicellular Life on Earth (continued)

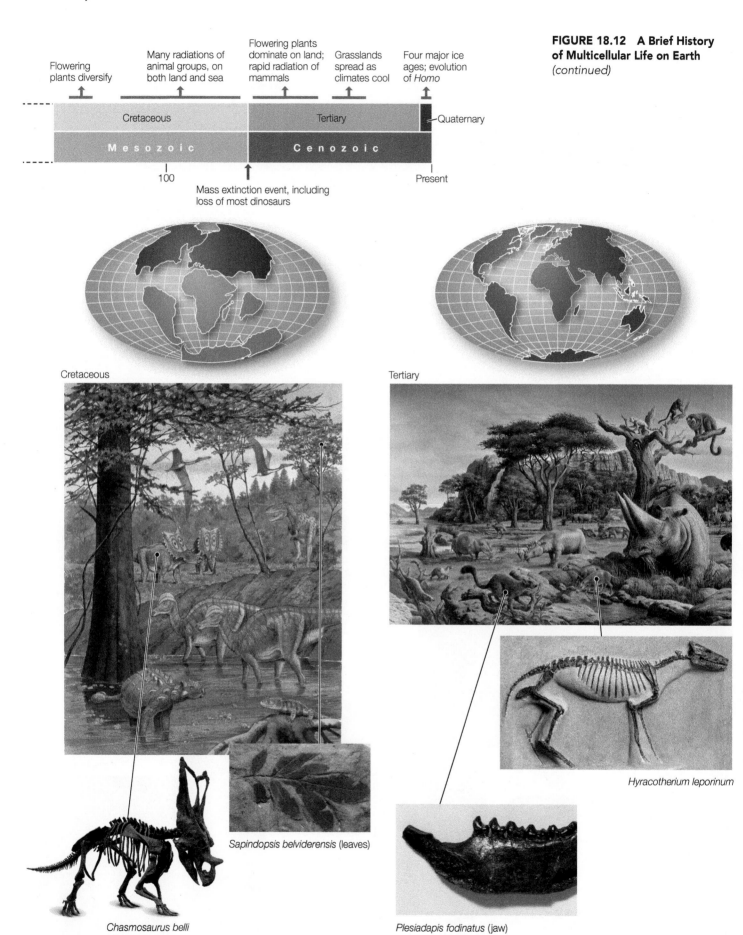

FIGURE 18.12   A Brief History of Multicellular Life on Earth (*continued*)

Flowering plants diversify

Many radiations of animal groups, on both land and sea

Flowering plants dominate on land; rapid radiation of mammals

Grasslands spread as climates cool

Four major ice ages; evolution of *Homo*

Cretaceous

Tertiary

Quaternary

M e s o z o i c

C e n o z o i c

100

Mass extinction event, including loss of most dinosaurs

Present

Cretaceous

Tertiary

Chasmosaurus belli

Sapindopsis belviderensis (leaves)

Plesiadapis fodinatus (jaw)

Hyracotherium leporinum

FIGURE 18.13 **Evidence of Insect Diversification** *(Page 362)*

TABLE 18.2	Subdivisions of the Cenozoic Era	
PERIOD	**EPOCH**	**ONSET (MYA)**
Quaternary	Holocene (Recent)	0.01 (~10,000 years ago)
	Pleistocene	2.6
Tertiary	Pliocene	5.3
	Miocene	23
	Oligocene	34
	Eocene	55.8
	Paleocene	65

(Page 363)

Bacteria, Archaea, and Viruses

19

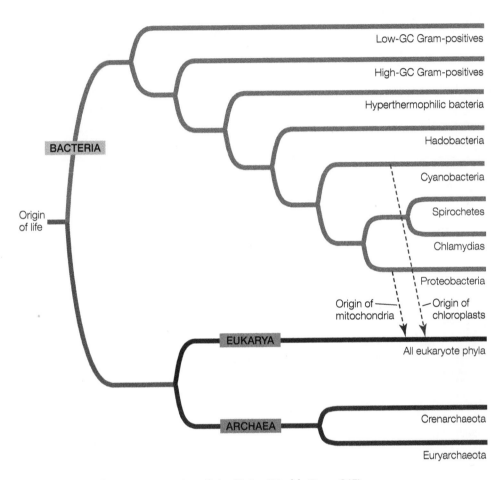

FIGURE 19.1 The Three Domains of the Living World *(Page 367)*

5

| TABLE 19.1 | The Three Domains of Life on Earth | | |

CHARACTERISTIC	BACTERIA	DOMAIN ARCHAEA	EUKARYA
Membrane-enclosed nucleus	Absent	Absent	Present
Membrane-enclosed organelles	Few	Absent	Many
Peptidoglycan in cell wall	Present	Absent	Absent
Membrane lipids	Ester-linked	Ether-linked	Ester-linked
	Unbranched	Branched	Unbranched
Ribosomes[a]	70S	70S	80S
Initiator tRNA	Formylmethionine	Methionine	Methionine
Operons	Yes	Yes	Rare
Plasmids	Yes	Yes	Rare
RNA polymerases	One	One[b]	Three
Ribosomes sensitive to chloramphenicol and streptomycin	Yes	No	No
Ribosomes sensitive to diphtheria toxin	No	Yes	Yes

[a]70S ribosomes are smaller than 80S ribosomes.
[b]Archaeal RNA polymerase is similar to eukaryotic polymerases.

(Page 368)

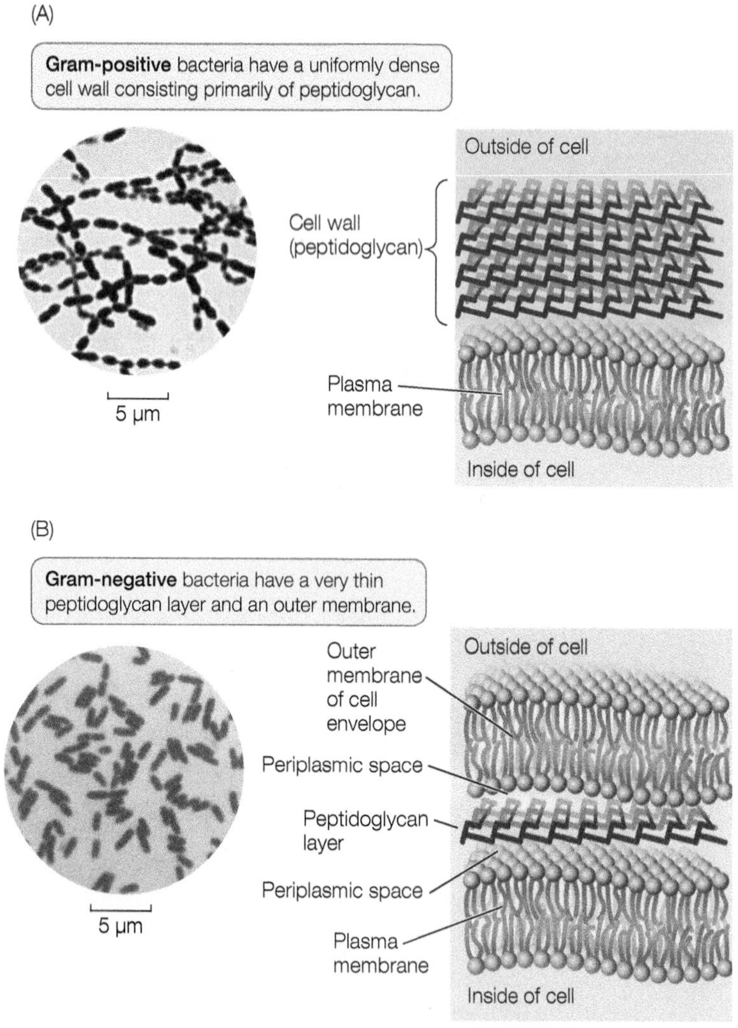

(A)

Gram-positive bacteria have a uniformly dense cell wall consisting primarily of peptidoglycan.

(B)

Gram-negative bacteria have a very thin peptidoglycan layer and an outer membrane.

FIGURE 19.2 The Gram Stain and the Bacterial Cell Wall (Page 369)

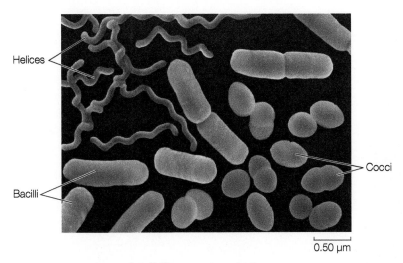

FIGURE 19.3 Bacterial Cell Shapes *(Page 369)*

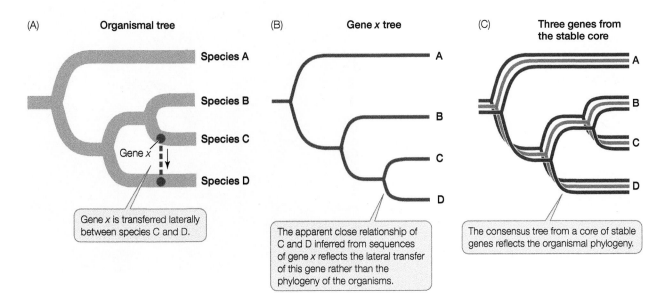

FIGURE 19.4 Lateral Gene Transfer Complicates Phylogenetic Relationships *(Page 370)*

Bacillus thuringiensis

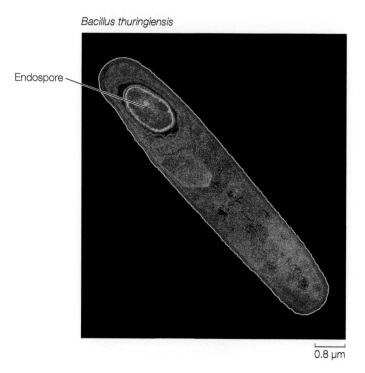

Endospore

0.8 μm

FIGURE 19.5   A Structure for Waiting Out Bad Times *(Page 372)*

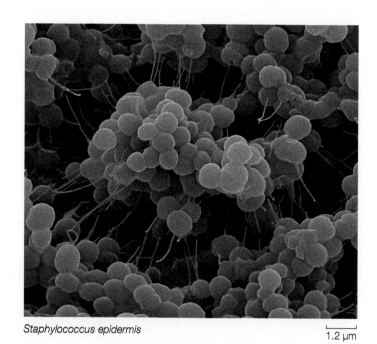

Staphylococcus epidermis

1.2 μm

FIGURE 19.6 Staphylococci *(Page 372)*

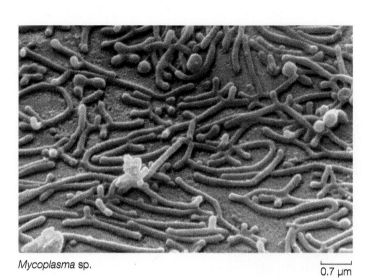

Mycoplasma sp.

0.7 µm

FIGURE 19.7   Tiny Cells *(Page 373)*

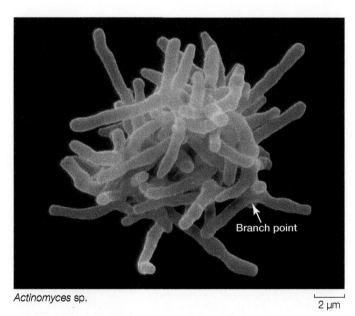

Branch point

Actinomyces sp.

2 µm

FIGURE 19.8   Actinomycetes are High-GC Gram-Positives
(Page 373)

(A) *Anabaena* sp.

(B) *Nostoc punctiforme*

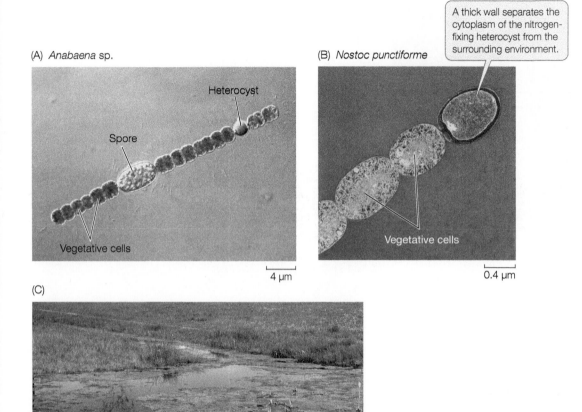

Heterocyst

Spore

Vegetative cells

4 µm

A thick wall separates the cytoplasm of the nitrogen-fixing heterocyst from the surrounding environment.

Vegetative cells

0.4 µm

(C)

FIGURE 19.9 Cyanobacteria *(Page 374)*

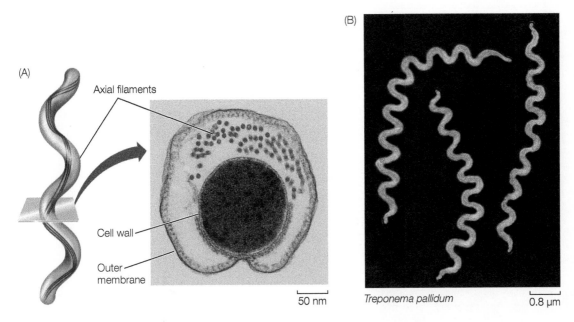

(A)

Axial filaments

Cell wall

Outer membrane

50 nm

(B)

Treponema pallidum

0.8 µm

FIGURE 19.10 Spirochetes Get Their Shape from Axial Filaments *(Page 374)*

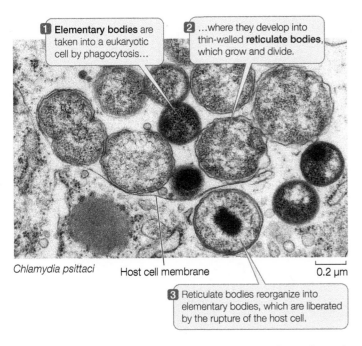

1 **Elementary bodies** are taken into a eukaryotic cell by phagocytosis...

2 ...where they develop into thin-walled **reticulate bodies**, which grow and divide.

Chlamydia psittaci   Host cell membrane   0.2 µm

3 Reticulate bodies reorganize into elementary bodies, which are liberated by the rupture of the host cell.

FIGURE 19.11 Chlamydias Change Form during Their Life Cycle *(Page 375)*

Salmonella typhimurium

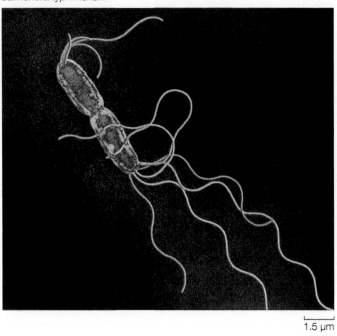

1.5 μm

FIGURE 19.12 Proteobacteria Include Human Pathogens
(Page 375)

FIGURE 19.13 Crown Gall *(Page 376)*

INVESTIGATION

FIGURE 19.14 What Is the Highest Temperature Compatible with Life? Can any organism thrive at temperatures above 120°C? This is the temperature used for sterilization, known to destroy all previously described organisms. Kazem Kashefi and Derek Lovley isolated an unidentified prokaryote from water samples taken near a hydrothermal vent and found it survived and even multiplied at 121°C. The organism was dubbed "Strain 121," and its gene sequencing results indicate that it is an archaeal species.

HYPOTHESIS

Some prokaryotes can survive at temperatures above the 120°C threshold of sterilization.

METHOD

1. Seal samples of unidentified, iron-reducing, thermal vent prokaryotes in tubes with a medium containing Fe^{3+} as an electron acceptor. Control tubes contain Fe^{3+} but no organisms.

2. Hold both tubes in a sterilizer at 121°C for 10 hours. If the iron-reducing organisms are metabolically active, they will reduce the Fe^{3+} to Fe^{2+} (as magnetite, which can be detected with a magnet).

RESULTS

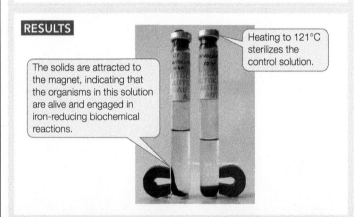

The solids are attracted to the magnet, indicating that the organisms in this solution are alive and engaged in iron-reducing biochemical reactions.

Heating to 121°C sterilizes the control solution.

CONCLUSION

This thermal vent organism (Strain 121) can survive at temperatures above the previously defined sterilization limit.

ANALYZE THE DATA

After Strain 121 was isolated, its growth was examined at various temperatures. The table shows generation time (the time between cell divisions) at nine temperatures.

Temperature (°C)	Generation time (hr)
85	10
90	4
95	3
100	2.5
105	2
110	4
115	6
120	20
130	No growth, but cells not killed

A. Make a graph showing generation time as a function of temperature.
B. Which temperature appears to be closest to the optimum for growth of Strain 121?
C. Note that no growth occurred at 130°C, but that the cells were not killed. How would you demonstrate that these cells were still alive?

Go to **yourBioPortal.com** for original citations, discussions, and relevant links for all INVESTIGATION figures.

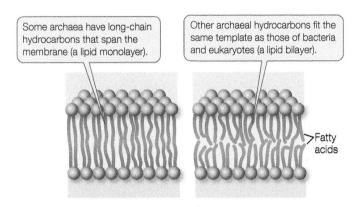

> Some archaea have long-chain hydrocarbons that span the membrane (a lipid monolayer).

> Other archaeal hydrocarbons fit the same template as those of bacteria and eukaryotes (a lipid bilayer).

Fatty acids

FIGURE 19.15 **Membrane Architecture in Archaea** *(Page 377)*

FIGURE 19.16 **Crenarchaeotes Like It Hot** *(Page 377)*

FIGURE 19.17 **Extreme Halophiles** *(Page 378)*

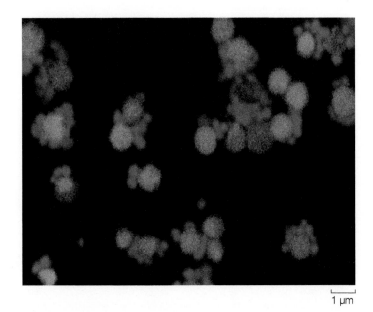

1 μm

FIGURE 19.18   A Nanoarchaeote Growing in Mixed Culture with a Crenarchaeote *(Page 378)*

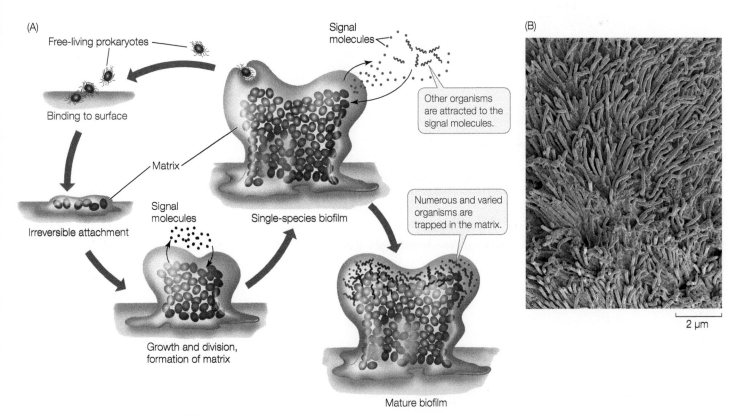

FIGURE 19.19   Forming a Biofilm *(Page 379)*

TABLE 19.2	How Organisms Obtain Their Energy and Carbon	
NUTRITIONAL CATEGORY SOURCE	**ENERGY SOURCE**	**CARBON**
Photoautotrophs (found in all three domains)	Light	Carbon dioxide
Photoheterotrophs (some bacteria)	Light	Organic compounds
Chemolithotrophs (some bacteria, many archaea)	Inorganic substances	Carbon dioxide
Chemoheterotrophs (found in all three domains)	Organic compounds	Organic compounds

(Page 380)

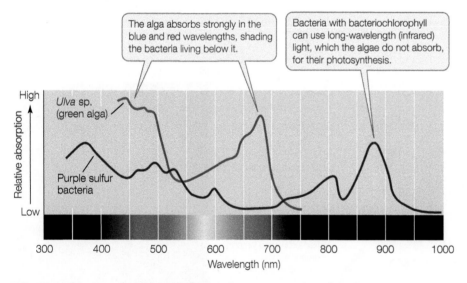

FIGURE 19.20 Bacteriochlorophyll Absorbs Long-Wavelength Light *(Page 380)*

Marshall and Warren set out to satisfy Koch's postulates:

Test 1

The microorganism must be present in every case of the disease.

Results: Biopsies from the stomachs of many patients revealed that the bacterium was always present if the stomach was inflamed or ulcerated.

Test 2

The microorganism must be cultured from a sick host.

Results: The bacterium was isolated from biopsy material and eventually grown in culture media in the laboratory.

Test 3

The isolated and cultured bacteria must be able to induce the disease.

Results: Marshall was examined and found to be free of bacteria and inflammation in his stomach. After drinking a pure culture of the bacterium, he developed stomach inflammation (gastritis).

Test 4

The bacteria must be recoverable from newly infected individuals.

Results: Biopsy of Marshall's stomach 2 weeks after he ingested the bacteria revealed the presence of the bacterium, now christened *Helicobacter pylori*, in the inflamed tissue.

Conclusion

Antibiotic treatment eliminated the bacteria and the inflammation in Marshall. The experiment was repeated on healthy volunteers, and many patients with gastric ulcers were cured with antibiotics. Thus Marshall and Warren demonstrated that the stomach inflammation leading to ulcers is caused by *H. pylori* infections in the stomach.

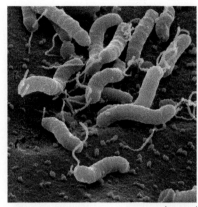

Helicobacter pylori   1.5 μm

FIGURE 19.21   Satisfying Koch's Postulates *(Page 382)*

(A)

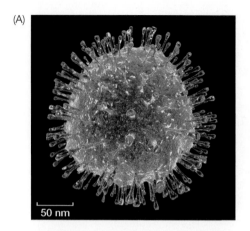

A negative-sense single-stranded RNA virus: The H1N1 influenza A virus prevalent in 2009–2010. Surface view.

(B)

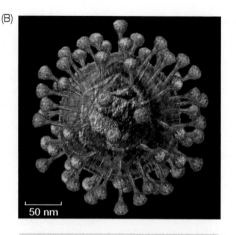

A positive-sense single-stranded RNA virus: Coronavirus of a type thought to be responsible for severe acute respiratory syndrome (SARS). Surface view.

(C)

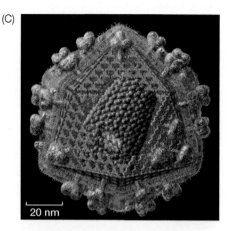

An RNA retrovirus: One of the human immunodeficiency viruses (HIV) that causes AIDS. Cutaway view.

(D)

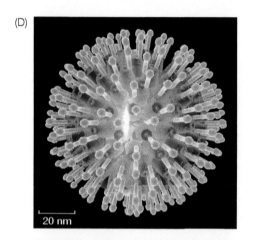

A double-stranded DNA virus: One of the many herpes viruses (Herpesviridae). Different herpes viruses are responsible for many human infections, including chicken pox, shingles, cold sores, and genital herpes (HSV1/2). Surface view.

(E)

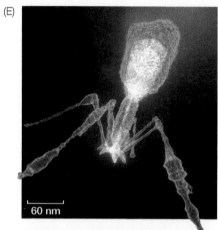

A double-stranded DNA virus: Bacteriophage T4. Viruses that infect bacteria are referred to as bacteriophage (or simply phage). T4 attaches leglike fibers to the outside of its host cell and injects its DNA into the cytoplasm through its "tail" (pink structure in this rendition).

(F)

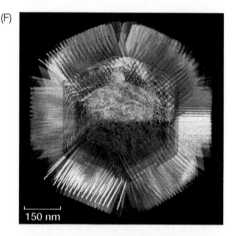

A double-stranded DNA mimivirus: This *Acanthamoeba polyphaga* mimivirus (APMV) has the largest diameter of all known viruses and a genome larger than some prokaryote genomes. Cutaway view.

FIGURE 19.22 Viruses Are Diverse *(Page 384)*

Yellow areas are dead leaf cells, killed by the mosaic virus.

FIGURE 19.23   Mosaic Viruses Are a Problem for Agriculture
(Page 385)

The Origin and Diversification of Eukaryotes

20

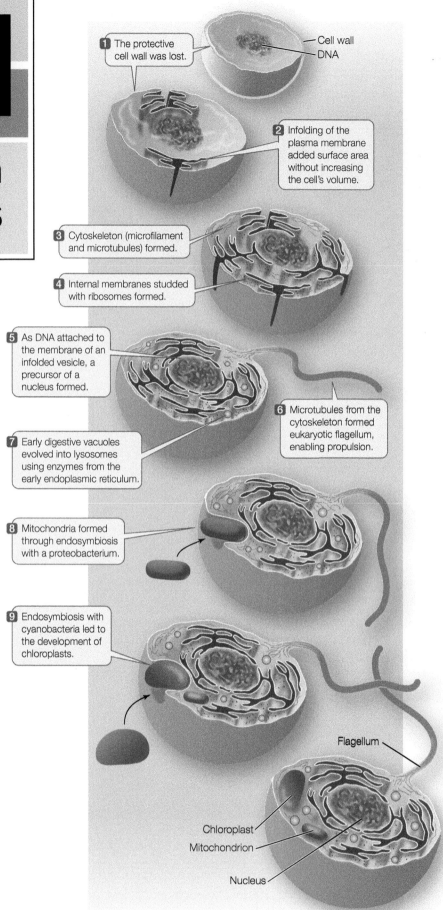

1 The protective cell wall was lost.

Cell wall
DNA

2 Infolding of the plasma membrane added surface area without increasing the cell's volume.

3 Cytoskeleton (microfilament and microtubules) formed.

4 Internal membranes studded with ribosomes formed.

5 As DNA attached to the membrane of an infolded vesicle, a precursor of a nucleus formed.

6 Microtubules from the cytoskeleton formed eukaryotic flagellum, enabling propulsion.

7 Early digestive vacuoles evolved into lysosomes using enzymes from the early endoplasmic reticulum.

8 Mitochondria formed through endosymbiosis with a proteobacterium.

9 Endosymbiosis with cyanobacteria led to the development of chloroplasts.

Flagellum

Chloroplast
Mitochondrion
Nucleus

FIGURE 20.1   Evolution of the Eukaryotic Cell *(Page 389)*

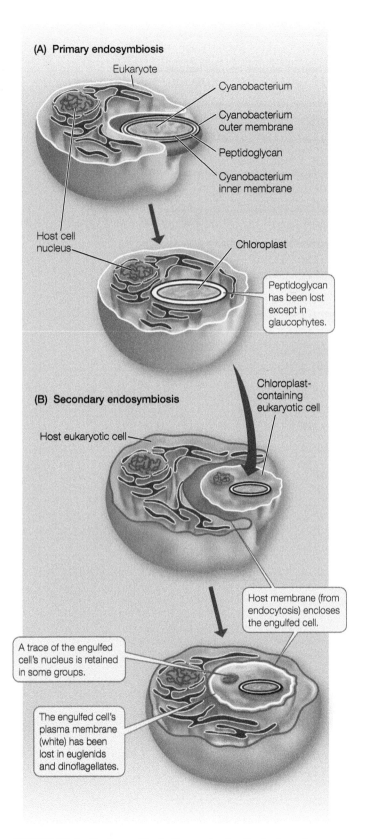

(A) Primary endosymbiosis

Eukaryote

Cyanobacterium

Cyanobacterium outer membrane

Peptidoglycan

Cyanobacterium inner membrane

Host cell nucleus

Chloroplast

Peptidoglycan has been lost except in glaucophytes.

(B) Secondary endosymbiosis

Chloroplast-containing eukaryotic cell

Host eukaryotic cell

Host membrane (from endocytosis) encloses the engulfed cell.

A trace of the engulfed cell's nucleus is retained in some groups.

The engulfed cell's plasma membrane (white) has been lost in euglenids and dinoflagellates.

FIGURE 20.2 Endosymbiotic Events in the Evolution of Chloroplasts *(Page 391)*

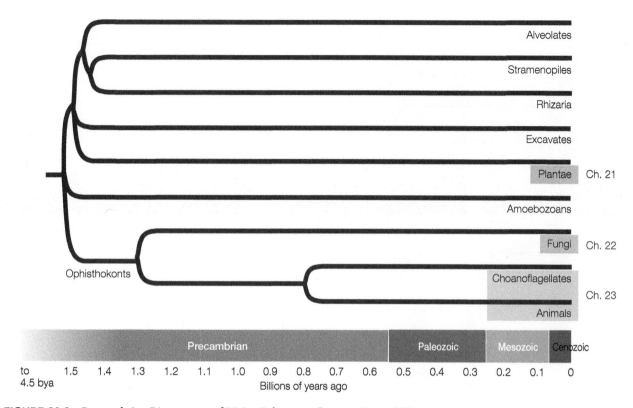

FIGURE 20.3 Precambrian Divergence of Major Eukaryote Groups *(Page 393)*

Peridinium sp.

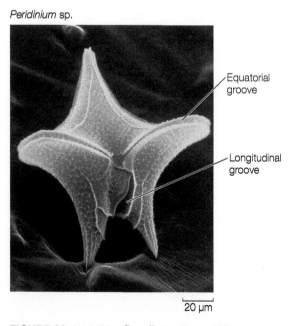

FIGURE 20.4 A Dinoflagellate *(Page 393)*

(A) *Paramecium* sp.

(B) *Didinium nasutum*

(C) *Euplotes* sp.

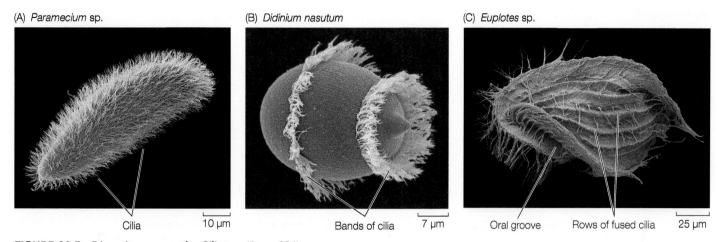

Cilia 10 μm

Bands of cilia 7 μm

Oral groove Rows of fused cilia 25 μm

FIGURE 20.5 Diversity among the Ciliates *(Page 394)*

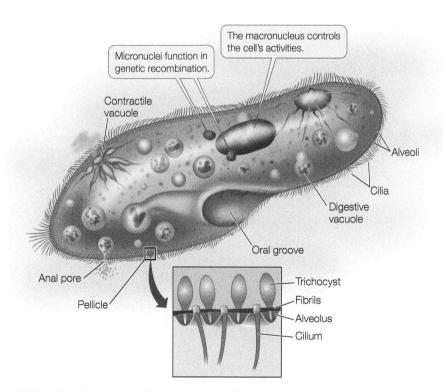

Micronuclei function in genetic recombination.

The macronucleus controls the cell's activities.

Contractile vacuole

Alveoli

Cilia

Digestive vacuole

Oral groove

Anal pore

Pellicle

Trichocyst

Fibrils

Alveolus

Cilium

FIGURE 20.6 Anatomy of a *Paramecium* *(Page 394)*

(A) *Giardia muris*

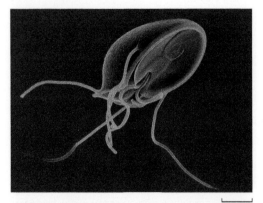

2 µm

(B) *Trichomonas vaginalis*

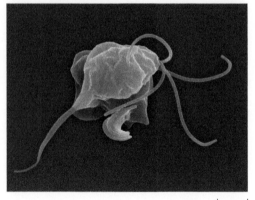

2 µm

FIGURE 20.7 Some Excavate Groups Lack Mitochondria *(Page 395)*

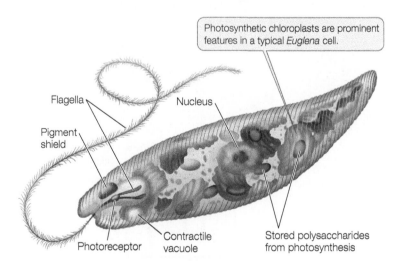

Photosynthetic chloroplasts are prominent features in a typical *Euglena* cell.

Flagella

Nucleus

Pigment shield

Photoreceptor

Contractile vacuole

Stored polysaccharides from photosynthesis

FIGURE 20.8 A Photosynthetic Euglenid *(Page 395)*

TABLE 20.1	A Comparison of Three Kinetoplastid Trypanosomes		
	TRYPANOSOMA BRUCEI	*TRYPANOSOMA CRUZI*	*LEISHMANIA MAJOR*
Human disease	Sleeping sickness	Chagas' disease	Leishmaniasis
Insect vector	Tsetse fly	Assassin bug	Sand fly
Vaccine or effective cure	None	None	None
Strategy for survival	Changes surface recognition molecules frequently	Causes changes in surface recognition molecules on host cell	Reduces effectiveness of macrophage hosts
Site in human body	Bloodstream; attacks nerve tissue in final stages	Enters cells, especially muscle cells	Enters cells, primarily macrophages
Approximate number of deaths per year	50,000	43,000	60,000

(Page 396)

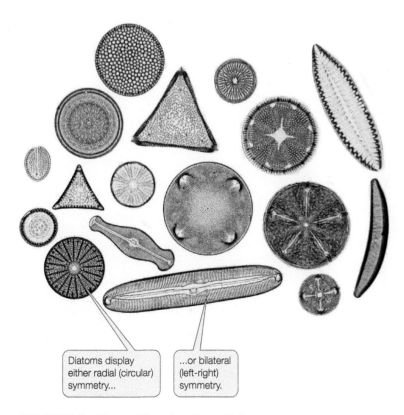

Diatoms display either radial (circular) symmetry...

...or bilateral (left-right) symmetry.

FIGURE 20.9 Diatom Diversity (Page 396)

(A) *Himanthalia elongata*

(B) *Postelsia palmaeformis*

Holdfasts

FIGURE 20.10 Brown Algae *(Page 397)*

Saprolegnia sp.

2 mm

FIGURE 20.11 An Oomycete *(Page 397)*

Elphidium crispum

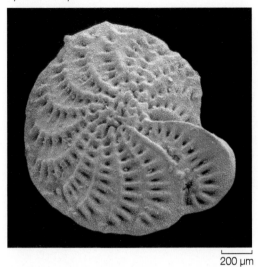

200 µm

FIGURE 20.12   Building Blocks of Limestone
(Page 398)

(A)

350 µm

(B) *Hexacontium* sp.   50 µm

**FIGURE 20.13   Radiolarians Exhibit Distinctive Pseudopods
and Radial Symmetry** (Page 398)

Pelomyxa carolinensis

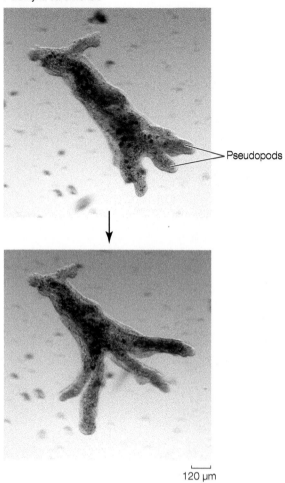

120 µm

FIGURE 20.14   An Amoeba in Motion *(Page 399)*

Nebela collaris

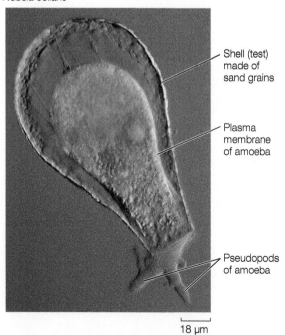

18 µm

FIGURE 20.15   Life in a Glass House *(Page 399)*

(A)

(B)

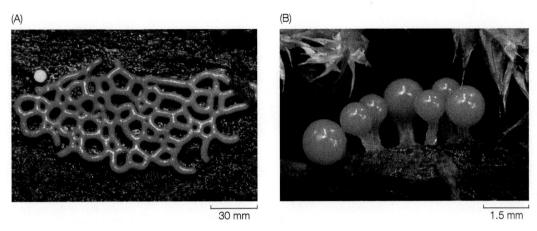

30 mm

1.5 mm

FIGURE 20.16 **Plasmodial Slime Molds** *(Page 399)*

Dictyostelium discoideum

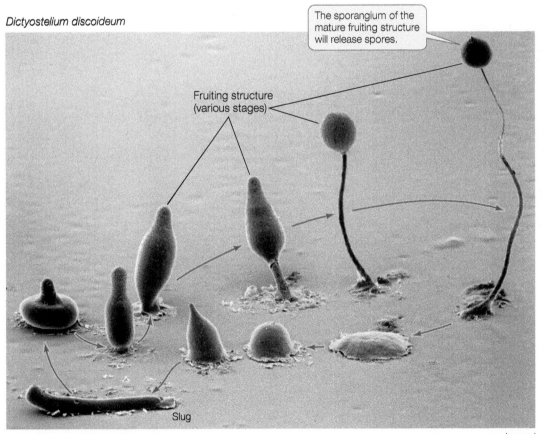

The sporangium of the mature fruiting structure will release spores.

Fruiting structure (various stages)

Slug

0.25 mm

FIGURE 20.17 **A Cellular Slime Mold** *(Page 400)*

Macronucleus

Micronucleus

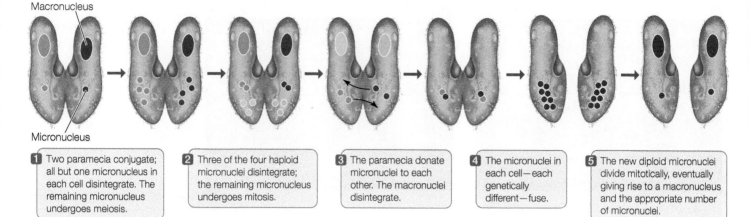

1. Two paramecia conjugate; all but one micronucleus in each cell disintegrate. The remaining micronucleus undergoes meiosis.

2. Three of the four haploid micronuclei disintegrate; the remaining micronucleus undergoes mitosis.

3. The paramecia donate micronuclei to each other. The macronuclei disintegrate.

4. The micronuclei in each cell—each genetically different—fuse.

5. The new diploid micronuclei divide mitotically, eventually giving rise to a macronucleus and the appropriate number of micronuclei.

FIGURE 20.18 Paramecia Achieve Genetic Recombination by Conjugating *(Page 402)*

INVESTIGATION

FIGURE 20.19 Can Corals Reacquire Dinoflagellate Endosymbionts Lost to Bleaching? Some corals lose their chief nutritional source when their photosynthetic endosymbionts die, often as a result of changing environmental conditions. This experiment by Cynthia Lewis and Mary Alice Coffroth investigated the ability of corals to acquire new endosymbionts after bleaching.

HYPOTHESIS

Bleached corals can acquire new photosynthetic endosymbionts from their environment.

METHOD

1. Count numbers of *Symbiodinium*, a photosynthetic dinoflagellate, living symbiotically in samples of a coral (*Briareum* sp.).
2. Stimulate bleaching by maintaining all *Briareum* colonies in darkness for 12 weeks.
3. After 12 weeks of darkness, count numbers of *Symbiodinium* in the coral samples; then return all colonies to light.
4. In some of the bleached colonies (the experimental group), introduce *Symbiodinium* strain B211—dinoflagellates that contain a unique molecular marker. A control group of bleached colonies is not exposed to strain B211. Maintain both groups in the light for 6 weeks.

RESULTS

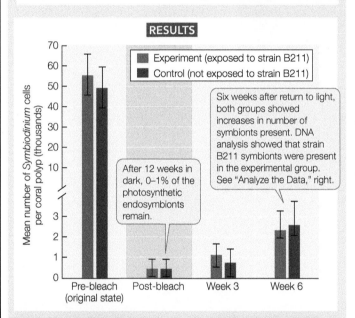

- Experiment (exposed to strain B211)
- Control (not exposed to strain B211)

After 12 weeks in dark, 0–1% of the photosynthetic endosymbionts remain.

Six weeks after return to light, both groups showed increases in number of symbionts present. DNA analysis showed that strain B211 symbionts were present in the experimental group. See "Analyze the Data," right.

Mean number of *Symbiodinium* cells per coral polyp (thousands)

CONCLUSION

Corals can acquire new strains of endosymbionts from their environment following bleaching.

ANALYZE THE DATA

These data—the results of DNA analysis of the *Symbiodinium* endosymbionts—reveal that many of the experimental colonies took up strain B211 from their environment. The control colonies recovered their native *Symbiodinium*, except in colonies in which endosymbionts were completely lost. Use these data to answer the questions below.

	Symbiodinium strain present (% of colonies)			
	Non-B211	B211	None*	Colony died
Experimental colonies (strain B211 added)				
Pre-bleach	100	0	0	0
Post-bleach	58	0	42	0
Week 3	0	92	0	8
Week 6	8	58	8	25
Control colonies (no strain B211)				
Pre-bleach	100	0	0	0
Post-bleach	67	0	33	0
Week 3	67	0	33	0
Week 6	67	0	17	17

*Colonies remained alive but no *Symbiodinium* were detected.

A. Are new strains of *Symbiodinium* taken up only by coral colonies that have lost all their original endosymbionts?

B. Does the acquisition of a new *Symbiodinium* strain always result in survival of a recovering *Briareum* colony?

C. In week 3, only strain B211 was detected in the experimental colonies, but in week 6, non-B211 *Symbiodinium* were detected in 8% of the experimental colonies. Can you suggest an explanation for this observation?

Pre-bleach

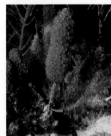

Post-bleach

Go to **yourBioPortal.com** for original citations, discussions, and relevant links for all INVESTIGATION figures.

FIGURE 20.20 **Light Up the Sea** *(Page 405)*

The Evolution of Plants

(A)

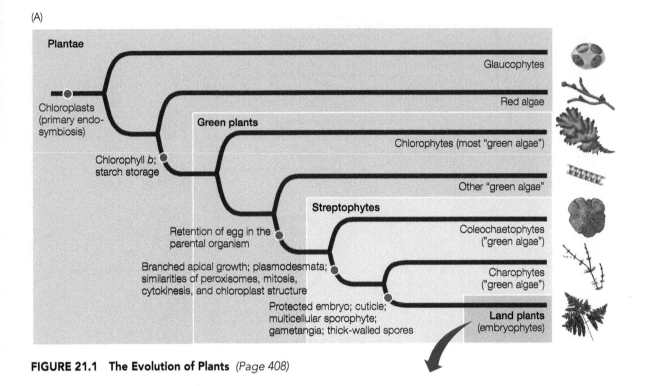

FIGURE 21.1 **The Evolution of Plants** *(Page 408)*

(B)

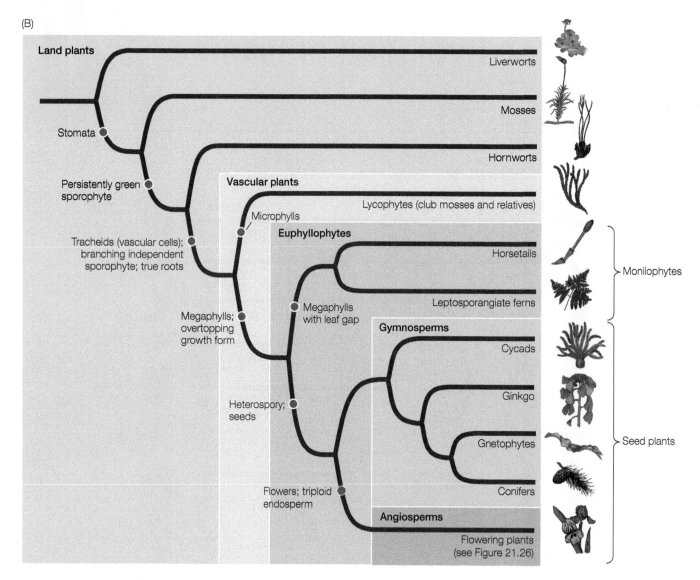

FIGURE 21.1 The Evolution of Plants *(continued)*

Nemalion helminthoides

FIGURE 21.2   A Red Alga *(Page 409)*

(A) *Ulva rigida*   (B) *Coleochaete* sp.   (C) *Chara* sp.

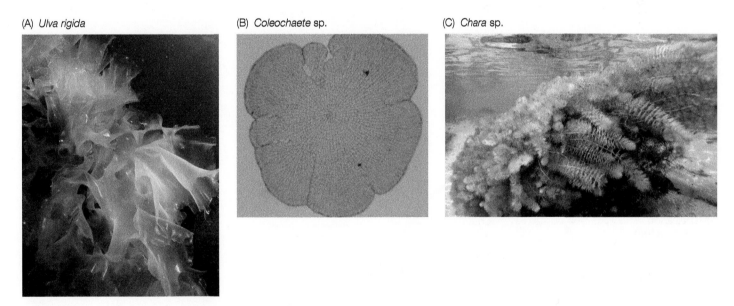

FIGURE 21.3   "Green Algae" Consist of Several Distantly Related Groups *(Page 410)*

TABLE 21.1	Classification of Land Plants	
GROUP	COMMON NAME	CHARACTERISTICS
Nonvascular Land plants		
Hepatophyta	Liverworts	No filamentous stage; gametophyte flat
Anthocerophyta	Hornworts	Embedded archegonia; sporophyte grows basally (from the ground)
Bryophyta	Mosses	Filamentous stage; sporophyte grows apically (from the tip)
Vascular plants		
Lycopodiophyta	Lycophytes: Club mosses and allies	Microphylls in spirals; sporangia in leaf axils
Monilophyta	Horsetails, ferns	Megaphylls with a leaf gap (a space in the stem from which the leaf emerges)
SEED PLANTS		
Gymnosperms		
Cycadophyta	Cycads	Compound leaves; swimming sperm; seeds on modified leaves
Ginkgophyta	Ginkgo	Deciduous; fan-shaped leaves; swimming sperm
Gnetophyta	Gnetophytes	Vessels in vascular tissue; opposite, simple leaves
Coniferophyta	Conifers	Seeds in cones; needlelike or scalelike leaves
Angiosperms	Flowering plants	Endosperm; carpels; gametophytes much reduced; seeds within fruit

(Page 410)

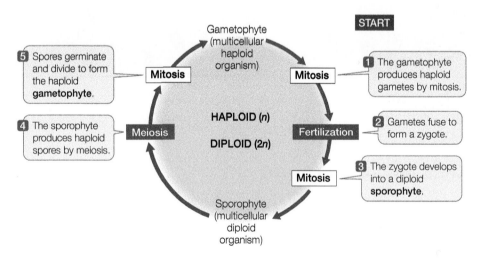

FIGURE 21.4 Alternation of Generations in Land Plants *(Page 412)*

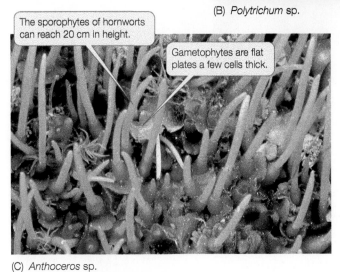

(A) *Marchantia* sp.

(B) *Polytrichum* sp.

- Spore case
- Sporophytes
- Gametophytes

The sporophytes of hornworts can reach 20 cm in height.

Gametophytes are flat plates a few cells thick.

(C) *Anthoceros* sp.

FIGURE 21.5   Diversity among Nonvascular Land Plants *(Page 413)*

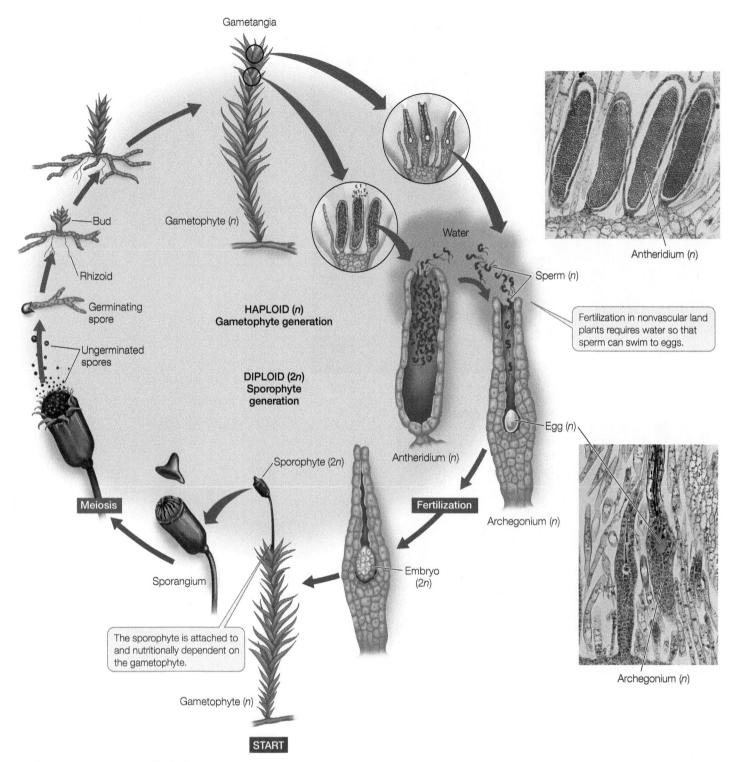

Gametangia

Gametophyte (n)

Bud

Rhizoid

Germinating spore

Ungerminated spores

HAPLOID (n) Gametophyte generation

DIPLOID (2n) Sporophyte generation

Water

Antheridium (n)

Sperm (n)

Fertilization in nonvascular land plants requires water so that sperm can swim to eggs.

Egg (n)

Antheridium (n)

Archegonium (n)

Meiosis

Sporophyte (2n)

Fertilization

Sporangium

Embryo (2n)

The sporophyte is attached to and nutritionally dependent on the gametophyte.

Archegonium (n)

Gametophyte (n)

START

FIGURE 21.6   A Moss Life Cycle *(Page 414)*

FIGURE 21.7   Reconstruction of an Ancient Forest *(Page 416)*

(A) *Lycopodium annotinum*

(B) *Equisetum pratense*

(C)   *Marsilea* sp.   *Salvinia* sp.

(D) *Dicksonia antarctica*

FIGURE 21.8 Lycophytes and Monilophytes *(Page 417)*

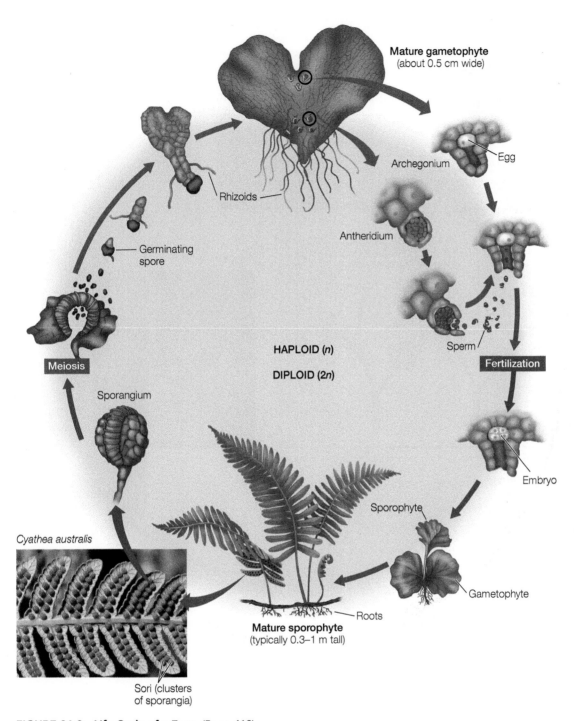

Mature gametophyte
(about 0.5 cm wide)

Archegonium

Egg

Rhizoids

Antheridium

Germinating
spore

Sperm

Fertilization

HAPLOID (*n*)

DIPLOID (2*n*)

Meiosis

Embryo

Sporangium

Sporophyte

Gametophyte

Cyathea australis

Roots

Mature sporophyte
(typically 0.3–1 m tall)

Sori (clusters
of sporangia)

FIGURE 21.9 Life Cycle of a Fern *(Page 418)*

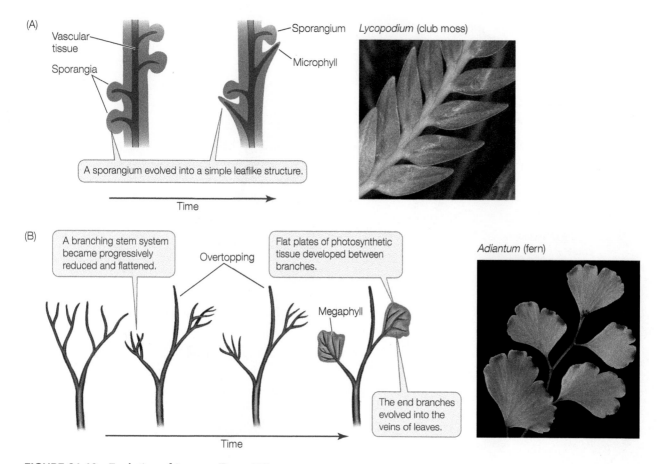

FIGURE 21.10 Evolution of Leaves *(Page 419)*

(A) Homospory

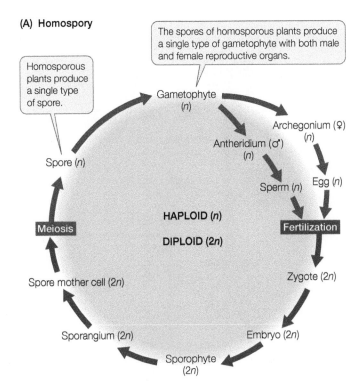

Homosporous plants produce a single type of spore.

The spores of homosporous plants produce a single type of gametophyte with both male and female reproductive organs.

Gametophyte (*n*)

Archegonium (♀) (*n*)

Antheridium (♂) (*n*)

Spore (*n*)

Sperm (*n*)

Egg (*n*)

HAPLOID (*n*)

DIPLOID (2*n*)

Meiosis

Fertilization

Spore mother cell (2*n*)

Zygote (2*n*)

Sporangium (2*n*)

Embryo (2*n*)

Sporophyte (2*n*)

FIGURE 21.11   Homospory and Heterospory *(Page 419)*

(B) Heterospory

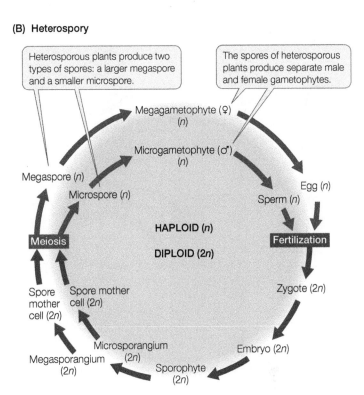

Heterosporous plants produce two types of spores: a larger megaspore and a smaller microspore.

The spores of heterosporous plants produce separate male and female gametophytes.

Megagametophyte (♀) (*n*)

Microgametophyte (♂) (*n*)

Megaspore (*n*)

Microspore (*n*)

Egg (*n*)

Sperm (*n*)

HAPLOID (*n*)

DIPLOID (2*n*)

Meiosis

Fertilization

Spore mother cell (2*n*)

Spore mother cell (2*n*)

Zygote (2*n*)

Microsporangium (2*n*)

Megasporangium (2*n*)

Embryo (2*n*)

Sporophyte (2*n*)

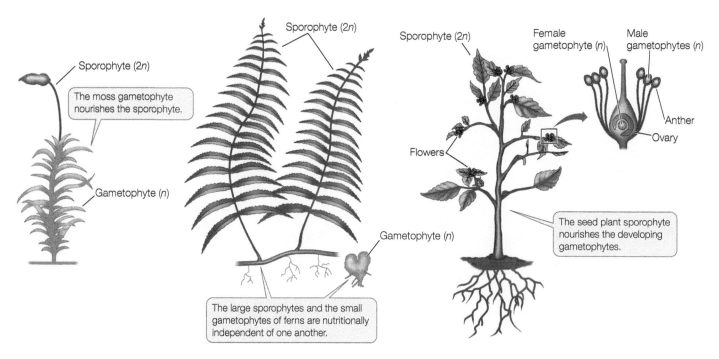

FIGURE 21.12 The Relationship between Sporophyte and Gametophyte *(Page 420)*

Salix cinerea

FIGURE 21.13 Pollen Grains *(Page 421)*

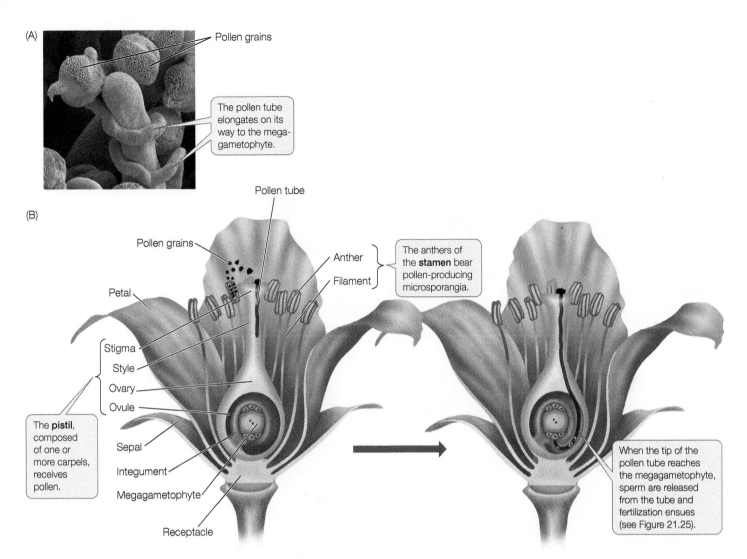

(A)

Pollen grains

The pollen tube elongates on its way to the mega-gametophyte.

(B)

Pollen tube

Pollen grains

Anther

Filament

The anthers of the **stamen** bear pollen-producing microsporangia.

Petal

Stigma

Style

Ovary

Ovule

The **pistil**, composed of one or more carpels, receives pollen.

Sepal

Integument

Megagametophyte

Receptacle

When the tip of the pollen tube reaches the megagametophyte, sperm are released from the tube and fertilization ensues (see Figure 21.25).

FIGURE 21.14   Pollination in Seed Plants *(Page 421)*

(A) *Encephalartos transvenosus*

(B) *Ginkgo biloba*

(D) *Pinus longaeva*

(C) *Welwitschia mirabilis*

FIGURE 21.15 Diversity among the Gymnosperms *(Page 423)*

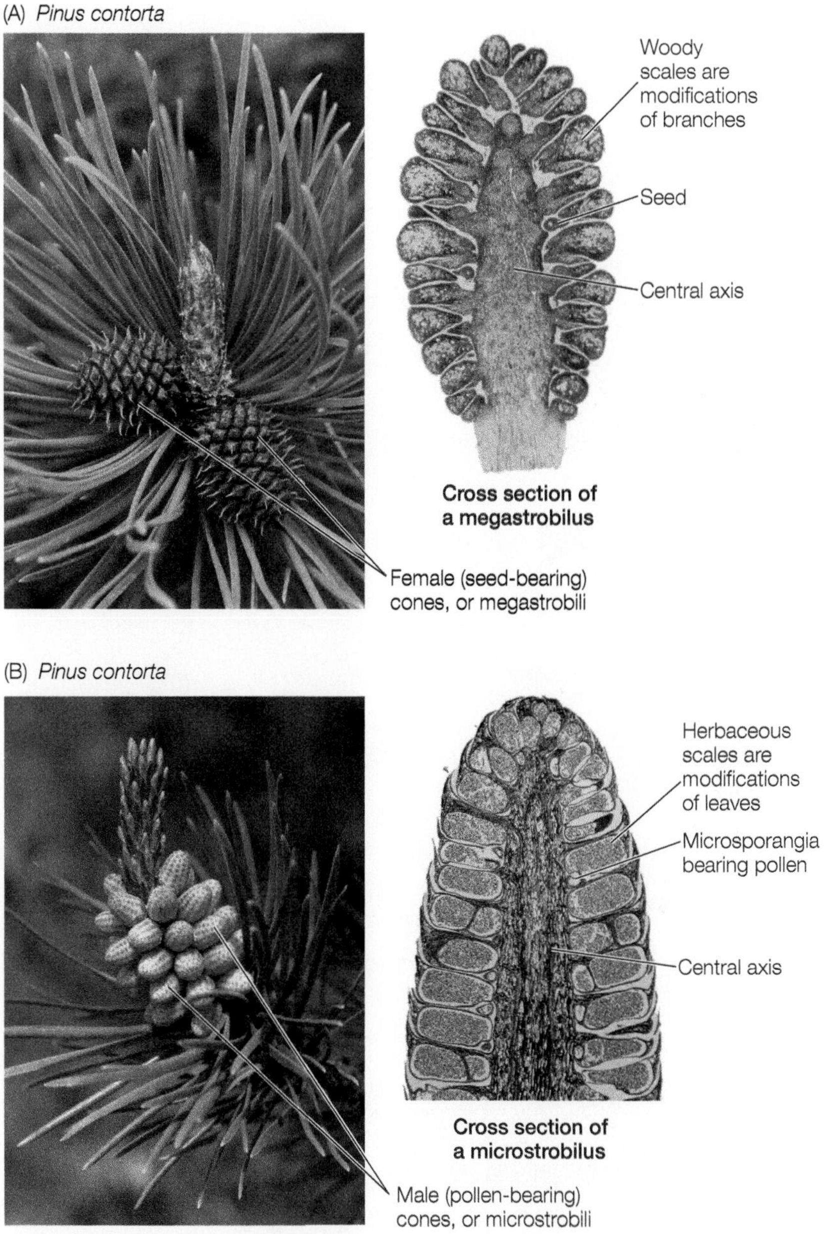

(A) *Pinus contorta*

Woody scales are modifications of branches

Seed

Central axis

Cross section of a megastrobilus

Female (seed-bearing) cones, or megastrobili

(B) *Pinus contorta*

Herbaceous scales are modifications of leaves

Microsporangia bearing pollen

Central axis

Cross section of a microstrobilus

Male (pollen-bearing) cones, or microstrobili

FIGURE 21.16 Female and Male Cones *(Page 424)*

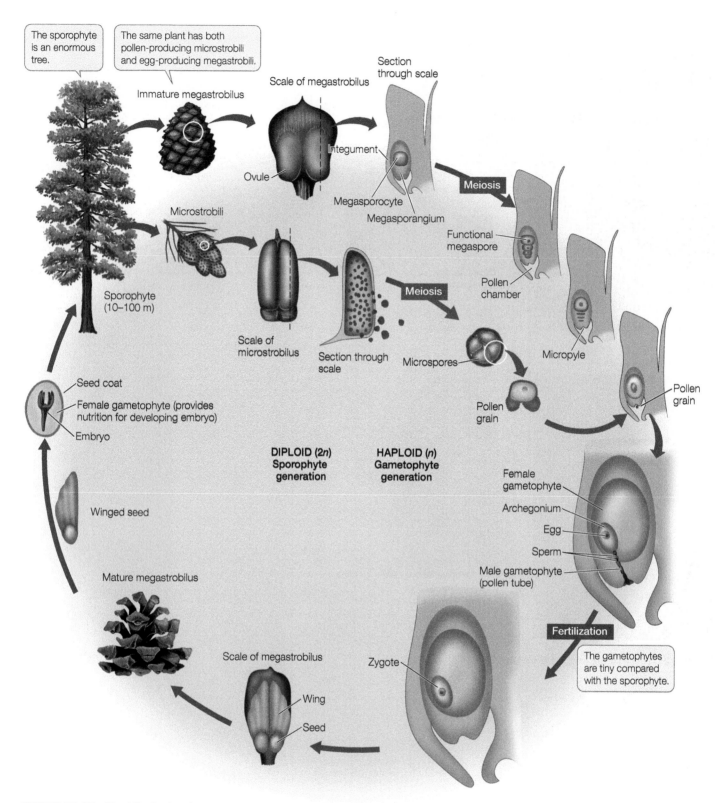

FIGURE 21.17 The Life Cycle of a Pine Tree *(Page 425)*

(A) *Aegopodium podagraria*

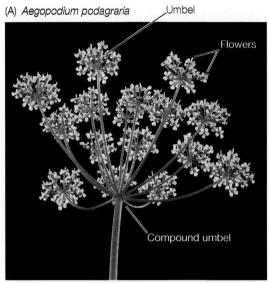

Umbel

Flowers

Compound umbel

(B) *Zinnia elegans*

Ray flowers Disc flowers

(C) *Agropyron repens*

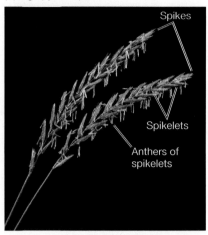

Spikes

Spikelets

Anthers of spikelets

FIGURE 21.18 Inflorescences *(Page 426)*

(A) *Nymphaea* sp.

(B) *Viola tricolor*

FIGURE 21.19 Flower Form and Evolution *(Page 427)*

(A) Carpel evolution

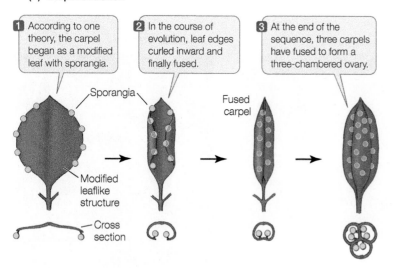

1 According to one theory, the carpel began as a modified leaf with sporangia.

2 In the course of evolution, leaf edges curled inward and finally fused.

3 At the end of the sequence, three carpels have fused to form a three-chambered ovary.

Sporangia

Fused carpel

Modified leaflike structure

Cross section

(B) Stamen evolution

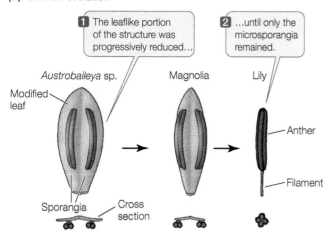

1 The leaflike portion of the structure was progressively reduced…

2 …until only the microsporangia remained.

Austrobaileya sp.

Magnolia

Lily

Modified leaf

Sporangia

Cross section

Anther

Filament

FIGURE 21.20 Carpels and Stamens Evolved from Leaflike Structures
(Page 428)

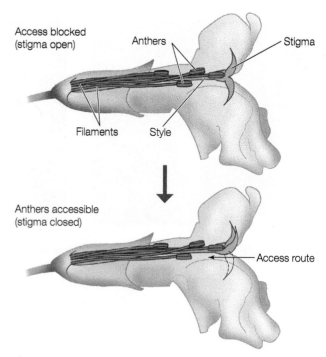

Access blocked (stigma open)

Anthers

Stigma

Filaments

Style

Anthers accessible (stigma closed)

Access route

FIGURE 21.21 An Unusual Way to Prevent Selfing
(Page 428)

INVESTIGATION

FIGURE 21.22   The Effect of Stigma Retraction in Monkeyflowers   Elizabeth Fetscher's experiments showed that the unusual stigma retraction response to pollination in monkeyflowers (illustrated in Figure 21.21) enhances the dispersal of pollen to other flowers.

HYPOTHESIS

The stigma-retraction response in *M. aurantiacus* increases the likelihood than an individual flower's pollen will be exported to another flower once pollen from another flower has been deposited on its stigma.

METHOD

1. Set up three groups of monkeyflower arrays. Each array consists of one pollen-donor flower and multiple pollen-recipient flowers (with the anthers removed to prevent pollen donation).
2. In control arrays, the stigma of the pollen donor is allowed to function normally.
3. In one set of experimental arrays, the stigma of the pollen donor is permanently propped open.
4. In a second set of experimental arrays, the stigma of the pollen donor is artificially sealed closed.
5. Allow hummingbirds to visit the arrays, then count the pollen grains transferred from each donor flower to the recipient flowers in the same array.

RESULTS

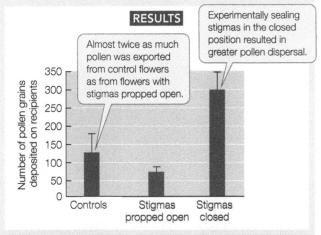

Almost twice as much pollen was exported from control flowers as from flowers with stigmas propped open.

Experimentally sealing stigmas in the closed position resulted in greater pollen dispersal.

CONCLUSION

The stigma-retraction response enhances the male function of the flower (dispersal of pollen) once the female function (receipt of pollen) has been performed.

Go to **yourBioPortal.com** for original citations, discussions, and relevant links for all INVESTIGATION figures.

Rubeckia fulgida

FIGURE 21.23   See Like a Bee *(Page 429)*

FIGURE 21.24 Fruits Come in Many Forms *(Page 430)*

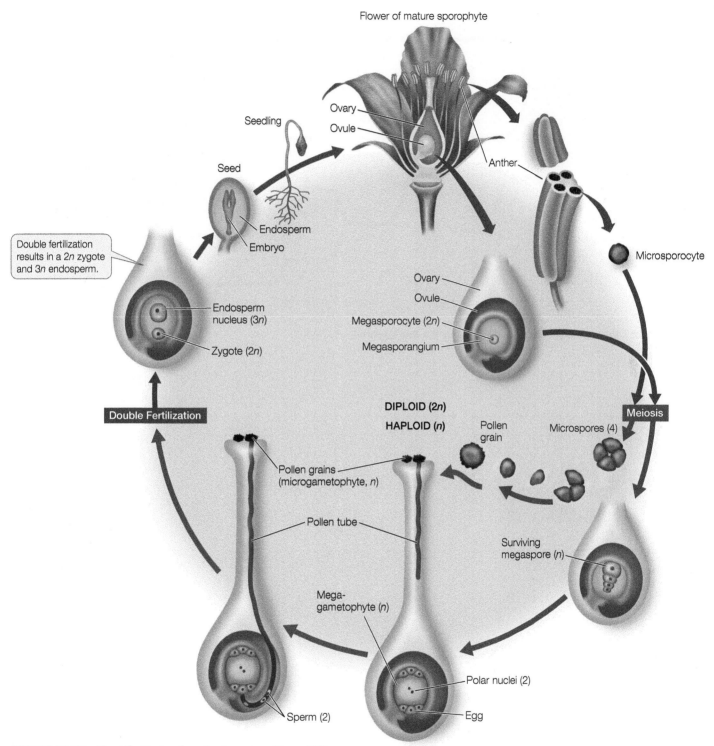

Flower of mature sporophyte

Ovary

Ovule

Seedling

Seed

Anther

Endosperm

Embryo

Microsporocyte

Double fertilization results in a 2*n* zygote and 3*n* endosperm.

Endosperm nucleus (3*n*)

Ovary

Ovule

Megasporocyte (2*n*)

Megasporangium

Zygote (2*n*)

DIPLOID (2*n*)

HAPLOID (*n*)

Pollen grain

Meiosis

Microspores (4)

Double Fertilization

Pollen grains (microgametophyte, *n*)

Surviving megaspore (*n*)

Pollen tube

Mega-gametophyte (*n*)

Polar nuclei (2)

Sperm (2)

Egg

FIGURE 21.25 The Life Cycle of an Angiosperm *(Page 431)*

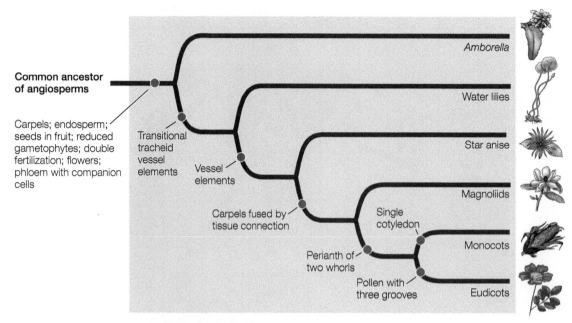

Common ancestor of angiosperms

Carpels; endosperm; seeds in fruit; reduced gametophytes; double fertilization; flowers; phloem with companion cells

Transitional tracheid vessel elements

Vessel elements

Carpels fused by tissue connection

Single cotyledon

Perianth of two whorls

Pollen with three grooves

Amborella

Water lilies

Star anise

Magnoliids

Monocots

Eudicots

FIGURE 21.26   Evolutionary Relationships among the Angiosperms *(Page 432)*

(A) *Amborella trichopoda*

False anthers

(B) *Victoria amazonica*

(C) *Illicium floridanum*

(D) *Magnolia* sp.

(E) *Aristolochia littoralis*

FIGURE 21.27 Monocots and Eudicots Are Not the Only Surviving Angiosperms *(Page 432)*

(A)

(B) *Saccharum* sp.

(C) *Posidonia oceanica*

(D) *Phoenix dactylifera*

FIGURE 21.28 Monocots *(Page 433)*

(A) *Laburnum* sp.

(B) *Passiflora caerulea*

Filaments of corona

(C) *Rafflesia arnoldii*

(D) *Echinocereus reichenbachii*

FIGURE 21.29 Eudicots *(Page 434)*

The Evolution and Diversity of Fungi

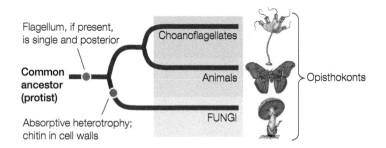

FIGURE 22.1 Fungi in Evolutionary Context *(Page 438)*

Saccharomyces cerevisiae

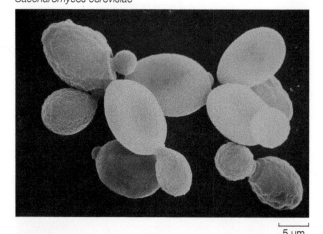

5 μm

FIGURE 22.2 Yeasts *(Page 438)*

(A)

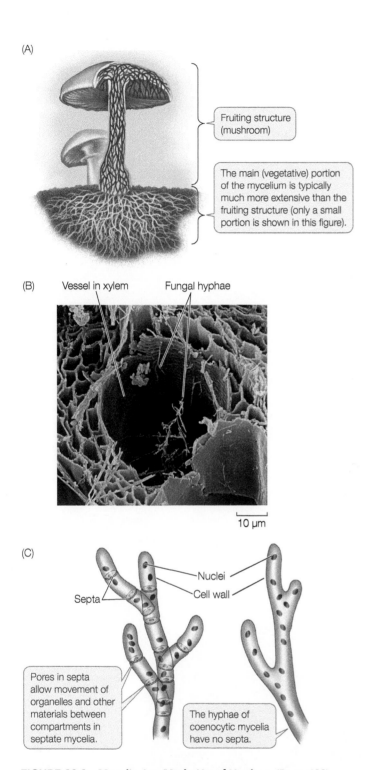

Fruiting structure (mushroom)

The main (vegetative) portion of the mycelium is typically much more extensive than the fruiting structure (only a small portion is shown in this figure).

(B)

Vessel in xylem   Fungal hyphae

10 μm

(C)

Nuclei

Cell wall

Septa

Pores in septa allow movement of organelles and other materials between compartments in septate mycelia.

The hyphae of coenocytic mycelia have no septa.

FIGURE 22.3 Mycelia Are Made Up of Hyphae *(Page 439)*

Lycoperdon perlatum

FIGURE 22.4   Spores Galore *(Page 440)*

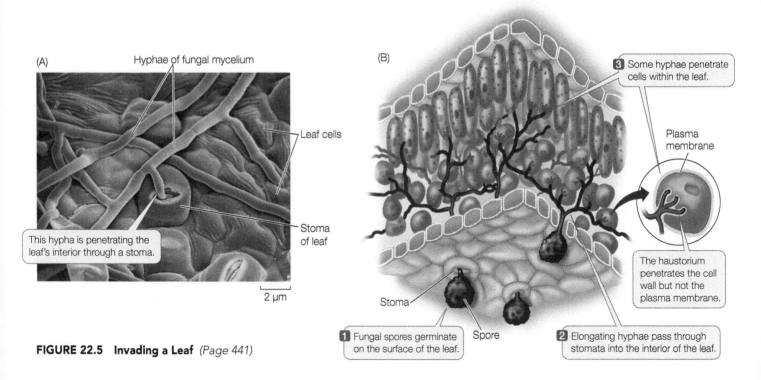

(A) Hyphae of fungal mycelium

Leaf cells

Stoma of leaf

This hypha is penetrating the leaf's interior through a stoma.

2 µm

(B) **3** Some hyphae penetrate cells within the leaf.

Plasma membrane

The haustorium penetrates the cell wall but not the plasma membrane.

Stoma

Spore

1 Fungal spores germinate on the surface of the leaf.

2 Elongating hyphae pass through stomata into the interior of the leaf.

FIGURE 22.5   Invading a Leaf *(Page 441)*

Nematode   Fungal hyphae

20 µm

FIGURE 22.6   Fungus as Predator *(Page 442)*

(A)   Crustose (*Caloplaca* sp.)

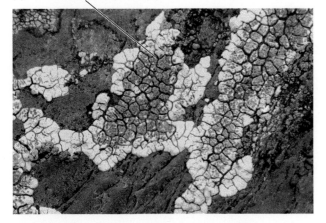

(B)   Fruticose (*Cladonia* sp.)

Foliose (*Parmotrema* sp.)

FIGURE 22.7   Lichen Body Forms *(Page 442)*

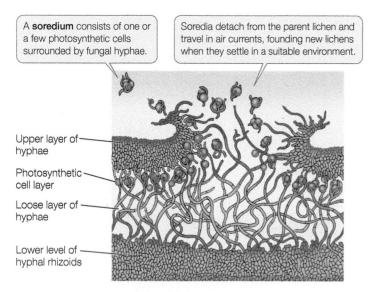

A **soredium** consists of one or a few photosynthetic cells surrounded by fungal hyphae.

Soredia detach from the parent lichen and travel in air currents, founding new lichens when they settle in a suitable environment.

Upper layer of hyphae

Photosynthetic cell layer

Loose layer of hyphae

Lower level of hyphal rhizoids

FIGURE 22.8 Lichen Anatomy *(Page 443)*

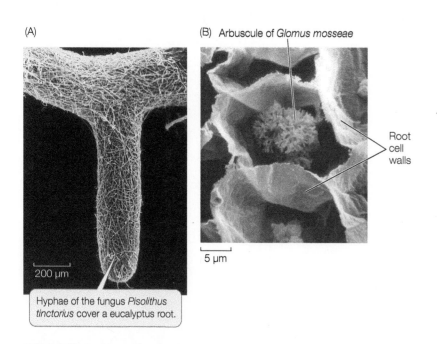

(A)

200 µm

Hyphae of the fungus *Pisolithus tinctorius* cover a eucalyptus root.

(B) Arbuscule of *Glomus mosseae*

Root cell walls

5 µm

FIGURE 22.9 Mycorrhizal Associations *(Page 443)*

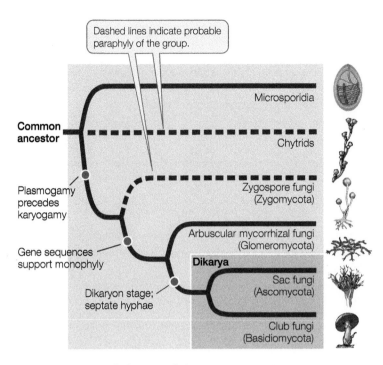

Dashed lines indicate probable paraphyly of the group.

Microsporidia

Common ancestor

Chytrids

Plasmogamy precedes karyogamy

Zygospore fungi (Zygomycota)

Gene sequences support monophyly

Arbuscular mycorrhizal fungi (Glomeromycota)

Dikarya

Sac fungi (Ascomycota)

Dikaryon stage; septate hyphae

Club fungi (Basidiomycota)

FIGURE 22.10 A Phylogeny of the Fungi *(Page 444)*

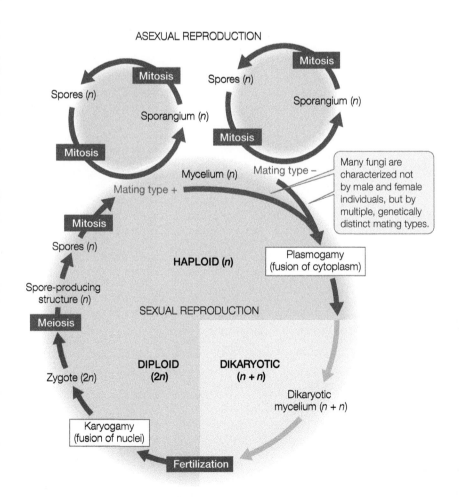

ASEXUAL REPRODUCTION

Mitosis

Spores (*n*)

Mitosis

Spores (*n*)

Sporangium (*n*)

Mitosis

Sporangium (*n*)

Mitosis

Mycelium (*n*)

Mating type −

Many fungi are characterized not by male and female individuals, but by multiple, genetically distinct mating types.

Mating type +

Mitosis

Spores (*n*)

HAPLOID (*n*)

Plasmogamy (fusion of cytoplasm)

Spore-producing structure (*n*)

SEXUAL REPRODUCTION

Meiosis

DIPLOID (2*n*)

DIKARYOTIC (*n* + *n*)

Zygote (2*n*)

Dikaryotic mycelium (*n* + *n*)

Karyogamy (fusion of nuclei)

Fertilization

FIGURE 22.11 A Fungal Life Cycle *(Page 445)*

TABLE 22.1 Classification of the Fungi

GROUP	COMMON NAME	FEATURES
Microsporidia	Microsporidia	Intracellular parasites of animals; greatly reduced, among smallest eukayotes known; polar tube used to infect hosts

Chytrids (paraphyletic)[a]
   Chytridiomycota
   Neocallimastigomycota
   Blastocladiomycota
	Chytrids	Mostly aquatic and microscopic; zoospores have flagella

Zygomycota (paraphyletic)[a]
   Entomophthoromycotina
   Kickxellomycotina
   Mucoromycotina
   Zoopagomycotina
	Zygospore fungi	Reproductive structure is a unicellular zygospore with many diploid nuclei in a zygosporangium; hyphae coenocytic; usually no fleshy fruiting body

Glomeromycota	Arbuscular mycorrhizal fungi	Form arbuscular mycorrhizae on plant roots; only asexual reproduction is known
Ascomycota	Sac fungi	Sexual reproductive saclike structure known as an ascus, which contains haploid ascospores; hyphae septate; dikaryon
Basidiomycota	Club fungi	Sexual reproductive structure is a basidium, a swollen cell at the tip of a specialized hypha that supports haploid basidiospores; hyphae septate; dikaryon

[a]The formally named groups within the chytrids and Zygomycota are each thought to be monophyletic, but their relationships to one another (and to Microsporidia) are not yet well resolved.

(Page 445)

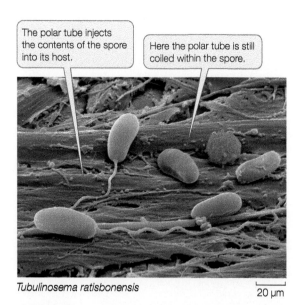

Tubulinosema ratisbonensis

FIGURE 22.12 Invasion of the Microsporidia Spores
(Page 446)

(A) Chytrids

The life cycle of some aquatic chytrids features alternation of generations.

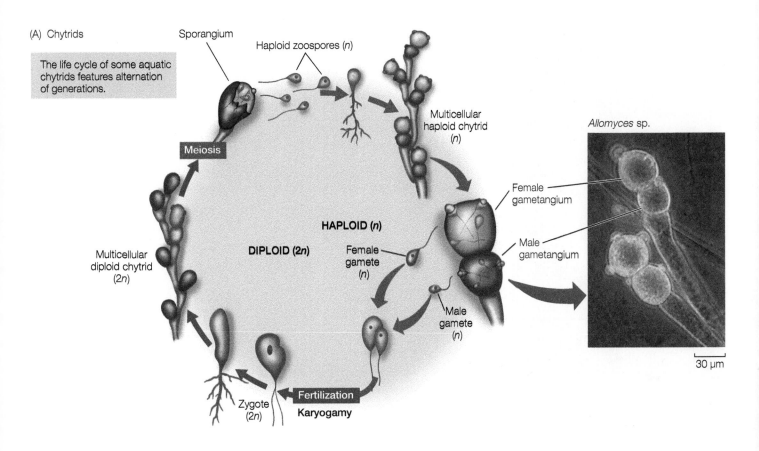

Sporangium

Haploid zoospores (*n*)

Multicellular haploid chytrid (*n*)

Meiosis

Allomyces sp.

Female gametangium

Male gametangium

HAPLOID (*n*)

DIPLOID (2*n*)

Multicellular diploid chytrid (2*n*)

Female gamete (*n*)

Male gamete (*n*)

30 μm

Zygote (2*n*)

Fertilization

Karyogamy

(B) Zygospore fungi (Zygomycota)

The sporangium of zygospore fungi contains haploid nuclei that are incorporated into spores.

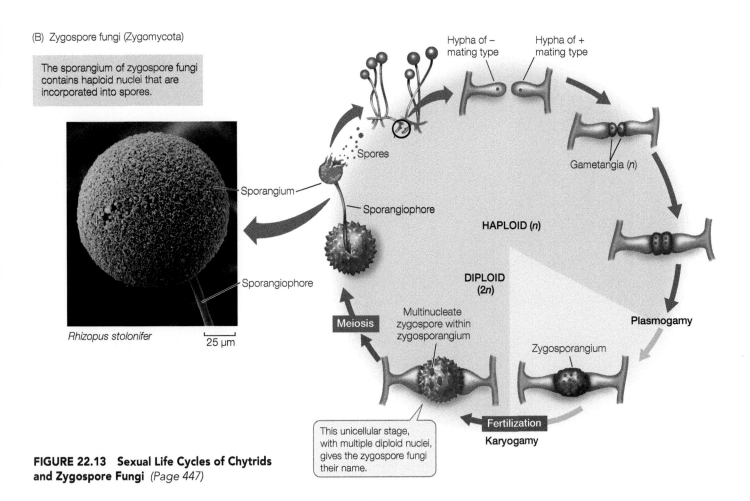

Hypha of – mating type

Hypha of + mating type

Spores

Gametangia (*n*)

Sporangium

Sporangiophore

HAPLOID (*n*)

DIPLOID (2*n*)

Plasmogamy

Sporangiophore

Meiosis

Multinucleate zygospore within zygosporangium

Zygosporangium

Rhizopus stolonifer

25 μm

This unicellular stage, with multiple diploid nuclei, gives the zygospore fungi their name.

Fertilization

Karyogamy

FIGURE 22.13 Sexual Life Cycles of Chytrids and Zygospore Fungi *(Page 447)*

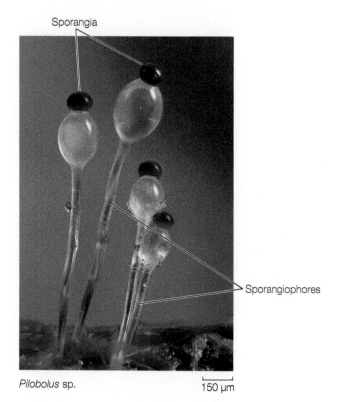

Sporangia

Sporangiophores

Pilobolus sp.

150 μm

FIGURE 22.14 Zygospore Fungi Produce Sporangiophores
(Page 448)

(A) Sac fungi (Ascomycota)

In sac fungi, the products of meiosis are borne in a microscopic sac called an ascus. The fleshy fruiting bodies consist of both dikaryotic and haploid hyphae.

(B) Club fungi (Basidiomycota)

In club fungi, the products of meiosis are borne on the surface of the gills on pedestals called basidia. Fruiting bodies consist solely of dikaryotic hyphae, and the dikaryotic phase can last a long time.

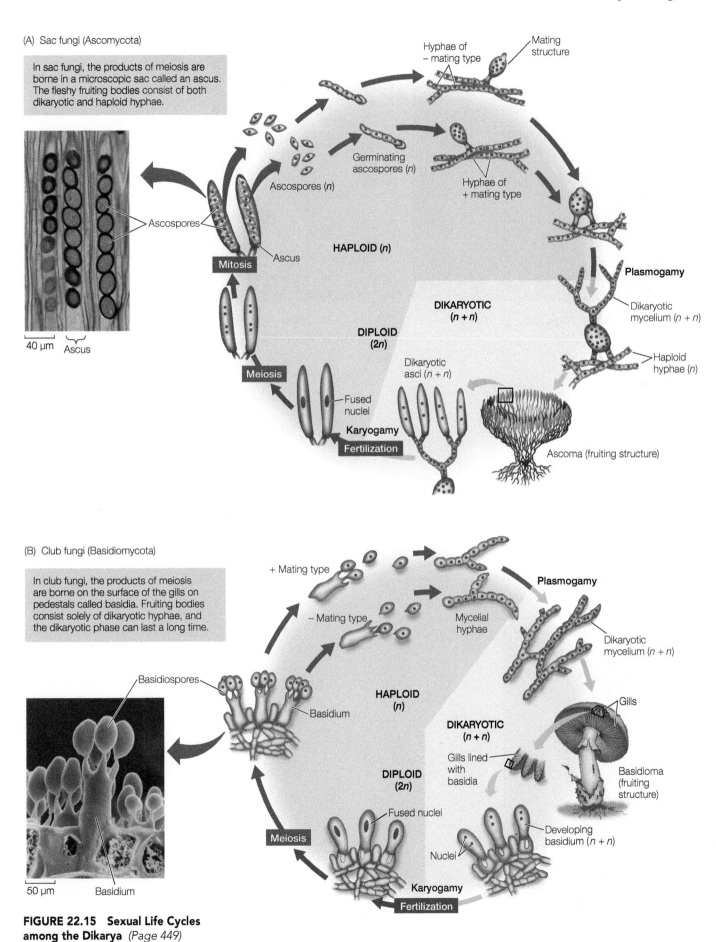

FIGURE 22.15 Sexual Life Cycles among the Dikarya (Page 449)

(B) *Morchella esculenta*

(A) *Aleuria aurantia*

FIGURE 22.16 Sac Fungi (Page 450)

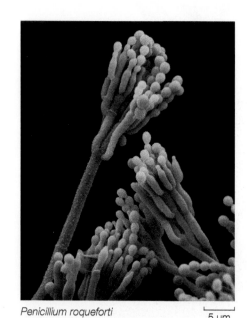

Penicillium roqueforti

5 μm

FIGURE 22.17 Conidia (Page 451)

(A) *Armillaria* sp.

(B) *Coriolus versicolor*

FIGURE 22.18 Club Fungus Basidiomata *(Page 451)*

(A)

(B)

FIGURE 22.19 More Lichens, Better Air *(Page 453)*

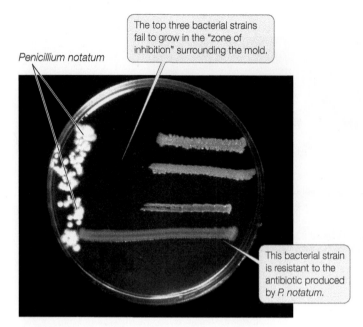

FIGURE 22.20 **Penicillin Resistance** *(Page 454)*

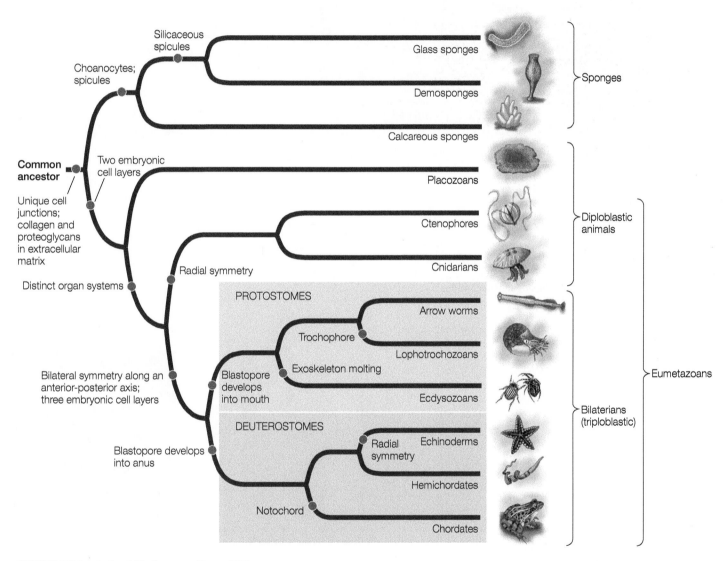

FIGURE 23.1 Animal Phylogeny *(Page 457)*

(A)

Water out
via osculum

Osculum

Water and
food particles
in via pores

Spicules

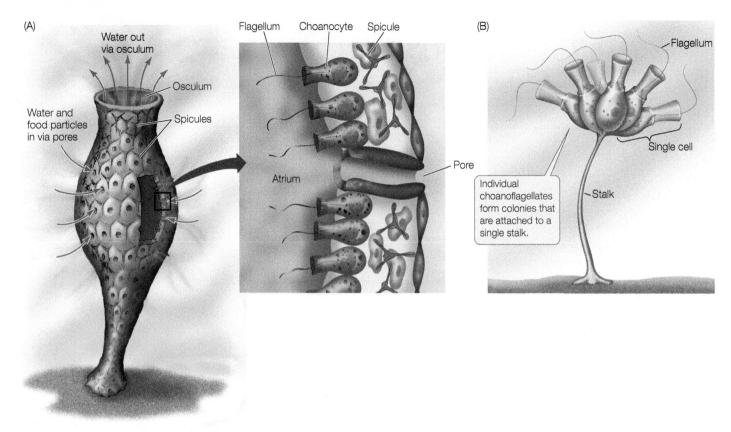

Flagellum   Choanocyte   Spicule

Atrium

Pore

(B)

Flagellum

Single cell

Individual
choanoflagellates
form colonies that
are attached to a
single stalk.

Stalk

**FIGURE 23.2 Choanocytes in Sponges Resemble
Choanoflagellate Protists** *(Page 458)*

Blastopore

IN-TEXT ART *(Page 459)*

Radial symmetry

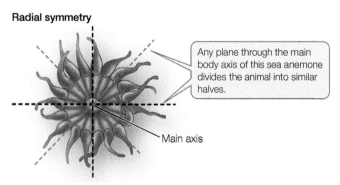

Any plane through the main
body axis of this sea anemone
divides the animal into similar
halves.

Main axis

IN-TEXT ART *(Page 459)*

Bilateral symmetry

Dorsal (back)

Anterior
(head)

> A single plane through
> the anterior–posterior
> midline divides the animal
> into mirror-image halves.

Posterior
(tail)

Ventral (belly)

IN-TEXT ART *(Page 459)*

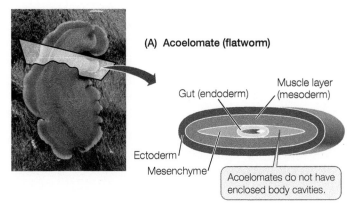

(A) Acoelomate (flatworm)

Muscle layer
(mesoderm)

Gut (endoderm)

Ectoderm

Mesenchyme

> Acoelomates do not have
> enclosed body cavities.

(B) Pseudocoelomate (roundworm)

Gut (endoderm)

Pseudocoel (cavity)

Muscle
(mesoderm)

Internal
organs

Ectoderm

> The pseudocoel is lined
> with mesoderm, but no
> mesoderm surrounds
> the internal organs.

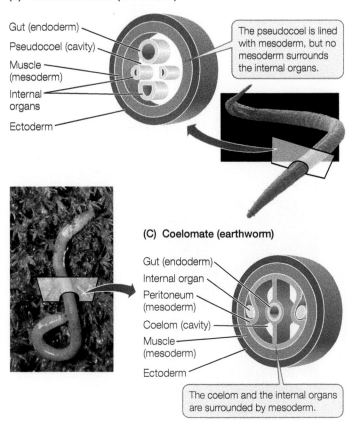

(C) Coelomate (earthworm)

Gut (endoderm)

Internal organ

Peritoneum
(mesoderm)

Coelom (cavity)

Muscle
(mesoderm)

Ectoderm

> The coelom and the internal organs
> are surrounded by mesoderm.

FIGURE 23.3 Animal Body Cavities *(Page 460)*

(A) *Hermodice carunculata*

The fireworm is a marine worm that displays an evenly segmented body plan.

Protective bristles

Anterior segments have fused and bear appendages for locomotion and feeding.

Tail segments are modified for hunting and defense.

Abdominal segments are modified for digestion and reproduction.

(B) *Ophistothalmus walberghi*

FIGURE 23.4 Body Segmentation *(Page 461)*

(A) *Xestospongia testudinaria* (B) *Staurocalyptus* sp. (C) *Sycon* sp.

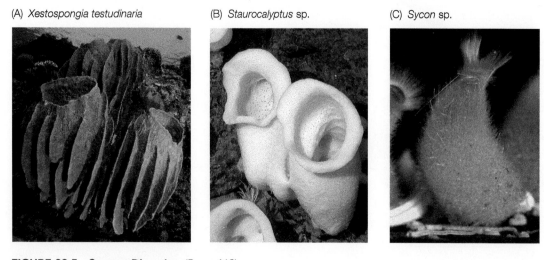

FIGURE 23.5 Sponge Diversity *(Page 462)*

TABLE 23.1 Summary of Living Members of the Major Animal Groups

	APPROXIMATE NUMBER OF LIVING SPECIES DESCRIBED	MAJOR GROUPS		APPROXIMATE NUMBER OF LIVING SPECIES DESCRIBED	MAJOR GROUPS
Sponges	9,000	Demosponges, glass sponges, calcareous sponges	**Ecdysozoans**		
			Kinorhynchs	150	
Placozoans	2		Loriciferans	100	
Ctenophores	150		Priapulids	16	
Cnidarians	11,000	Anthozoans: Corals, sea anemones	Horsehair worms	320	
			Nematodes	25,000	
		Hydrozoans: Hydras and hydroids	Onychophorans	150	
		Scyphozoans: Jellyfishes	Tardigrades	800	
			Arthropods:		
PROTOSTOMES			Crustaceans	52,000	Crabs, shrimps, lobsters, barnacles, copepods
Arrow worms	100				
Lophotrochozoans			Hexapods	1,000,000	Insects and relatives
Bryozoans	4,500		Myriapods	14,000	Millipedes, centipedes
Flatworms	25,000	Free-living flatworms; flukes and tapeworms (all parasitic); monogeneans (ectoparasites of fishes)	Chelicerates	98,000	Horseshoe crabs, arachnids (scorpions, harvestmen, spiders, mites, ticks)
			DEUTEROSTOMES		
Rotifers	1,800		Echinoderms	7,000	Crinoids (sea lilies and feather stars); brittle stars; sea stars; sea urchins; sea cucumbers
Ribbon worms	1,000				
Phoronids	20				
Brachiopods	335		Hemichordates	100	Acorn worms and pterobranchs
Annelids	16,500	Polychaetes (all marine)			
		Clitellates: Earthworms, freshwater worms, leeches	Urochordates	3,000	Ascidians (sea squirts)
			Cephalochordates	30	Lancelets
Mollusks	100,000	Monoplacophorans	Vertebrates	62,000	Hagfish; lampreys
		Chitons			Cartilaginous fishes
		Bivalves: Clams, oysters, mussels			Ray-finned fishes
		Gastropods: Snails, slugs, limpets			Coelacanths; lungfishes
		Cephalopods: Squids, octopuses, nautiloids			Amphibians
					Reptiles (including birds)
					Mammals

(Page 462)

(A)

(B)

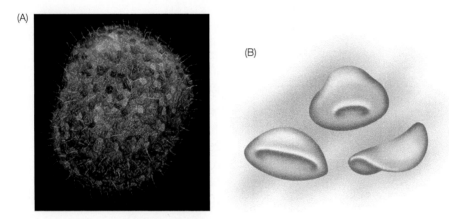

FIGURE 23.6   Placozoan Simplicity *(Page 463)*

(B) *Mnemiopsis* sp.

(A)

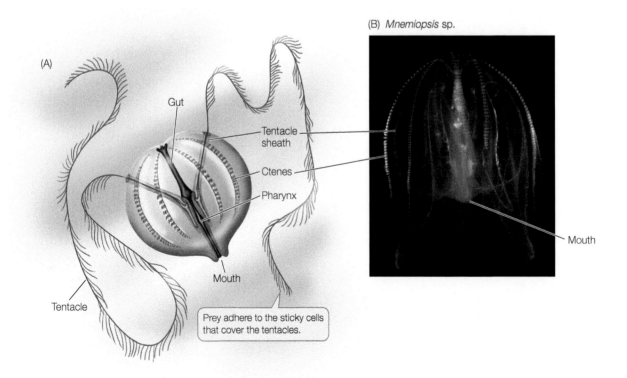

Gut

Tentacle
sheath

Ctenes

Pharynx

Mouth

Tentacle

Prey adhere to the sticky cells
that cover the tentacles.

Mouth

FIGURE 23.7   Comb Jellies Feed with Tentacles *(Page 464)*

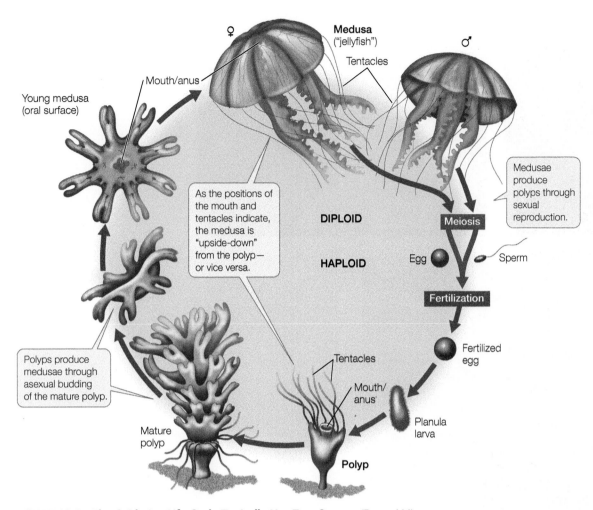

FIGURE 23.8 The Cnidarian Life Cycle Typically Has Two Stages *(Page 464)*

(A) *Sagartia modesta*

(B) *Gonionemus vertens*

(C)

FIGURE 23.9 Diversity among Cnidarians *(Page 465)*

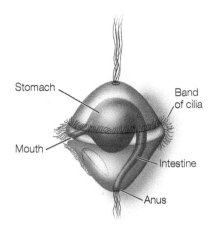

Stomach

Band
of cilia

Mouth

Intestine

Anus

IN-TEXT ART *(Page 466)*

(A) *Cristatella mucedo*

Mouth

Lophophore

Tentacles of
lophophore

(B) *Cabera boryi*

FIGURE 23.10 Bryozoans Form Colonies *(Page 466)*

(A) Diagram of a typical parasitic flatworm

(B) *Pseudobiceros* sp.

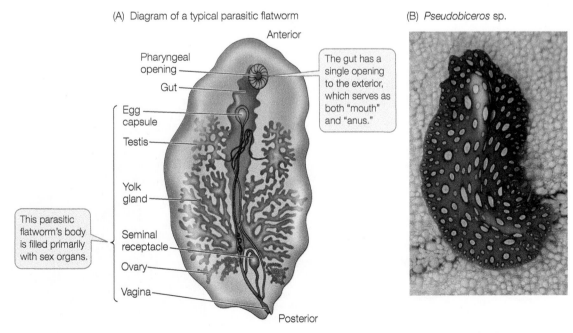

Anterior

Pharyngeal
opening

Gut

The gut has a
single opening
to the exterior,
which serves as
both "mouth"
and "anus."

Egg
capsule

Testis

Yolk
gland

This parasitic
flatworm's body
is filled primarily
with sex organs.

Seminal
receptacle

Ovary

Vagina

Posterior

FIGURE 23.11 Flatworms *(Page 467)*

(A) *Philodina roseola*

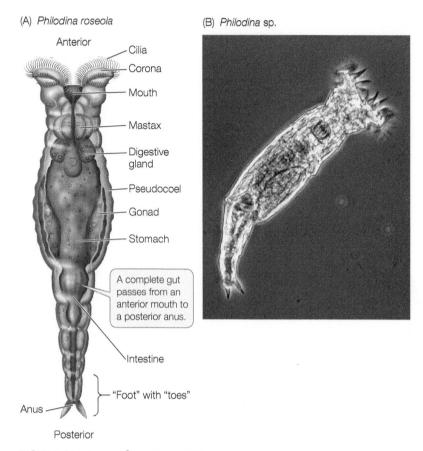

Anterior

Cilia

Corona

Mouth

Mastax

Digestive gland

Pseudocoel

Gonad

Stomach

A complete gut passes from an anterior mouth to a posterior anus.

Intestine

"Foot" with "toes"

Anus

Posterior

(B) *Philodina* sp.

FIGURE 23.12 **Rotifers** *(Page 467)*

(A)

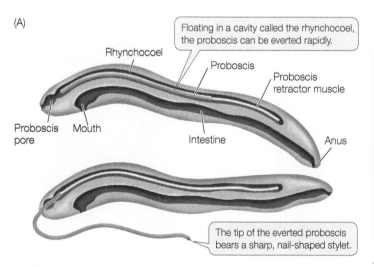

Rhynchocoel

Floating in a cavity called the rhynchocoel, the proboscis can be everted rapidly.

Proboscis

Proboscis retractor muscle

Proboscis pore

Mouth

Intestine

Anus

The tip of the everted proboscis bears a sharp, nail-shaped stylet.

(B) *Tubulanus annulatus*

FIGURE 23.13 **Ribbon Worms** *(Page 468)*

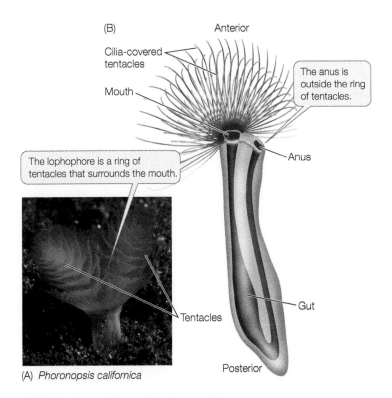

(B)

Anterior

Cilia-covered tentacles

Mouth

The anus is outside the ring of tentacles.

Anus

The lophophore is a ring of tentacles that surrounds the mouth.

Tentacles

Gut

(A) *Phoronopsis californica*

Posterior

FIGURE 23.14   Phoronids *(Page 468)*

Terebraulina septentrionalis

Lophophore rings

Tentacles

FIGURE 23.15   Brachiopods *(Page 469)*

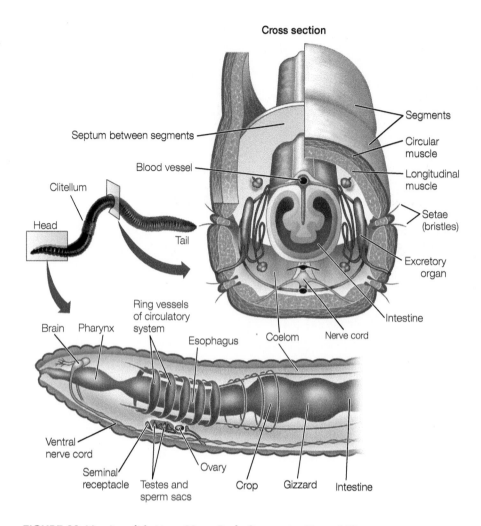

Cross section

Septum between segments

Segments

Circular muscle

Blood vessel

Longitudinal muscle

Clitellum

Head

Tail

Setae (bristles)

Excretory organ

Ring vessels of circulatory system

Brain   Pharynx

Esophagus

Coelom

Nerve cord

Intestine

Ventral nerve cord

Seminal receptacle   Testes and sperm sacs

Ovary

Crop

Gizzard

Intestine

FIGURE 23.16   Annelids Have Many Body Segments *(Page 469)*

(A) *Spirographis spallanzanii*

(B) *Riftia* sp.

(C) *Hirudo medicinalis*

FIGURE 23.17 Diversity among the Annelids *(Page 470)*

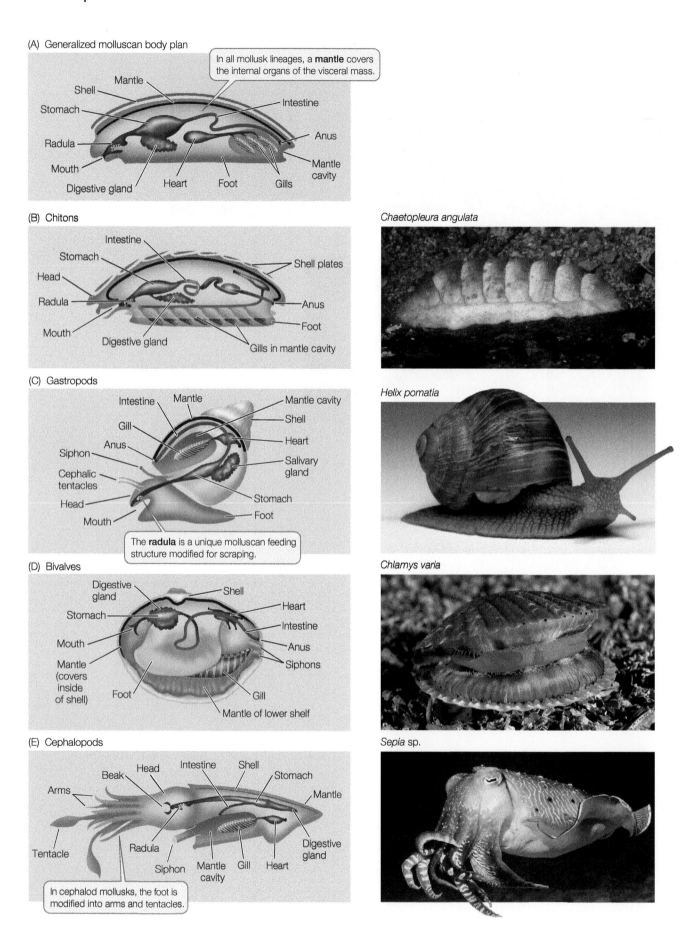

(A) Generalized molluscan body plan

In all mollusk lineages, a **mantle** covers the internal organs of the visceral mass.

Mantle
Shell
Stomach
Intestine
Radula
Anus
Mouth
Mantle cavity
Digestive gland
Heart
Foot
Gills

(B) Chitons

Chaetopleura angulata

Intestine
Stomach
Shell plates
Head
Radula
Anus
Mouth
Foot
Digestive gland
Gills in mantle cavity

(C) Gastropods

Helix pomatia

Intestine
Mantle
Mantle cavity
Gill
Shell
Anus
Heart
Siphon
Salivary gland
Cephalic tentacles
Head
Stomach
Mouth
Foot

The **radula** is a unique molluscan feeding structure modified for scraping.

(D) Bivalves

Chlamys varia

Digestive gland
Shell
Stomach
Heart
Intestine
Mouth
Anus
Mantle (covers inside of shell)
Siphons
Foot
Gill
Mantle of lower shelf

(E) Cephalopods

Sepia sp.

Beak
Head
Intestine
Shell
Stomach
Arms
Mantle
Tentacle
Radula
Digestive gland
Siphon
Mantle cavity
Gill
Heart

In cephalod mollusks, the foot is modified into arms and tentacles.

FIGURE 23.18 Organization and Diversity of Molluscan Bodies *(Page 472)*

(A) *Hermissenda crassicornis*

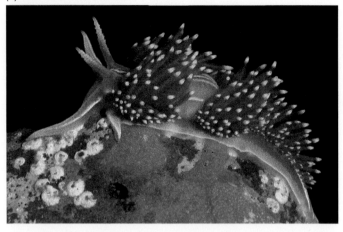

(B) *Octopus macropus*

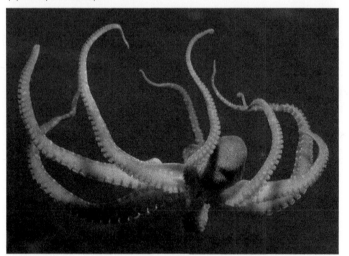

FIGURE 23.19   Mollusks in Some Groups Have Lost Their Shells *(Page 473)*

(A)

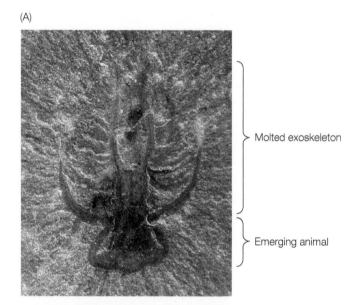

Molted exoskeleton

Emerging animal

(B) *Heterophrynus batesi*   Molted exoskeleton

The newly emerged whip scorpion's body is still soft and vulnerable.

FIGURE 23.20   Molting, Past and Present *(Page 473)*

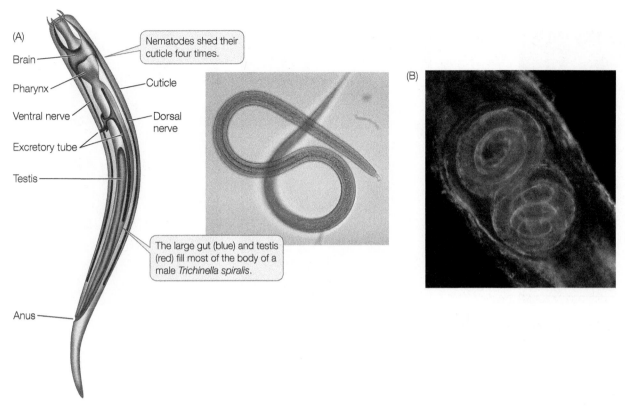

(A)

Brain

Pharynx

Ventral nerve

Excretory tube

Testis

Anus

Nematodes shed their cuticle four times.

Cuticle

Dorsal nerve

The large gut (blue) and testis (red) fill most of the body of a male *Trichinella spiralis*.

(B)

FIGURE 23.21 Nematodes *(Page 474)*

An adult horsehair worm exits the wood cricket it parasitized during its larval development.

FIGURE 23.22 Horsehair Worm Larvae Are Parasitic *(Page 475)*

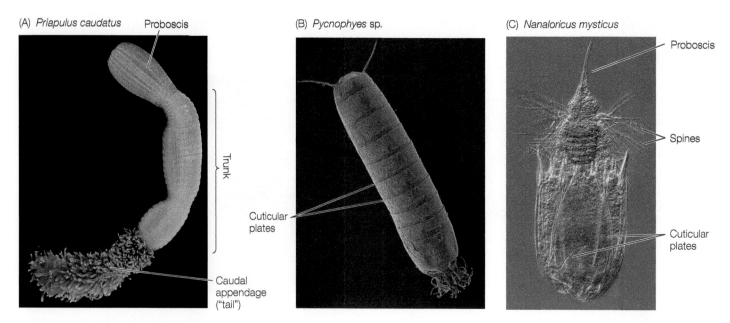

(A) *Priapulus caudatus*   Proboscis

Trunk

Caudal
appendage
("tail")

(B) *Pycnophyes* sp.

Cuticular
plates

(C) *Nanaloricus mysticus*

Proboscis

Spines

Cuticular
plates

FIGURE 23.23   Benthic Marine Ecdysozoans *(Page 476)*

(A) *Peripatus* sp.

(B) *Echiniscus* sp.

**FIGURE 23.24   Arthropod Relatives with Unjointed
Appendages** *(Page 477)*

(A) *Anoplodactylus* sp.

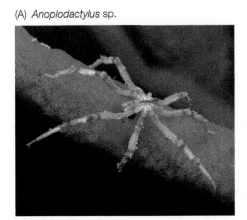

(B) *Limulus polyphemus*

FIGURE 23.25   Two Small Chelicerate Groups *(Page 477)*

(A) *Peucetia* sp.

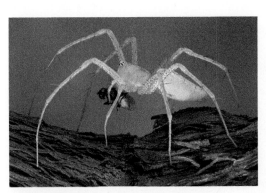

(B) *Opistophthalmus carinatus*

(C) *Leiobunum rotundum*

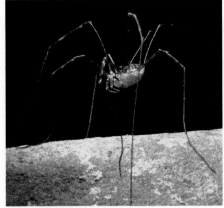

(D) *Lorryia formosa*

FIGURE 23.26   Arachnid Diversity *(Page 478)*

(A) *Scolopendra angulata*

(B) *Sigmoria trimaculata*

FIGURE 23.27   Myriapods *(Page 478)*

(A) *Grapsus grapsus*

(B) *Armadillium vulgare*

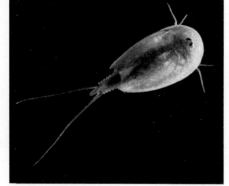

(C) *Eudiaptomus gracilis*

(D) *Lepidurus* sp.

(E) *Lepas anatifera*

FIGURE 23.28   Crustacean Diversity *(Page 479)*

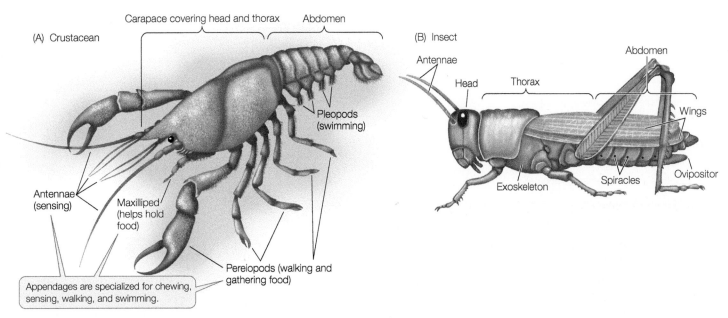

(A) Crustacean

Carapace covering head and thorax

Abdomen

Pleopods
(swimming)

Antennae
(sensing)

Maxilliped
(helps hold
food)

Pereiopods (walking and
gathering food)

Appendages are specialized for chewing,
sensing, walking, and swimming.

(B) Insect

Antennae

Head

Thorax

Abdomen

Wings

Ovipositor

Spiracles

Exoskeleton

FIGURE 23.29 Two Segmented Body Plans *(Page 480)*

TABLE 23.2	The Major Insect Groups[a]
GROUP	**APPROXIMATE NUMBER OF DESCRIBED LIVING SPECIES**
Jumping bristletails (Archaeognatha)	300
Silverfish (Thysanura)	370
PTERYGOTE (WINGED) INSECTS (PTERYGOTA)	
Mayflies (Ephemeroptera)	2,000
Dragonflies and damselflies (Odonata)	5,000
Neopterans (Neoptera)[b]	
Ice-crawlers (Grylloblattodea)	25
Gladiators (Mantophasmatodea)	15
Stoneflies (Plecoptera)	1,700
Webspinners (Embioptera)	300
Angel insects (Zoraptera)	30
Earwigs (Dermaptera)	1,800
Grasshoppers and crickets (Orthoptera)	20,000
Stick insects (Phasmida)	3,000
Cockroaches (Blattodea)	3,500
Termites (Isoptera)	2,750
Mantids (Mantodea)	2,300
Booklice and barklice (Psocoptera)	3,000
Thrips (Thysanoptera)	5,000
Lice (Phthiraptera)	3,100
True bugs, cicadas, aphids, leafhoppers (Hemiptera)	80,000
Holometabolous neopterans (Holometabola)[c]	
Ants, bees, wasps (Hymenoptera)	125,000
Beetles (Coleoptera)	375,000
Twisted-wing parasites (Strepsiptera)	600
Lacewings, ant lions, dobsonflies (Neuropterida)	4,700
Scorpionflies (Mecoptera)	600
Fleas (Siphonaptera)	2,400
True flies (Diptera)	120,000
Caddisflies (Trichoptera)	5,000
Butterflies and moths (Lepidoptera)	250,000

[a] The hexapod relatives of insects include the springtails (Collembola; 3,000 spp.), two-pronged bristletails (Diplura; 600 spp.), and proturans (Protura; 10 spp.). All are wingless and have internal mouthparts.

[b] Neopteran insects can tuck their wings close to their bodies

[c] Holometabolous insects are neopterans that undergo complete metamorphosis.

(Page 481)

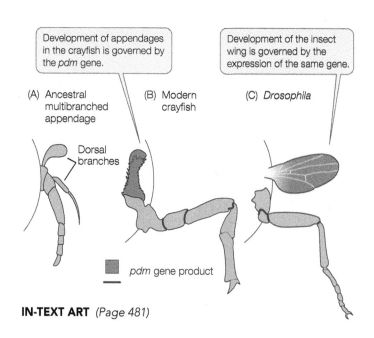

IN-TEXT ART *(Page 481)*

(A) *Libellula saturata,* Odonata

(B) *Melanoplus differentialis,* Orthoptera

(C) *Anisocelis flavolineata,* Hemiptera

(D) *Limnephilus* (larva), Trichoptera

(E) *Trachelophorus giraffa,* Coleoptera

(F) *Junonia coenia,* Lepidoptera

(G) *Scathophaga stercoraria,* Diptera

(H) *Polistes gallicus,* Hymenoptera

FIGURE 23.30 Diverse Winged Insects *(Page 482)*

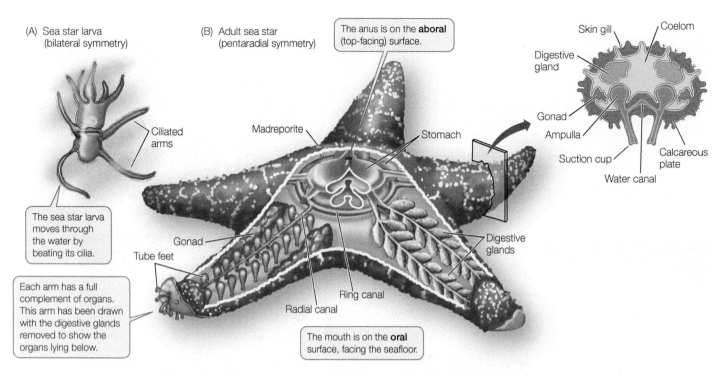

(A) Sea star larva
(bilateral symmetry)

Ciliated
arms

The sea star larva
moves through
the water by
beating its cilia.

Each arm has a full
complement of organs.
This arm has been drawn
with the digestive glands
removed to show the
organs lying below.

(B) Adult sea star
(pentaradial symmetry)

The anus is on the **aboral**
(top-facing) surface.

Madreporite

Stomach

Gonad

Tube feet

Digestive
glands

Radial canal

Ring canal

The mouth is on the **oral**
surface, facing the seafloor.

Skin gill

Coelom

Digestive
gland

Gonad

Ampulla

Suction cup

Water canal

Calcareous
plate

FIGURE 23.31   Bilaterally Symmetrical Echinoderm Larvae become Radially Symmetrical Adults *(Page 484)*

(A) *Comanthina schlegeli*

(B) *Sphaerechinus granularis*

(C) *Thelenota* sp.

(D) *Marthasterias glacialis*

(E) *Ophiopholis aculeata*

FIGURE 23.32 **Echinoderm Diversity** *(Page 484)*

(A)

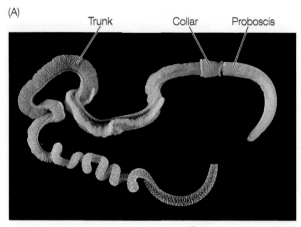

Trunk   Collar   Proboscis

Saccoglossus kowalevskii

(B)

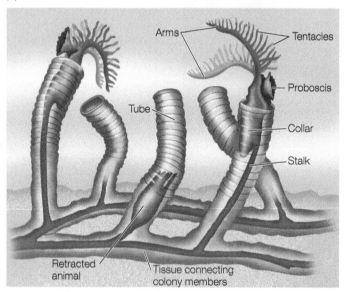

Arms   Tentacles

Proboscis

Tube

Collar

Stalk

Retracted animal

Tissue connecting colony members

FIGURE 23.33   Hemichordates *(Page 485)*

(A)

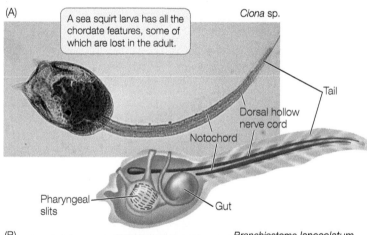

A sea squirt larva has all the chordate features, some of which are lost in the adult.

Ciona sp.

Tail

Dorsal hollow nerve cord

Notochord

Pharyngeal slits

Gut

(B)

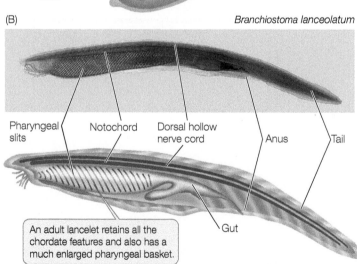

Branchiostoma lanceolatum

Pharyngeal slits   Notochord   Dorsal hollow nerve cord   Anus   Tail

An adult lancelet retains all the chordate features and also has a much enlarged pharyngeal basket.

Gut

FIGURE 23.34   The Key Features of Chordates Are Most Apparent in Early Developmental Stages *(Page 486)*

Polycarpa aurata

FIGURE 23.35   An Adult Urochordate *(Page 486)*

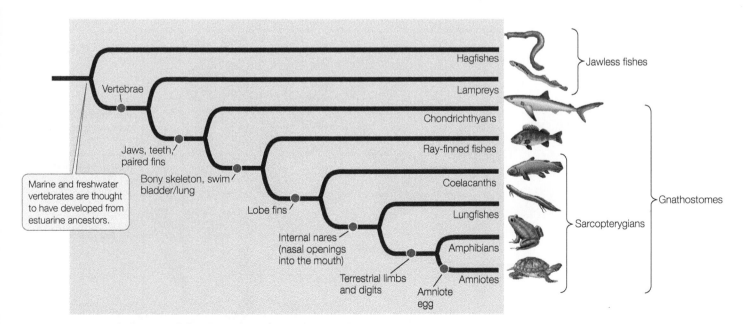

FIGURE 23.36   Phylogeny of the Living Vertebrates *(Page 487)*

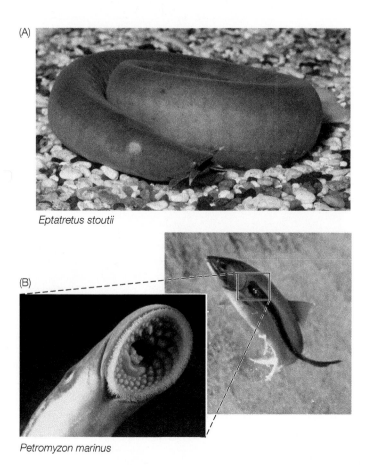

(A)

Eptatretus stoutii

(B)

Petromyzon marinus

FIGURE 23.37   Modern Jawless Fishes *(Page 487)*

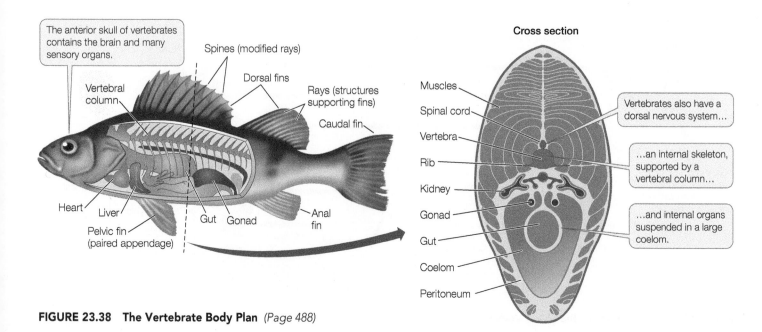

The anterior skull of vertebrates contains the brain and many sensory organs.

Spines (modified rays)

Dorsal fins

Rays (structures supporting fins)

Caudal fin

Vertebral column

Heart

Liver

Pelvic fin (paired appendage)

Gut   Gonad

Anal fin

Cross section

Muscles

Spinal cord

Vertebra

Rib

Kidney

Gonad

Gut

Coelom

Peritoneum

Vertebrates also have a dorsal nervous system...

...an internal skeleton, supported by a vertebral column...

...and internal organs suspended in a large coelom.

FIGURE 23.38   The Vertebrate Body Plan *(Page 488)*

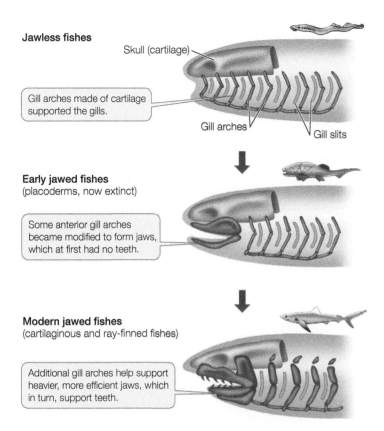

Jawless fishes

Skull (cartilage)

Gill arches made of cartilage supported the gills.

Gill arches

Gill slits

Early jawed fishes
(placoderms, now extinct)

Some anterior gill arches became modified to form jaws, which at first had no teeth.

Modern jawed fishes
(cartilaginous and ray-finned fishes)

Additional gill arches help support heavier, more efficient jaws, which in turn, support teeth.

FIGURE 23.39 Verterbrate Jaw Evolution *(Page 489)*

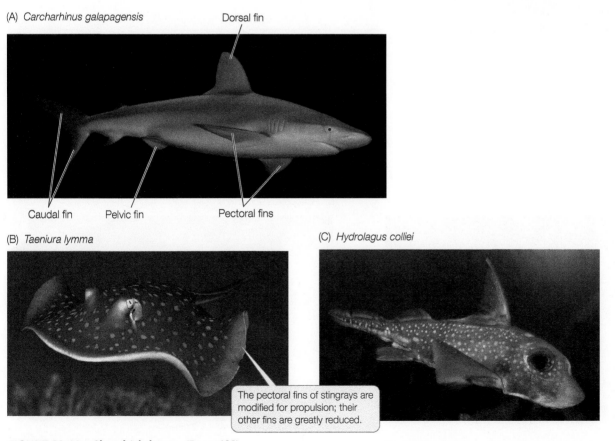

(A) *Carcharhinus galapagensis*

Dorsal fin

Caudal fin Pelvic fin Pectoral fins

(B) *Taeniura lymma*

(C) *Hydrolagus colliei*

The pectoral fins of stingrays are modified for propulsion; their other fins are greatly reduced.

FIGURE 23.40 Chondrichthyans *(Page 489)*

(A)

Cleaner wrasse (*Labroides dimidiatus*) feed on parasites off the body of a much larger ribbon sweetlips (*Plectorhincus polytaenia*).

(B) *Gymnothorax meleagris*

FIGURE 23.41   Ray-Finned Fishes *(Page 490)*

(A) *Latimeria chalumnae*

(B) *Protopterus annectens*

FIGURE 23.42   The Closest Relatives of Tetrapods *(Page 491)*

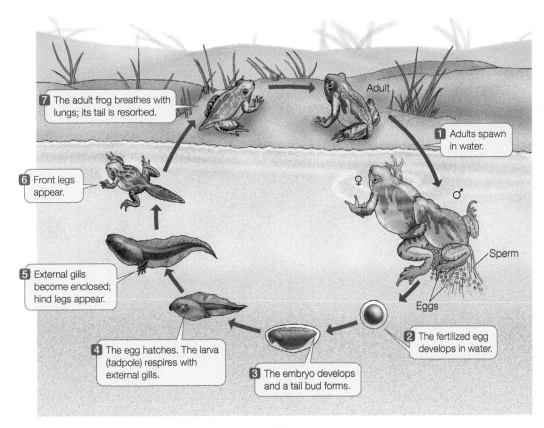

7 The adult frog breathes with lungs; its tail is resorbed.

Adult

1 Adults spawn in water.

6 Front legs appear.

♀ ♂

Sperm

5 External gills become enclosed; hind legs appear.

Eggs

4 The egg hatches. The larva (tadpole) respires with external gills.

2 The fertilized egg develops in water.

3 The embryo develops and a tail bud forms.

FIGURE 23.43 In and Out of the Water *(Page 491)*

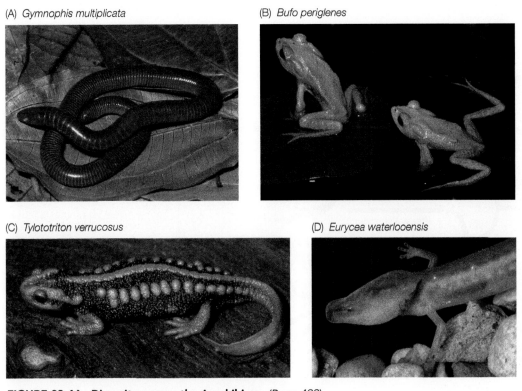

(A) *Gymnophis multiplicata*

(B) *Bufo periglenes*

(C) *Tylototriton verrucosus*

(D) *Eurycea waterlooensis*

FIGURE 23.44 Diversity among the Amphibians *(Page 492)*

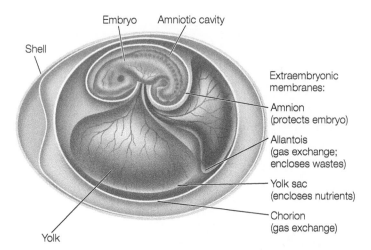

Shell

Embryo

Amniotic cavity

Extraembryonic
membranes:

Amnion
(protects embryo)

Allantois
(gas exchange;
encloses wastes)

Yolk sac
(encloses nutrients)

Chorion
(gas exchange)

Yolk

IN-TEXT ART *(Page 493)*

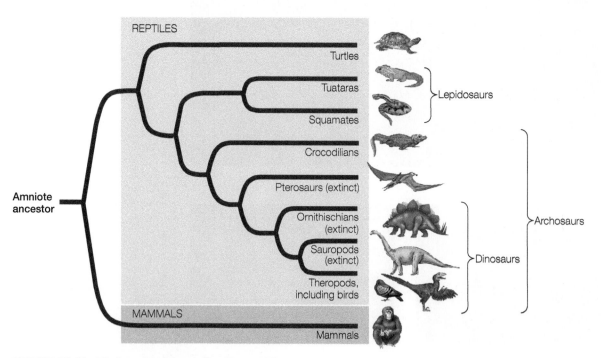

FIGURE 23.45   Phylogeny of Amniotes *(Page 493)*

(A) *Emydoidea blandingii*

(B) *Sphenodon punctatus*

(C) *Eublepharis macularius*

(D) *Lampropeltis triangulum*

FIGURE 23.46 Reptilian Diversity *(Page 494)*

(A) *Crocodylus niloticus*

(B) *Rhea americana*

FIGURE 23.47 Archosaurs *(Page 495)*

(A)

(B)

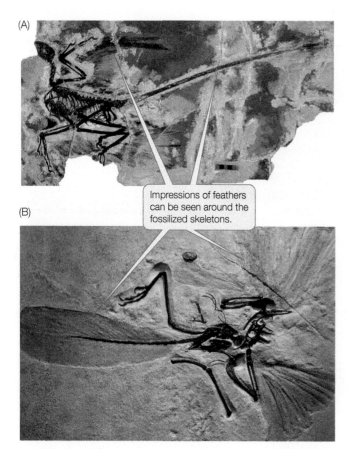

Impressions of feathers can be seen around the fossilized skeletons.

FIGURE 23.48 Mesozoic Bird Relatives *(Page 496)*

(A) *Balearica regulorum gibbericeps*

(B) *Megascops asio*

(C) *Carduelis carduelis*

FIGURE 23.49 Some Diverse Birds *(Page 496)*

(A) *Ornithorhynchus anatinus*

(B) *Didelphis virginiana*

(C) *Spermophilus mexicanus*

(E)

(F) *Megatera novaeangliae*

(D) *Macroderma gigas*

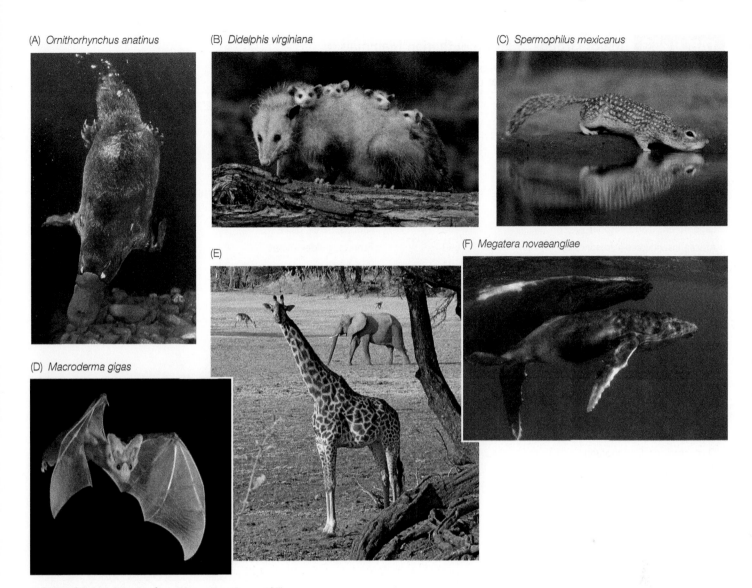

FIGURE 23.50 Mammalian Diversity *(Page 497)*

TABLE 23.3 | Major Groups of Living Eutherian Mammals

GROUP	APPROXIMATE NUMBER OF LIVING SPECIES	EXAMPLES
Gnawing mammals (Rodentia)	2,300	Rats, mice, squirrels, woodchucks, ground squirrels, beaver, capybara
Flying mammals (Chiroptera)	1,100	Bats
Soricomorph insectivores (Soricomorpha)	430	Shrews, moles
Even-toed hoofed mammals and cetaceans (Cetartiodactyla)	320	Deer, sheep, goats, cattle, antelopes, giraffes, camels, swine, hippopotamus, whales, dolphins
Carnivores (Carnivora)	290	Wolves, dogs, bears, cats, weasels, pinnipeds (seals, sea lions, walruses)
Primates (Primates)	235	Lemurs, monkeys, apes, humans
Lagomorphs (Lagomorpha)	80	Rabbits, hares, pikas
African insectivores (Afrosoricida)	50	Tenrecs, golden moles
Spiny insectivores (Erinaceomorpha)	24	Hedgehogs
Armored mammals (Cingulata)	21	Armadillos
Tree shrews (Scandentia)	20	Tree shrews
Odd-toed hoofed mammals (Perissodactyla)	20	Horses, zebras, tapirs, rhinoceroses
Long-nosed insectivores (Macroscelidea)	16	Elephant shrews
Pilosans (Pilosa)	10	Anteaters, sloths
Pholidotans (Pholidota)	8	Pangolins
Sirenians (Sirenia)	5	Manatees, dugongs
Hyracoids (Hyracoidea)	4	Hyraxes, dassies
Elephants (Proboscidea)	3	African and Indian elephants
Dermopterans (Dermoptera)	2	Flying lemurs
Aardvark (Tubulidentata)	1	Aardvark

(Page 498)

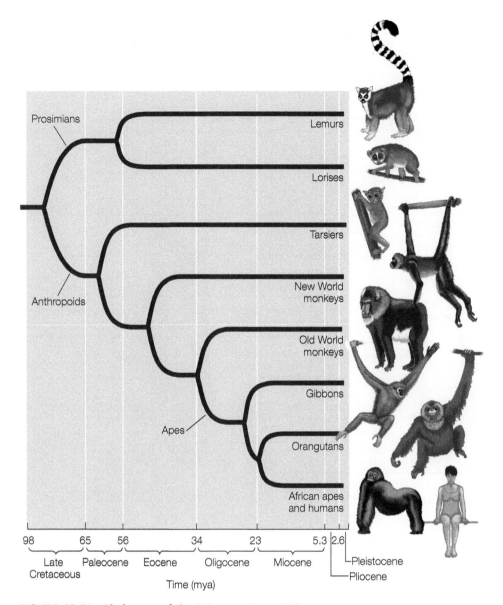

FIGURE 23.51   Phylogeny of the Primates *(Page 499)*

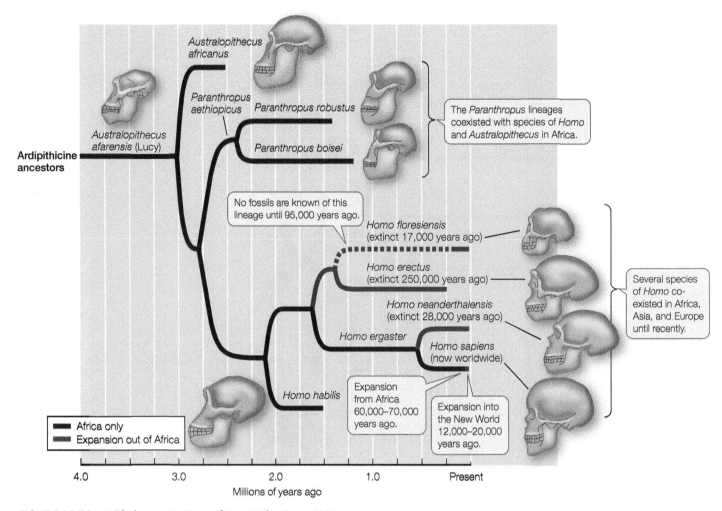

FIGURE 23.52 A Phylogenetic Tree of Hominids *(Page 500)*

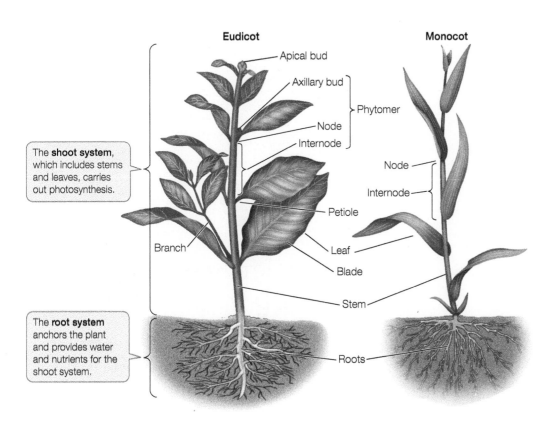

FIGURE 24.1 Vegetative Plant Organs and System *(Page 507)*

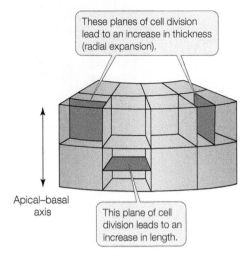

FIGURE 24.2 **Cytokinesis and Morphogenesis** (*Page 508*)

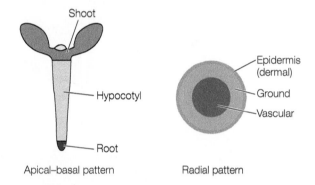

FIGURE 24.3 **Two Patterns for Plant Morphogenesis** (*Page 508*)

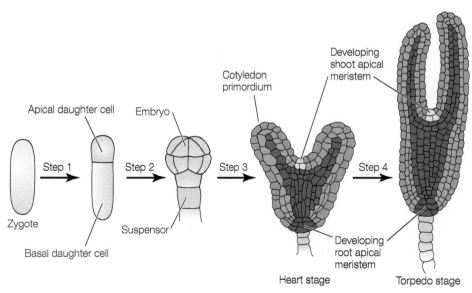

FIGURE 24.4 **Plant Embryogenesis** (*Page 509*)

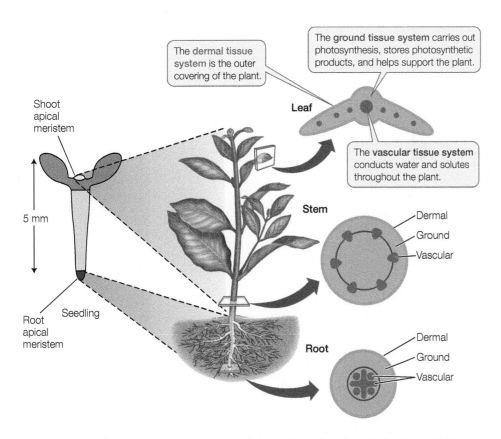

FIGURE 24.5 Three Tissue Systems Extend throughout the Plant Body *(Page 509)*

Parenchyma cells

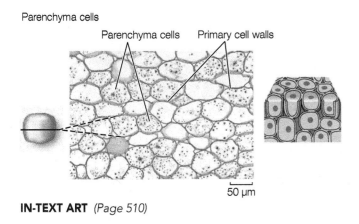

IN-TEXT ART *(Page 510)*

Collenchyma cells

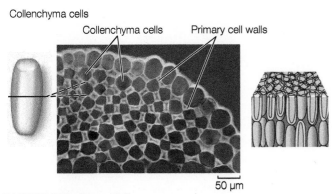

IN-TEXT ART *(Page 510)*

Fibers

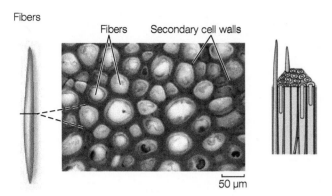

Fibers   Secondary cell walls

50 μm

IN-TEXT ART *(Page 510)*

Sclereids

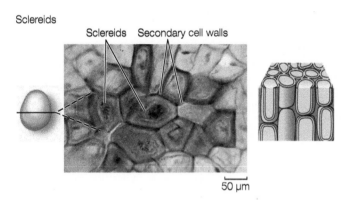

Sclereids   Secondary cell walls

50 μm

IN-TEXT ART *(Page 510)*

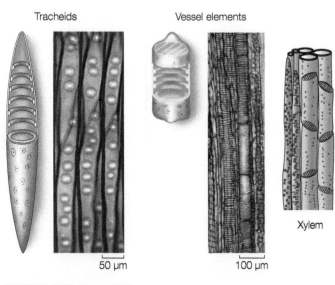

Tracheids   Vessel elements

Xylem

50 μm   100 μm

IN-TEXT ART *(Page 510)*

Sieve tube elements

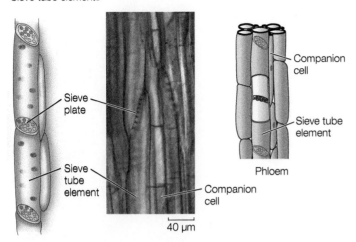

Sieve plate

Sieve tube element

Companion cell

40 µm

Companion cell

Sieve tube element

Phloem

IN-TEXT ART *(Page 511)*

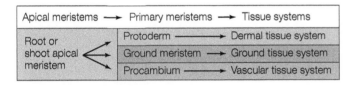

Apical meristems → Primary meristems → Tissue systems		
Root or shoot apical meristem	Protoderm ────────→ Dermal tissue system	
	Ground meristem ──→ Ground tissue system	
	Procambium ────────→ Vascular tissue system	

IN-TEXT ART *(Page 511)*

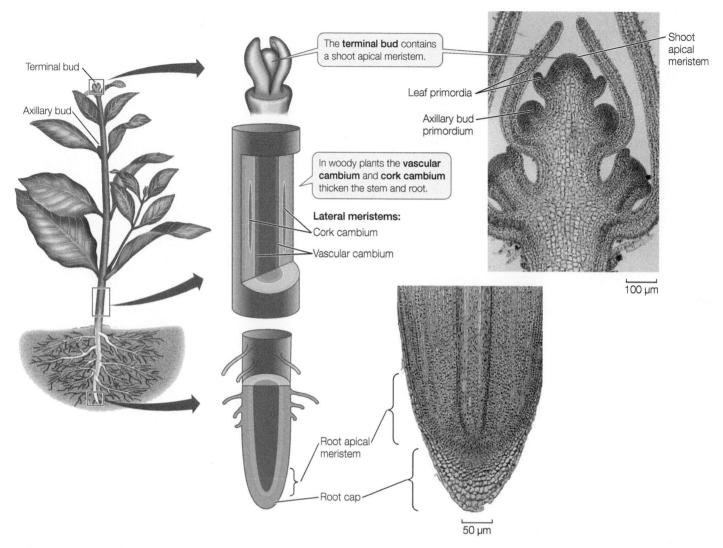

The **terminal bud** contains a shoot apical meristem.

In woody plants the **vascular cambium** and **cork cambium** thicken the stem and root.

Lateral meristems:
Cork cambium
Vascular cambium

Terminal bud
Axillary bud

Shoot apical meristem
Leaf primordia
Axillary bud primordium

100 µm

Root apical meristem
Root cap

50 µm

FIGURE 24.6   Apical and Lateral Meristems *(Page 512)*

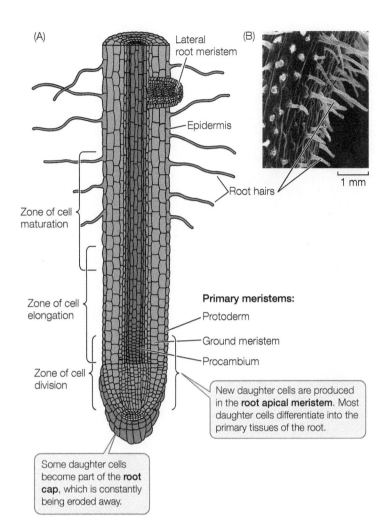

(A)

Lateral root meristem

Epidermis

Root hairs

Zone of cell maturation

Zone of cell elongation

Zone of cell division

Primary meristems:

Protoderm

Ground meristem

Procambium

New daughter cells are produced in the **root apical meristem**. Most daughter cells differentiate into the primary tissues of the root.

Some daughter cells become part of the **root cap**, which is constantly being eroded away.

(B)

1 mm

FIGURE 24.7 Tissues and Regions of the Root Tip *(Page 513)*

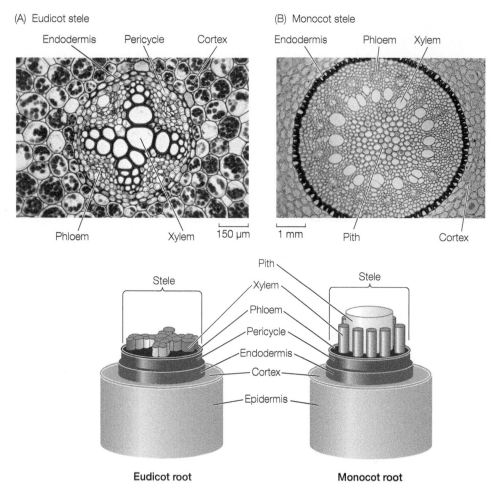

(A) Eudicot stele

Endodermis   Pericycle   Cortex

Phloem   Xylem   150 μm

(B) Monocot stele

Endodermis   Phloem   Xylem

1 mm   Pith   Cortex

Pith
Xylem
Phloem
Pericycle
Endodermis
Cortex
Epidermis

Stele   Stele

Eudicot root   Monocot root

FIGURE 24.8   Products of the Root's Primary Meristems *(Page 514)*

(A) Taproots

(B) Fibrous root system

(C) Prop roots

FIGURE 24.9   Root Systems of Eudicots and Monocots *(Page 514)*

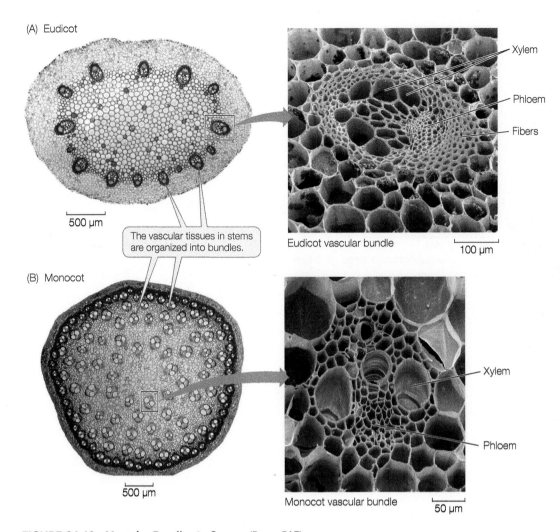

(A) Eudicot

500 µm

The vascular tissues in stems are organized into bundles.

Eudicot vascular bundle

Xylem

Phloem

Fibers

100 µm

(B) Monocot

500 µm

Monocot vascular bundle

Xylem

Phloem

50 µm

FIGURE 24.10 Vascular Bundles in Stems *(Page 515)*

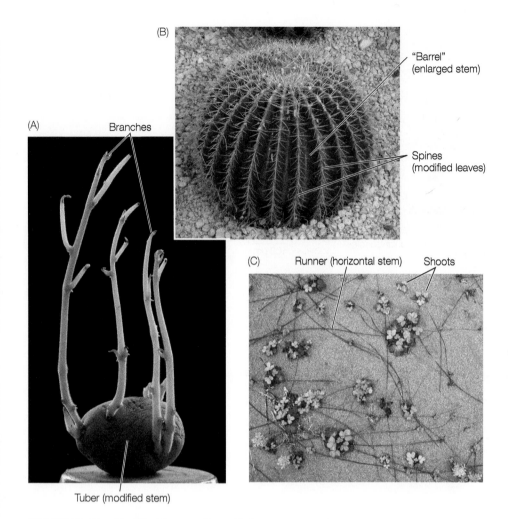

(A)

Branches

(B)

"Barrel"
(enlarged stem)

Spines
(modified leaves)

(C) Runner (horizontal stem)   Shoots

Tuber (modified stem)

FIGURE 24.11 Modified Stems *(Page 516)*

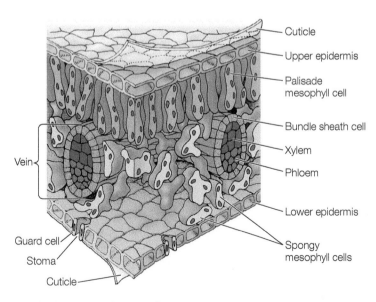

Cuticle

Upper epidermis

Palisade
mesophyll cell

Bundle sheath cell

Xylem

Phloem

Vein

Lower epidermis

Guard cell

Stoma

Spongy
mesophyll cells

Cuticle

FIGURE 24.12 Eudicot Leaf Anatomy *(Page 516)*

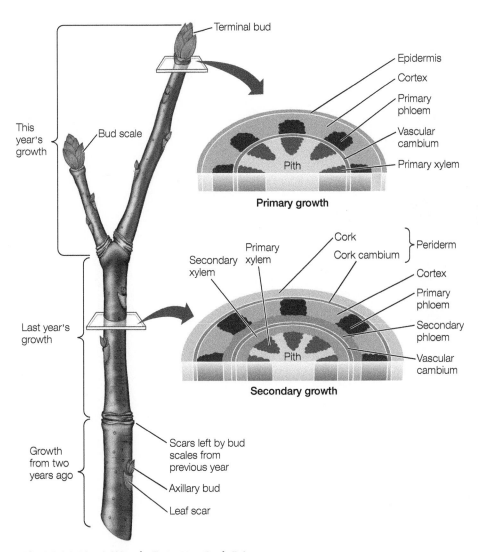

FIGURE 24.13 A Woody Twig Has Both Primary and Secondary Tissues *(Page 517)*

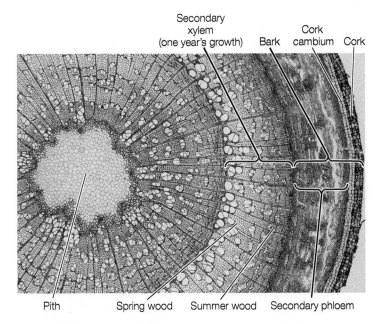

FIGURE 24.14 Annual Rings *(Page 518)*

Teosinte Corn

FIGURE 24.15   Corn Was Domesticated from the Wild Grass Teosinte *(Page 519)*

FIGURE 24.16   Kenaf Stems *(Page 519)*

Plant Nutrition and Transport

25

FIGURE 25.1   Mineral Nutrient Deficiency Symptoms *(Page 522)*

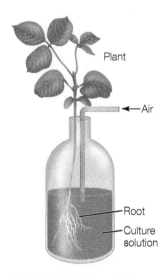

Plant

← Air

Root

Culture solution

IN-TEXT ART *(Page 522)*

INVESTIGATION

FIGURE 25.2 **Nickel Is an Essential Element for Plants** Using highly purified minerals in a hydroponic solution, Patrick Brown and his colleagues tested whether barley can complete its life cycle in the absence of nickel. Other investigators showed that no other element could substitute for nickel.

HYPOTHESIS

Nickel is an essential element for plants.

METHOD

1. Grow barley plants for three generations in hydroponic solutions containing 0, 0.6, and 1.0 μM nickel sulfate ($NiSO_4$).
2. Harvest seeds from 5–6 third-generation plants in each of the groups.
3. Determine the nickel concentration in seeds from each plant.
4. Germinate other seeds from the same plants in a nickel-free hydroponic solution and plot the success of germination against nickel concentration.

RESULTS

There was a positive correlation between seed germination and nickel concentration. There was significantly less germination at the lowest nickel concentrations.

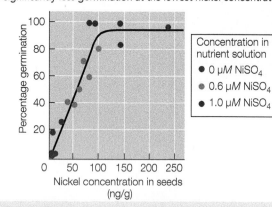

Concentration in nutrient solution
- 0 μM $NiSO_4$
- 0.6 μM $NiSO_4$
- 1.0 μM $NiSO_4$

CONCLUSION

Barley seeds require nickel in order to germinate and complete their life cycle.

ANALYZE THE DATA

A. What do the blue points have in common? Why are there five blue points instead of just one?

B. What is the biological meaning of the zero/zero point?

C. Why didn't the investigators examine only the plants grown without nickel in their hydroponic solution?

D. Plant biologists define the *critical value* for a mineral nutrient as that concentration in plant tissue that results in a 15 percent reduction in the optimal yield of the plant. Using maximum germination percentage in this experiment as the optimal yield, calculate the critical value for nickel.

For more, go to Working with Data 25.1 at **yourBioPortal.com**.

Go to **yourBioPortal.com** for original citations, discussions, and relevant links for all INVESTIGATION figures.

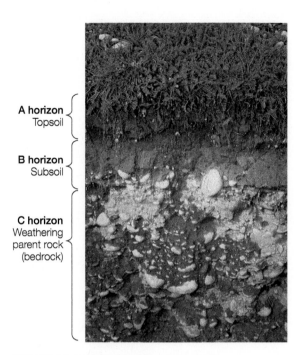

A horizon
Topsoil

B horizon
Subsoil

C horizon
Weathering
parent rock
(bedrock)

FIGURE 25.3 A Soil Profile *(Page 523)*

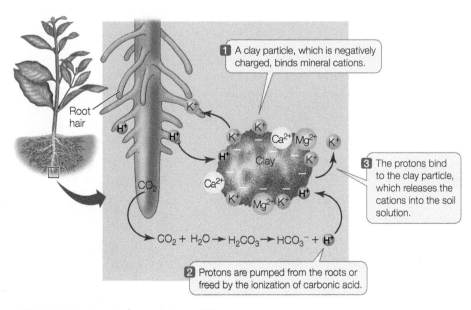

1 A clay particle, which is negatively charged, binds mineral cations.

Root hair

K^+

H^+

H^+

K^+

K^+

K^+

Ca^{2+} Mg^{2+}

K^+

H^+

Clay

K^+

Ca^{2+}

K^+

Mg^{2+} K^+

H^+

CO_2

3 The protons bind to the clay particle, which releases the cations into the soil solution.

$CO_2 + H_2O \rightarrow H_2CO_3 \rightarrow HCO_3^- + H^+$

2 Protons are pumped from the roots or freed by the ionization of carbonic acid.

FIGURE 25.4 Ion Exchange *(Page 524)*

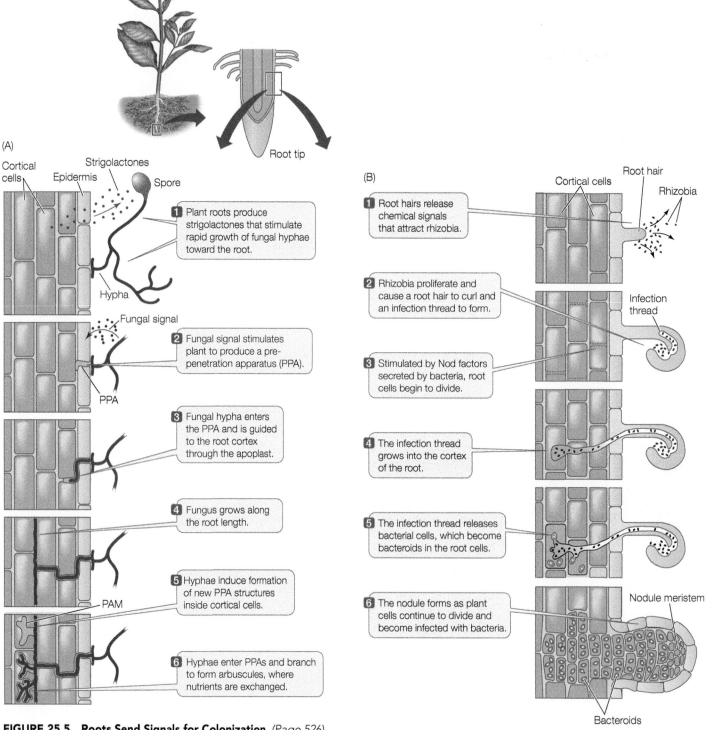

(A)

Cortical cells   Epidermis   Strigolactones   Spore

1 Plant roots produce strigolactones that stimulate rapid growth of fungal hyphae toward the root.

Hypha

Fungal signal

2 Fungal signal stimulates plant to produce a pre-penetration apparatus (PPA).

PPA

3 Fungal hypha enters the PPA and is guided to the root cortex through the apoplast.

4 Fungus grows along the root length.

5 Hyphae induce formation of new PPA structures inside cortical cells.

PAM

6 Hyphae enter PPAs and branch to form arbuscules, where nutrients are exchanged.

Root tip

(B)   Cortical cells   Root hair   Rhizobia

1 Root hairs release chemical signals that attract rhizobia.

2 Rhizobia proliferate and cause a root hair to curl and an infection thread to form.

Infection thread

3 Stimulated by Nod factors secreted by bacteria, root cells begin to divide.

4 The infection thread grows into the cortex of the root.

5 The infection thread releases bacterial cells, which become bacteroids in the root cells.

6 The nodule forms as plant cells continue to divide and become infected with bacteria.

Nodule meristem

Bacteroids

FIGURE 25.5 Roots Send Signals for Colonization (Page 526)

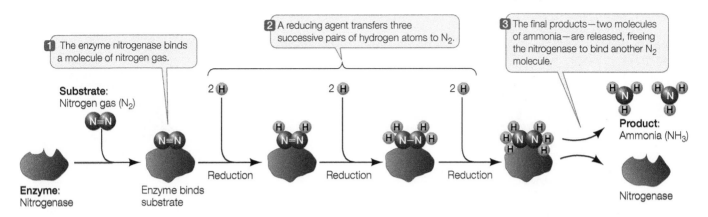

FIGURE 25.6   Nitrogenase Fixes Nitrogen *(Page 527)*

FIGURE 25.7   Nutrients from Other Organisms *(Page 528)*

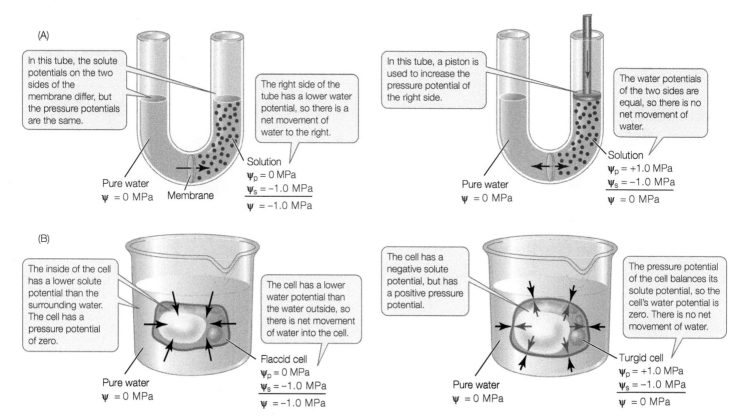

(A)

In this tube, the solute potentials on the two sides of the membrane differ, but the pressure potentials are the same.

The right side of the tube has a lower water potential, so there is a net movement of water to the right.

Pure water
ψ = 0 MPa

Membrane

Solution
ψ_p = 0 MPa
ψ_s = −1.0 MPa
ψ = −1.0 MPa

In this tube, a piston is used to increase the pressure potential of the right side.

The water potentials of the two sides are equal, so there is no net movement of water.

Pure water
ψ = 0 MPa

Solution
ψ_p = +1.0 MPa
ψ_s = −1.0 MPa
ψ = 0 MPa

(B)

The inside of the cell has a lower solute potential than the surrounding water. The cell has a pressure potential of zero.

The cell has a lower water potential than the water outside, so there is net movement of water into the cell.

Pure water
ψ = 0 MPa

Flaccid cell
ψ_p = 0 MPa
ψ_s = −1.0 MPa
ψ = −1.0 MPa

The cell has a negative solute potential, but has a positive pressure potential.

The pressure potential of the cell balances its solute potential, so the cell's water potential is zero. There is no net movement of water.

Pure water
ψ = 0 MPa

Turgid cell
ψ_p = +1.0 MPa
ψ_s = −1.0 MPa
ψ = 0 MPa

FIGURE 25.8   Water Potential, Solute Potential, and Pressure Potential *(Page 529)*

The water potential of cells of this plant is zero because the negative solute potential is balanced by an equally positive pressure potential.

The cells of this plant have a negative water potential due to negative solute potential and no pressure potential.

FIGURE 25.9   A Wilted Plant *(Page 530)*

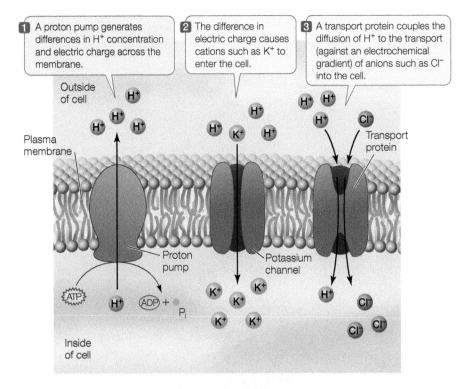

1 A proton pump generates differences in H⁺ concentration and electric charge across the membrane.

2 The difference in electric charge causes cations such as K⁺ to enter the cell.

3 A transport protein couples the diffusion of H⁺ to the transport (against an electrochemical gradient) of anions such as Cl⁻ into the cell.

Outside of cell

Plasma membrane

Proton pump

Potassium channel

Transport protein

ATP

ADP + Pᵢ

Inside of cell

FIGURE 25.10 Ion Transport into Plant Cells *(Page 530)*

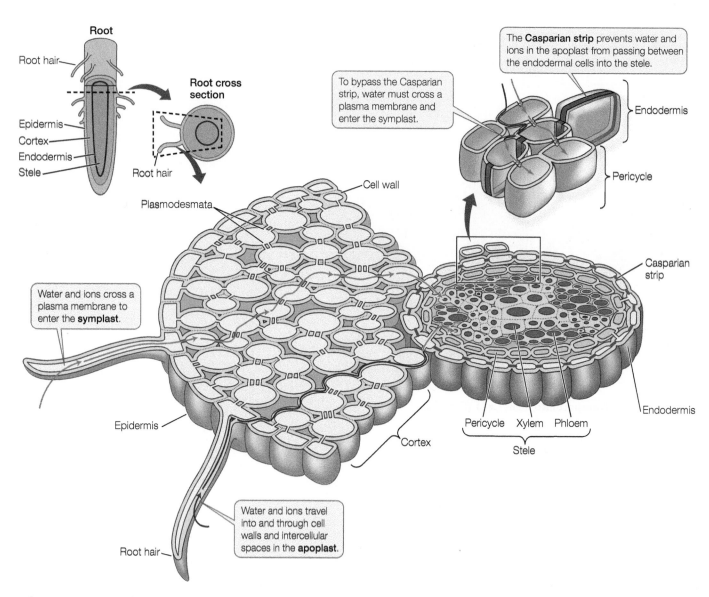

Root

Root hair

Root cross section

Epidermis
Cortex
Endodermis
Stele

Root hair

The **Casparian strip** prevents water and ions in the apoplast from passing between the endodermal cells into the stele.

To bypass the Casparian strip, water must cross a plasma membrane and enter the symplast.

Endodermis

Pericycle

Plasmodesmata

Cell wall

Water and ions cross a plasma membrane to enter the **symplast**.

Casparian strip

Epidermis

Cortex

Pericycle Xylem Phloem

Stele

Endodermis

Water and ions travel into and through cell walls and intercellular spaces in the **apoplast**.

Root hair

FIGURE 25.11 Apoplast and Symplast *(Page 531)*

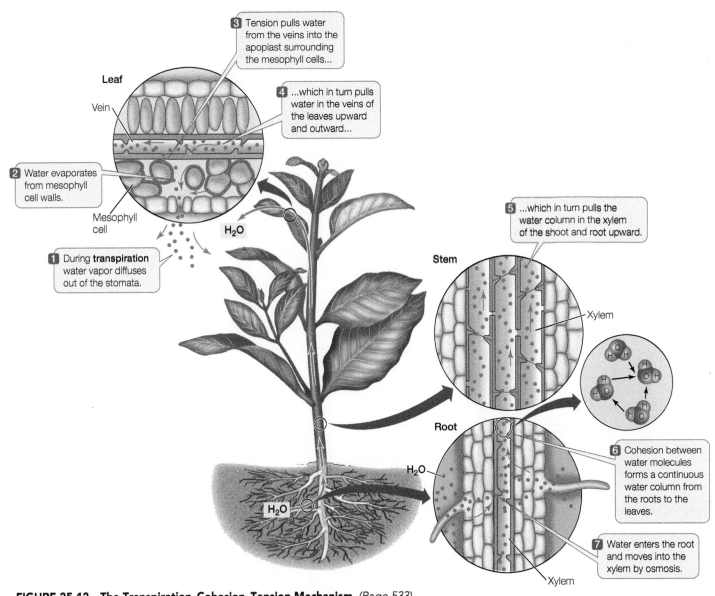

FIGURE 25.12 The Transpiration–Cohesion–Tension Mechanism *(Page 533)*

(A)

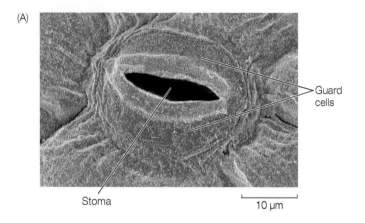

FIGURE 25.13 Stomata Regulate Gas Exchange and Transpiration *(Page 534)*

(B)

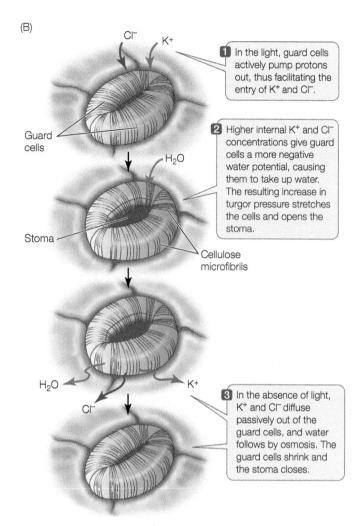

1 In the light, guard cells actively pump protons out, thus facilitating the entry of K^+ and Cl^-.

2 Higher internal K^+ and Cl^- concentrations give guard cells a more negative water potential, causing them to take up water. The resulting increase in turgor pressure stretches the cells and opens the stoma.

3 In the absence of light, K^+ and Cl^- diffuse passively out of the guard cells, and water follows by osmosis. The guard cells shrink and the stoma closes.

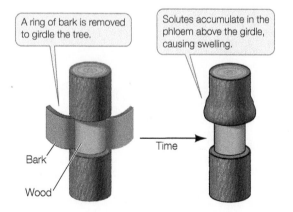

A ring of bark is removed to girdle the tree.

Solutes accumulate in the phloem above the girdle, causing swelling.

Time

Bark

Wood

IN-TEXT ART *(Page 535)*

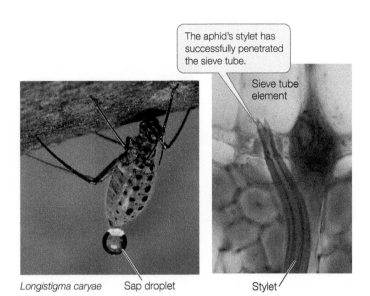

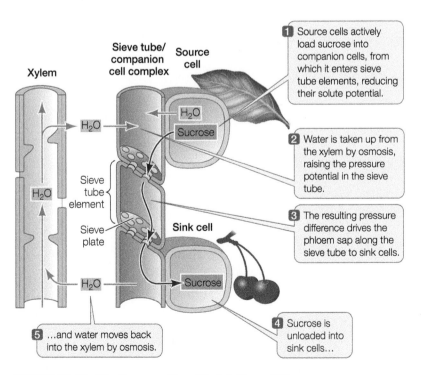

FIGURE 25.14 The Pressure Flow Model *(Page 536)*

Seedlings of current crop   Residue from previous crop

FIGURE 25.15 Conservation Tillage *(Page 537)*

Plant Growth and Development

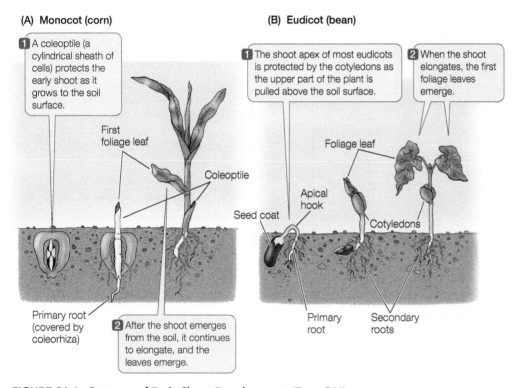

(A) Monocot (corn)

1 A coleoptile (a cylindrical sheath of cells) protects the early shoot as it grows to the soil surface.

First foliage leaf

Coleoptile

Primary root (covered by coleorhiza)

2 After the shoot emerges from the soil, it continues to elongate, and the leaves emerge.

(B) Eudicot (bean)

1 The shoot apex of most eudicots is protected by the cotyledons as the upper part of the plant is pulled above the soil surface.

2 When the shoot elongates, the first foliage leaves emerge.

Foliage leaf

Apical hook

Seed coat

Cotyledons

Primary root

Secondary roots

FIGURE 26.1 Patterns of Early Shoot Development *(Page 541)*

TABLE 26.1	Comparison of Plant and Animal Hormones	
CHARACTERISTIC	**PLANT HORMONES**	**ANIMAL HORMONES**
Size, chemistry	Small organic molecules	Peptides, proteins, small molecules
Site of synthesis	Throughout the plant	Specialized glands or cells
Site of action	Local or distant	Distant, transported
Effects	Diverse	Often specific
Regulation	Decentralized	By central nervous system

(Page 541)

RESEARCH TOOLS

FIGURE 26.2 A Genetic Screen Genetics of the model plant *Arabidopsis thaliana* can be used to identify the steps of a signal transduction pathway. If a mutant strain does not respond to a hormone (in this case, ethylene), the corresponding wild-type gene must be essential for the pathway (in this case, ethylene response). This method has been instrumental to scientists in understanding plant growth regulation.

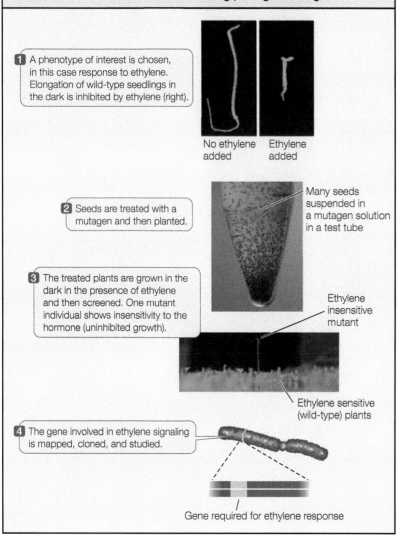

1 A phenotype of interest is chosen, in this case response to ethylene. Elongation of wild-type seedlings in the dark is inhibited by ethylene (right).

No ethylene added   Ethylene added

2 Seeds are treated with a mutagen and then planted.

Many seeds suspended in a mutagen solution in a test tube

3 The treated plants are grown in the dark in the presence of ethylene and then screened. One mutant individual shows insensitivity to the hormone (uninhibited growth).

Ethylene insensitive mutant

Ethylene sensitive (wild-type) plants

4 The gene involved in ethylene signaling is mapped, cloned, and studied.

Gene required for ethylene response

TABLE 26.2 Plant Growth Hormones

HORMONE	STRUCTURE	TYPICAL ACTIVITIES
Abscisic acid		Maintains seed dormancy; closes stomata
Auxin (indole-3-acetic acid)		Promotes stem elongation, lateral root initiation, and fruit development; inhibits axillary bud outgrowth, leaf abscission, and root elongation
Brassinosteroids		Promote stem and pollen tube elongation; promote vascular tissue differentiation
Cytokinins		Inhibit leaf senescence; promote cell division and axillary bud outgrowth; affect root growth
Ethylene		Promotes fruit ripening and leaf abscission; inhibits stem elongation
Gibberellins		Promote seed germination, stem growth, and fruit development; break winter dormancy; mobilize nutrient reserves in grass seeds

(Page 543)

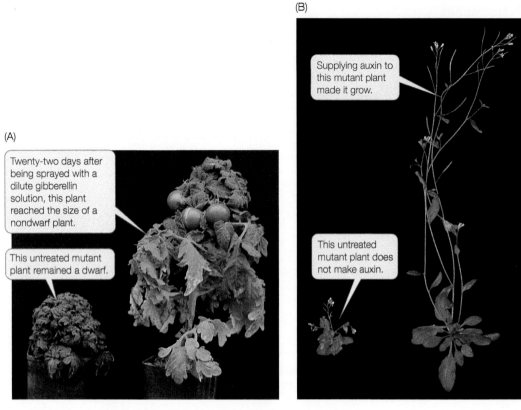

(A)

(B)

FIGURE 26.3 Hormones Reverse a Mutant Phenotype *(Page 543)*

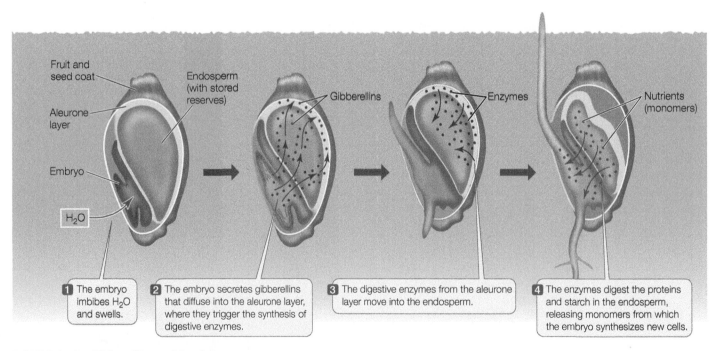

FIGURE 26.4 Gibberellins and Seed Germination *(Page 544)*

Untreated grapes

Grapes treated with gibberellin

IN-TEXT ART *(Page 544)*

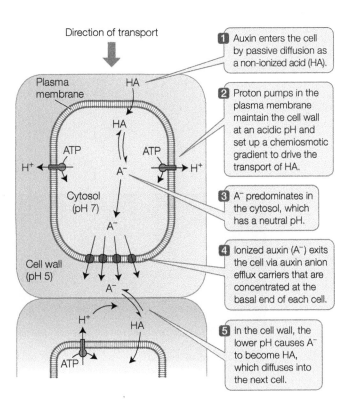

Direction of transport

Plasma membrane

HA

HA

ATP

ATP

H⁺

H⁺

A⁻

Cytosol (pH 7)

A⁻

Cell wall (pH 5)

A⁻

H⁺

HA

ATP

1 Auxin enters the cell by passive diffusion as a non-ionized acid (HA).

2 Proton pumps in the plasma membrane maintain the cell wall at an acidic pH and set up a chemiosmotic gradient to drive the transport of HA.

3 A⁻ predominates in the cytosol, which has a neutral pH.

4 Ionized auxin (A⁻) exits the cell via auxin anion efflux carriers that are concentrated at the basal end of each cell.

5 In the cell wall, the lower pH causes A⁻ to become HA, which diffuses into the next cell.

FIGURE 26.5 Polar Transport of Auxin *(Page 545)*

(A) Phototropism

1 Auxin moves to the shaded side within the tip.

2 The redistributed auxin moves down the coleoptile.

3 A higher auxin concentration causes more rapid growth by cell elongation on the shaded side. The tip curves toward the light.

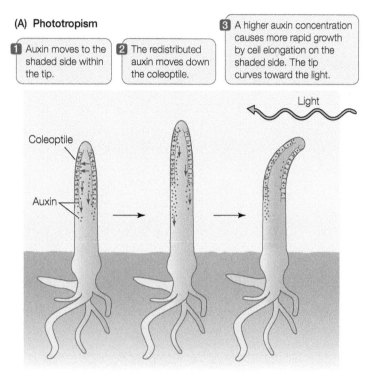

Light

Coleoptile

Auxin

(B) Negative gravitropism of shoot

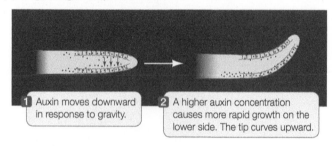

1 Auxin moves downward in response to gravity.

2 A higher auxin concentration causes more rapid growth on the lower side. The tip curves upward.

FIGURE 26.6 Plants Respond to Light and Gravity *(Page 545)*

Light

IN-TEXT ART *(Page 545)*

Auxin concentration

High

Low

IN-TEXT ART *(Page 546)*

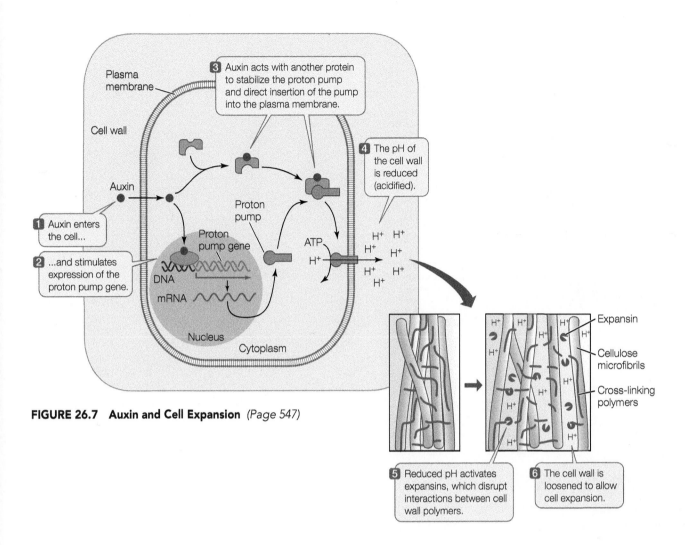

FIGURE 26.7 Auxin and Cell Expansion *(Page 547)*

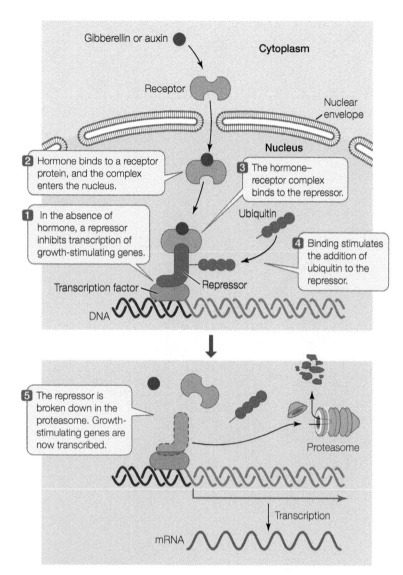

2 Hormone binds to a receptor protein, and the complex enters the nucleus.

3 The hormone–receptor complex binds to the repressor.

1 In the absence of hormone, a repressor inhibits transcription of growth-stimulating genes.

4 Binding stimulates the addition of ubiquitin to the repressor.

5 The repressor is broken down in the proteasome. Growth-stimulating genes are now transcribed.

FIGURE 26.8 Gibberellins and Auxin Have Similar Signal Transduction Pathways *(Page 548)*

These stored tomatoes were treated with ethylene to promote ripening.

IN-TEXT ART *(Page 549)*

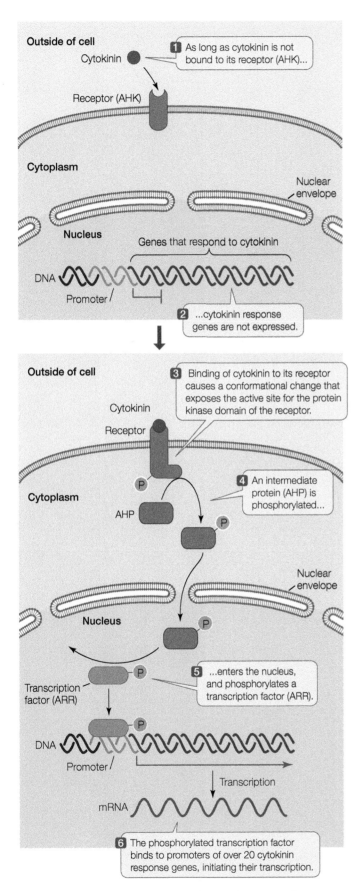

FIGURE 26.9 **The Cytokinin Signal Transduction Pathway**
(Page 550)

IN-TEXT ART *(Page 550)*

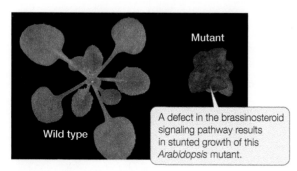

IN-TEXT ART *(Page 551)*

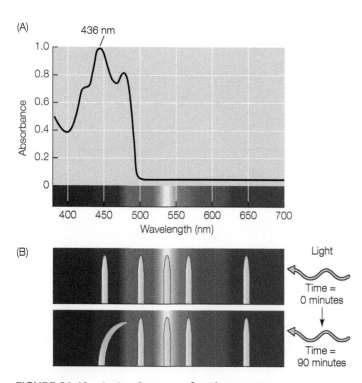

FIGURE 26.10 Action Spectrum for Phototropism *(Page 551)*

INVESTIGATION

FIGURE 26.11 Photomorphogenesis and Red Light Lettuce seeds will germinate if exposed to a brief period of light. The action spectrum for germination indicated that red light was most effective in promoting it, but far-red light would reverse the effect if presented right after a red-light flash. Harry Borthwick and his colleagues asked what the effect of repeated alternating flashes of red and far-red light would be. In each case, the final exposure determined the germination response. This observation led to the conclusion that a single, photoreversible molecule was involved. That molecule turned out to be phytochrome.

HYPOTHESIS

The effects of red and far-red light on lettuce seed germination are mutually reversible.

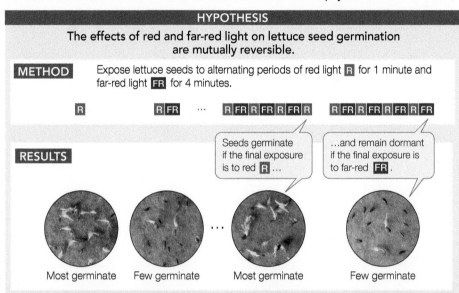

METHOD Expose lettuce seeds to alternating periods of red light R for 1 minute and far-red light FR for 4 minutes.

R   R FR   ⋯   R FR R FR R FR R   R FR R FR R FR R FR

RESULTS

Seeds germinate if the final exposure is to red R …

…and remain dormant if the final exposure is to far-red FR .

Most germinate   Few germinate   ⋯   Most germinate   Few germinate

CONCLUSION

Red light and far-red light reverse each other's effects.

ANALYZE THE DATA

Seven groups of 200 lettuce seeds each were incubated in water for 16 hours in the dark. One group was then exposed to white light for 1 min. A second group (controls) remained in the dark. Five other groups were exposed to red (R) and/or far-red (FR) light. All the seeds were then returned to darkness for 2 more days. Germination was then observed.

Condition	Seeds germinated
1. White light	199
2. Dark	17
3. R	196
4. R then FR	108
5. R then FR then R	200
6. R then FR then R then FR	86
7. R then FR then R then FR then R	198

A. Calculate the percentage of seeds that germinated in each case.

B. What can you conclude about the photoreceptors involved?

Go to **yourBioPortal.com** for original citations, discussions, and relevant links for all INVESTIGATION figures.

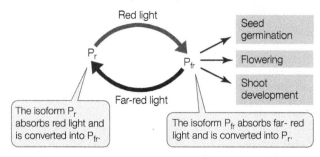

IN-TEXT ART *(Page 553)*

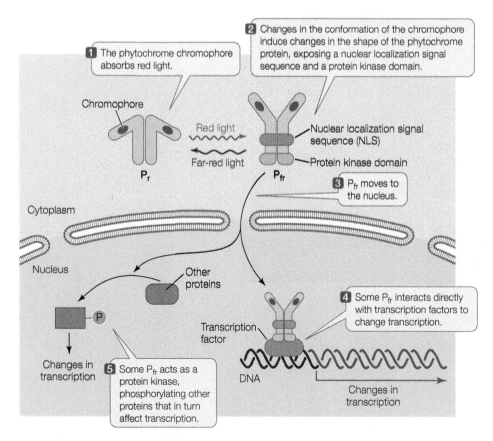

FIGURE 26.12 Phytochrome Stimulates Gene Transcription *(Page 553)*

FIGURE 26.13 **Semi-Dwarf Rice** *(Page 554)*

(A) Perfect: lily (*Lilium* sp.)

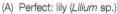

Carpel

Stamens

(B) Imperfect monoecious: corn (*Zea mays*)

Male flower
with stamens

Female flower
with carpels

(C) Imperfect dioecious: American holly (*Ilex opaca*)

Male flower with stamens

Female flower with carpels

FIGURE 27.1 Perfect and Imperfect Flowers *(Page 557)*

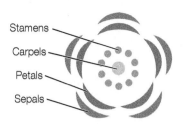

Stamens
Carpels
Petals
Sepals

IN-TEXT ART *(Page 557)*

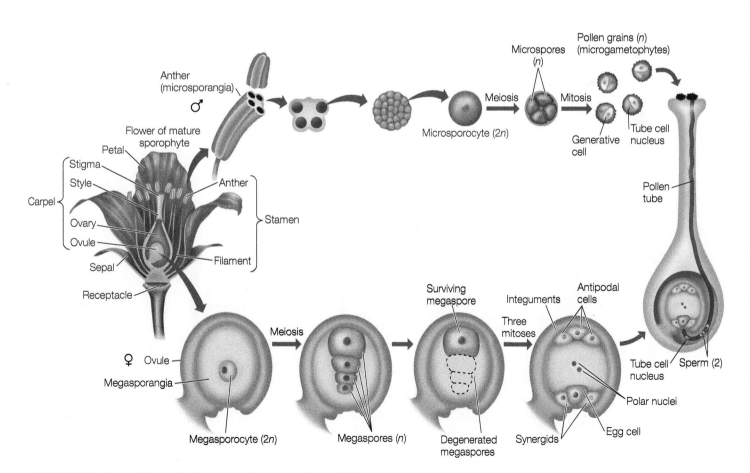

FIGURE 27.2   Sexual Reproduction in Angiosperms *(Page 558)*

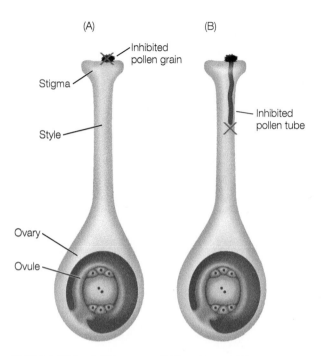

(A)   (B)

Inhibited pollen grain

Stigma

Style

Inhibited pollen tube

Ovary

Ovule

FIGURE 27.3 Self-incompatibility *(Page 559)*

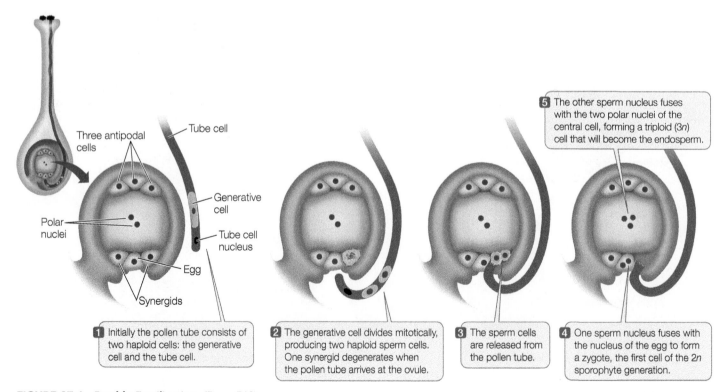

Three antipodal cells

Tube cell

Polar nuclei

Generative cell

Tube cell nucleus

Egg

Synergids

5 The other sperm nucleus fuses with the two polar nuclei of the central cell, forming a triploid (3*n*) cell that will become the endosperm.

1 Initially the pollen tube consists of two haploid cells: the generative cell and the tube cell.

2 The generative cell divides mitotically, producing two haploid sperm cells. One synergid degenerates when the pollen tube arrives at the ovule.

3 The sperm cells are released from the pollen tube.

4 One sperm nucleus fuses with the nucleus of the egg to form a zygote, the first cell of the 2*n* sporophyte generation.

FIGURE 27.4 Double Fertilization *(Page 560)*

(A)   Seed with embryo   Fruit (ovary wall)

(B)

Seed with embryo

(C)

Seed with embryo

Seed with embryo   Fruit (ovary wall)

Fruit (ovary wall)

FIGURE 27.5   Angiosperm Fruits   *(Page 561)*

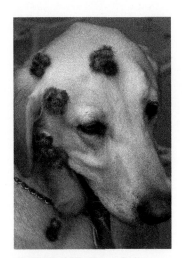

IN-TEXT ART   *(Page 561)*

IN-TEXT ART   *(Page 561)*

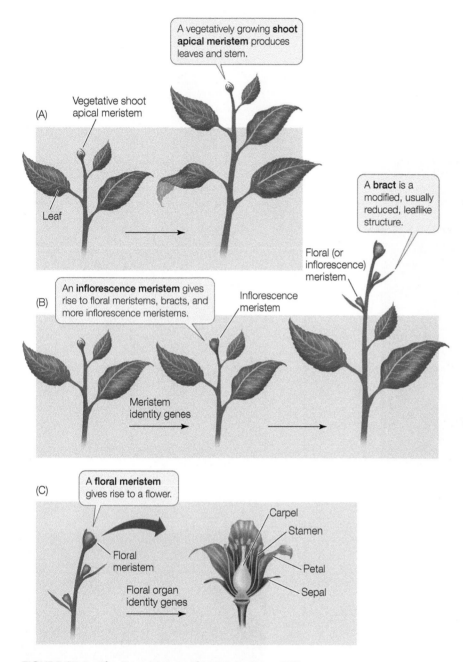

FIGURE 27.6 The Transition to Flowering *(Page 562)*

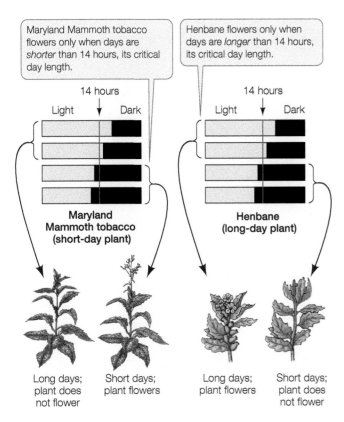

Maryland Mammoth tobacco flowers only when days are *shorter* than 14 hours, its critical day length.

Henbane flowers only when days are *longer* than 14 hours, its critical day length.

14 hours

Light | Dark

14 hours

Light | Dark

Maryland
Mammoth tobacco
(short-day plant)

Henbane
(long-day plant)

Long days;
plant does
not flower

Short days;
plant flowers

Long days;
plant flowers

Short days;
plant does
not flower

FIGURE 27.7 Photoperiod and Flowering *(Page 563)*

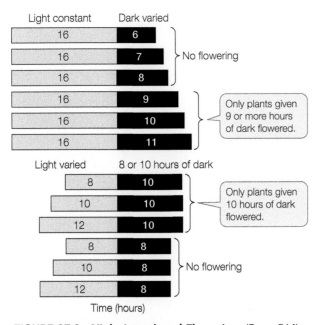

Light constant | Dark varied

16 | 6
16 | 7
16 | 8

No flowering

16 | 9
16 | 10
16 | 11

Only plants given
9 or more hours
of dark flowered.

Light varied | 8 or 10 hours of dark

8 | 10
10 | 10
12 | 10

Only plants given
10 hours of dark
flowered.

8 | 8
10 | 8
12 | 8

No flowering

Time (hours)

FIGURE 27.8 Night Length and Flowering *(Page 564)*

INVESTIGATION

FIGURE 27.9   The Flowering Signal Moves from Leaf to Bud
Phytochrome, the receptor for photoperiod, is in the leaf, but flowering occurs in the shoot apical meristem. To investigate whether there is a diffusible substance that travels from leaf to bud, James Knott exposed a single leaf of cocklebur plants to the inductive dark period.

HYPOTHESIS

The leaves measure the photoperiod.

METHOD   Grow cocklebur plants under long days and short nights. Mask a leaf on some plants and see if flowering occurs.

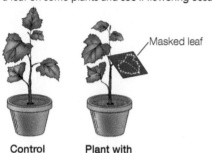

Control   Plant with masked leaf

RESULTS   If even one leaf is masked for part of the day—thus shifting that leaf to short days and long nights—the plant will flower.

CONCLUSION

The leaves measure the photoperiod. Therefore, some signal must move from the induced leaf to the flowering parts of the plant.

ANALYZE THE DATA

In related experiments, leaves were removed from plants before the plants were exposed to the inductive dark period. There were six plants in each condition.

Condition	Number of plants that flowered
No inductive dark period, intact plant	0
Inductive dark period, intact plant	6
Inductive dark period, all leaves removed	0
Inductive dark period, all but one leaf removed	6

A. Based on these data, which part of the plant senses photoperiod?

B. What do these data tell you about the signal that is generated by the plant in response to the photoperiod and that induces the shoot apical meristem to produce flowers?

Go to **yourBioPortal.com** for original citations, discussions, and relevant links for all INVESTIGATION figures.

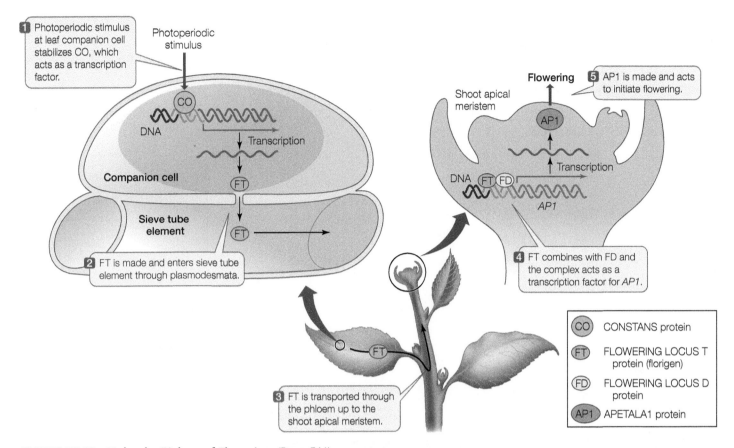

1 Photoperiodic stimulus at leaf companion cell stabilizes CO, which acts as a transcription factor.

Photoperiodic stimulus

CO

DNA

Transcription

Companion cell

FT

Sieve tube element

FT

2 FT is made and enters sieve tube element through plasmodesmata.

3 FT is transported through the phloem up to the shoot apical meristem.

Shoot apical meristem

Flowering

5 AP1 is made and acts to initiate flowering.

AP1

DNA

FT FD

Transcription

AP1

4 FT combines with FD and the complex acts as a transcription factor for *AP1*.

CO	CONSTANS protein
FT	FLOWERING LOCUS T protein (florigen)
FD	FLOWERING LOCUS D protein
AP1	APETALA1 protein

FIGURE 27.10   Molecular Biology of Flowering *(Page 566)*

Winter-annual *Arabidopsis* without vernalization

Winter-annual *Arabidopsis* with vernalization

FIGURE 27.11   Vernalization *(Page 567)*

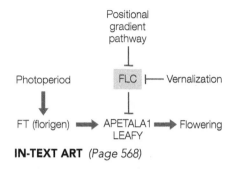

Positional gradient pathway

Photoperiod

FLC ⊣ Vernalization

FT (florigen) ➡ APETALA1 LEAFY ➡ Flowering

IN-TEXT ART *(Page 568)*

(A) These bamboo shoots all arise from the same underground stem.

(B) Each clove of garlic is a bulb that can give rise to a new plant.

(C) The plantlets forming on the margin of this *Kalanchoe* leaf will fall to the ground and become independent plants.

FIGURE 27.12 Vegetative Reproduction *(Page 568)*

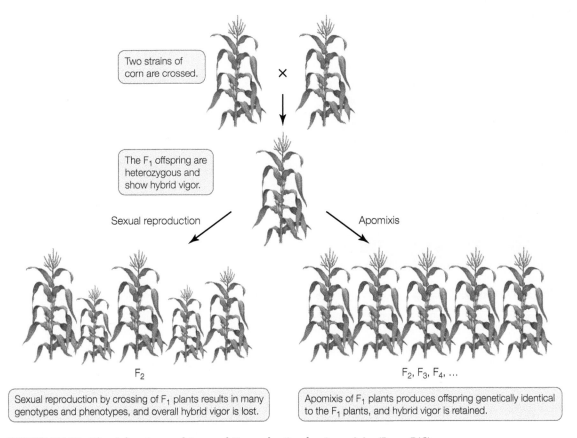

Two strains of corn are crossed.

The F$_1$ offspring are heterozygous and show hybrid vigor.

Sexual reproduction

Apomixis

F$_2$

F$_2$, F$_3$, F$_4$, …

Sexual reproduction by crossing of F$_1$ plants results in many genotypes and phenotypes, and overall hybrid vigor is lost.

Apomixis of F$_1$ plants produces offspring genetically identical to the F$_1$ plants, and hybrid vigor is retained.

FIGURE 27.13 The Advantage of Asexual Reproduction by Apomixis *(Page 569)*

Scion

In grafting, the scion is aligned so that its vascular cambium is adjacent to the vascular cambium in the stock.

Stock

FIGURE 27.14 Grafting *(Page 570)*

FIGURE 27.15   A Wild Relative of Poinsettia *(Page 570)*

Plants in the Environment

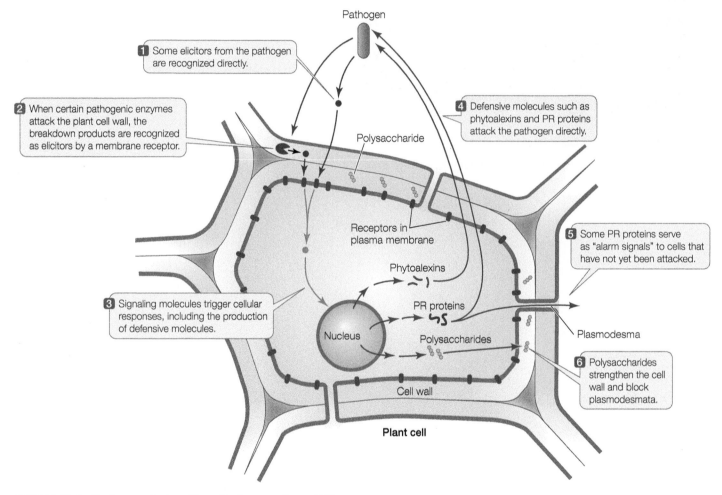

FIGURE 28.1 Pathogens Induce Plant Resistance *(Page 573)*

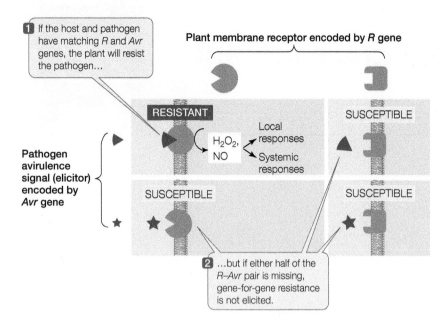

1 If the host and pathogen have matching *R* and *Avr* genes, the plant will resist the pathogen...

Plant membrane receptor encoded by *R* gene

RESISTANT

H_2O_2, NO

Local responses

Systemic responses

SUSCEPTIBLE

Pathogen avirulence signal (elicitor) encoded by *Avr* gene

SUSCEPTIBLE

SUSCEPTIBLE

2 ...but if either half of the *R–Avr* pair is missing, gene-for-gene resistance is not elicited.

FIGURE 28.2   Genes and the Response to a Pathogen *(Page 574)*

COOH

Tryptophan

Camalexin

IN-TEXT ART *(Page 574)*

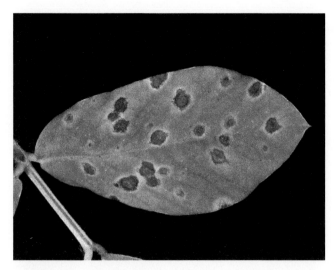

FIGURE 28.3   Sealing Off the Pathogen and the Damage
(Page 575)

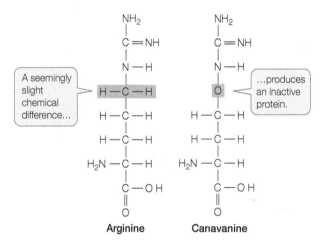

A seemingly slight chemical difference...

...produces an inactive protein.

Arginine   Canavanine

IN-TEXT ART (Page 576)

(A) *Locusta migratoria*

(B) *Manduca sexta*

FIGURE 28.4   Insect Herbivores (Page 576)

TABLE 28.1	Secondary Metabolites Used in Plant Defense		
CLASS	**TYPE**	**ROLE**	**EXAMPLE**
Nitrogen-containing	Alkaloids	Neurotoxin	Nicotine in tobacco
	Glycosides	Inhibit electron transport	Dhurrin in sorghum
	Nonprotein amino acids	Disrupt protein structure	Canavanine in jack bean
Ephedrine (an alkaloid)			
Nitrogen- and sulfur-containing	Glucosinolates	Inhibit respiration	Methylglucosinolate in cabbage
Methylglucosinolate			
Phenolics	Coumarins	Block cell division	Umbelliferone in carrots
	Flavonoids	Phytoalexins	Capsidol in peppers
	Tannins	Inhibit enzymes	Gallotannin in oak trees
Umbelliferone			
Terpenes	Monoterpenes	Neurotoxins	Pyrethrin in chrysanthemums
	Diterpenes	Disrupt reproduction and muscle function	Gossypol in cotton
	Triterpenes	Inhibit ion transport	Digitalis in foxglove
	Sterols	Block animal hormones	Spinasterol in spinach
	Polyterpenes	Deter feeding	Latex in *Euphorbia*
Pyrethrin			

(Page 577)

INVESTIGATION

FIGURE 28.5 Nicotine Is a Defense against Herbivores
The secondary metabolite nicotine, made by tobacco plants, is an insecticide, yet most commercial varieties of tobacco are suscep-tible to insect attack. Ian Baldwin demonstrated that a tobacco strain with a reduced nicotine concentration was much more susceptible to insect damage.

HYPOTHESIS
Nicotine helps protect tobacco plants against insects.

CONCLUSION
Nicotine provides tobacco plants with at least some protection against insects.

METHOD

Create a strain of low-nicotine tobacco plants.

Plant normal (control) and low-nicotine (mutant) plants together in a field where they are accessible to insects.

Assess the extent of leaf damage at 2-day intervals.

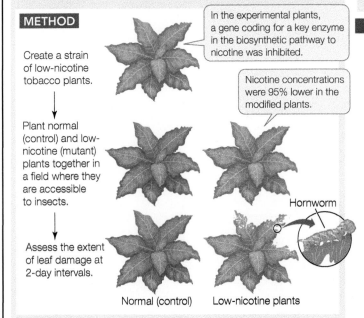

In the experimental plants, a gene coding for a key enzyme in the biosynthetic pathway to nicotine was inhibited.

Nicotine concentrations were 95% lower in the modified plants.

Hornworm

Normal (control)   Low-nicotine plants

ANALYZE THE DATA

In a separate experiment, Baldwin and his colleagues showed that treatment with jasmonic acid (jasmonate) increased the concentration of nicotine in normal tobacco plants, but not in the low-nicotine plants. The researchers planted a group of normal and low-nicotine plants and treated them with jasmonate seven days after planting. The plants were assessed for herbivore damage every 2 days after being planted. Here are the results:

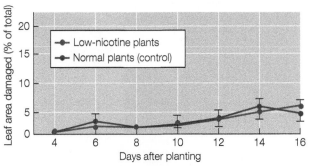

A. Compare these data to those at left for the untreated plants. What was the effect of jasmonate treatment on the resistance of normal plants to herbivore damage? What was the effect on low-nicotine plants?

B. What do these data reveal about the role of nicotine in preventing herbivore damage?

C. Explain how jasmonate could have had the effect it did on the low-nicotine plants, even though their nicotine levels were still low after jasmonate treatment.

D. The error bars at each data point are the standard error of the mean (SEM). What statistical test would you use to determine the possible significance of differences between the jasmonate-treated and untreated plants? At 10 days, the mean damage ± SEMs for untreated low-nicotine plants was 6.0 ± 1.5 percent ($n = 36$), and for treated low-nicotine plants it was 2.2 ± 0.6 percent ($n = 28$). Run a statistical test comparing the two results, calculate the P-value, and comment on significance.

RESULTS
The low-nicotine plants suffered more than twice as much leaf damage as did the normal controls.

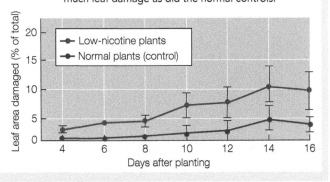

For more, go to Working with Data 28.1 at **yourBioPortal.com**.

Go to **yourBioPortal.com** for original citations, discussions, and relevant links for all INVESTIGATION figures.

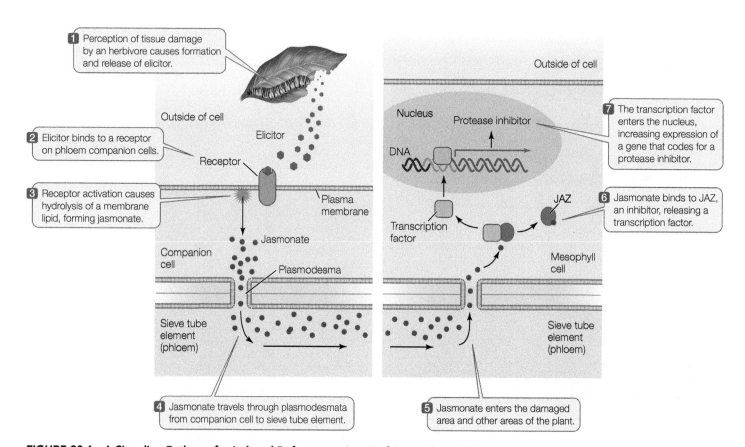

Jasmonic acid

IN-TEXT ART *(Page 578)*

1 Perception of tissue damage by an herbivore causes formation and release of elicitor.

Outside of cell

Elicitor

2 Elicitor binds to a receptor on phloem companion cells.

Receptor

3 Receptor activation causes hydrolysis of a membrane lipid, forming jasmonate.

Plasma membrane

Jasmonate

Companion cell

Plasmodesma

Sieve tube element (phloem)

4 Jasmonate travels through plasmodesmata from companion cell to sieve tube element.

Outside of cell

Nucleus

Protease inhibitor

7 The transcription factor enters the nucleus, increasing expression of a gene that codes for a protease inhibitor.

DNA

Transcription factor

JAZ

6 Jasmonate binds to JAZ, an inhibitor, releasing a transcription factor.

Mesophyll cell

Sieve tube element (phloem)

5 Jasmonate enters the damaged area and other areas of the plant.

FIGURE 28.6   A Signaling Pathway for Induced Defenses against Herbivory *(Page 579)*

Latex from laticifer

IN-TEXT ART *(Page 580)*

FIGURE 28.7   Desert Annuals Avoid Drought *(Page 580)*

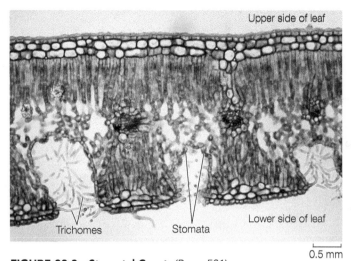

Upper side of leaf

Lower side of leaf

Trichomes

Stomata

0.5 mm

FIGURE 28.8 Stomatal Crypt *(Page 581)*

FIGURE 28.9 Succulence *(Page 581)*

FIGURE 28.10 **Mining Water with Deep Taproots** (Page 582)

(A)

(B)

Pneumatophores are root extensions that grow out of the water, under which the rest of the roots are submerged.

Open channel

Cells obtain oxygen through projections into the open channels of air-filled aerenchyma tissue.

Vascular bundle

75 μm

FIGURE 28.11 **Plant Adaptations to Saturated Habitats** (Page 582)

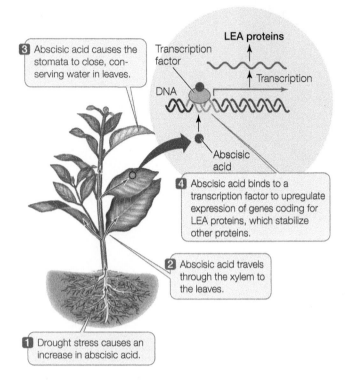

3 Abscisic acid causes the stomata to close, conserving water in leaves.

Transcription factor

LEA proteins

Transcription

DNA

Abscisic acid

4 Abscisic acid binds to a transcription factor to upregulate expression of genes coding for LEA proteins, which stabilize other proteins.

2 Abscisic acid travels through the xylem to the leaves.

1 Drought stress causes an increase in abscisic acid.

FIGURE 28.12 A Signaling Pathway in Response to Drought Stress *(Page 583)*

FIGURE 28.13 Salty Soil *(Page 584)*

FIGURE 28.14   Excreting Salt *(Page 585)*

FIGURE 28.15 Phytoremediation *(Page 585)*

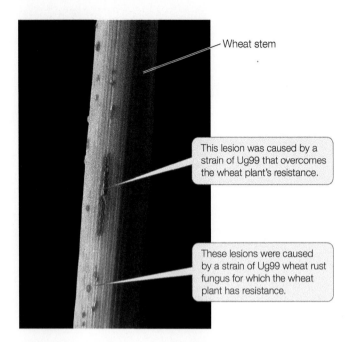

FIGURE 28.16 Overcoming Resistance to Pathogens *(Page 586)*

Physiology, Homeostasis, and Temperature Regulation

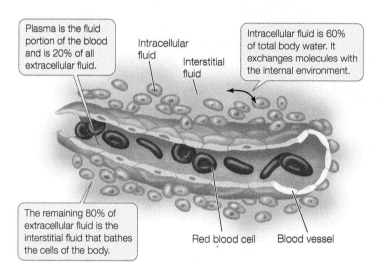

Plasma is the fluid portion of the blood and is 20% of all extracellular fluid.

Intracellular fluid

Interstitial fluid

Intracellular fluid is 60% of total body water. It exchanges molecules with the internal environment.

The remaining 80% of extracellular fluid is the interstitial fluid that bathes the cells of the body.

Red blood cell

Blood vessel

FIGURE 29.1 The Internal Environment *(Page 589)*

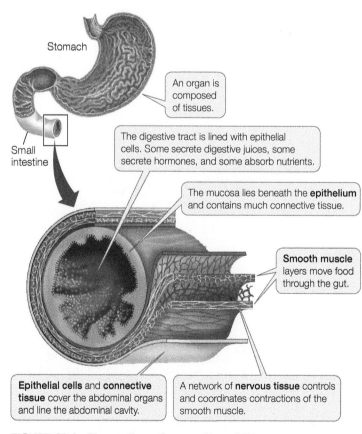

Stomach

Small intestine

An organ is composed of tissues.

The digestive tract is lined with epithelial cells. Some secrete digestive juices, some secrete hormones, and some absorb nutrients.

The mucosa lies beneath the **epithelium** and contains much connective tissue.

Smooth muscle layers move food through the gut.

Epithelial cells and **connective tissue** cover the abdominal organs and line the abdominal cavity.

A network of **nervous tissue** controls and coordinates contractions of the smooth muscle.

FIGURE 29.2 Tissues Form Organs *(Page 590)*

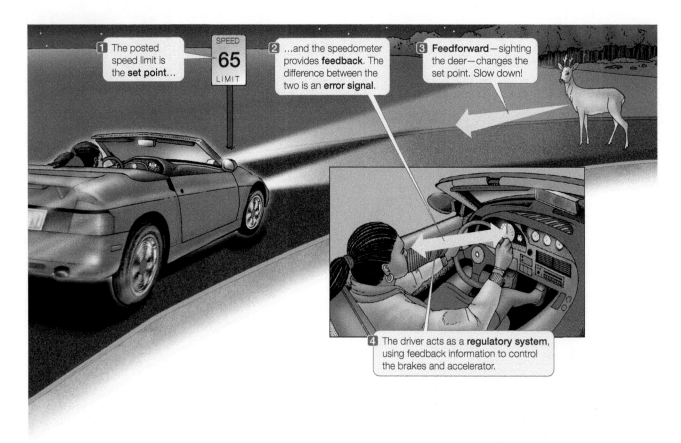

FIGURE 29.3 **Control, Regulation, and Feedback** *(Page 591)*

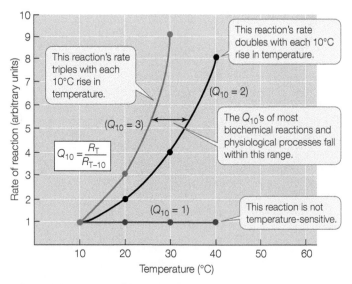

FIGURE 29.4 **Q_{10} and Reaction Rate** *(Page 593)*

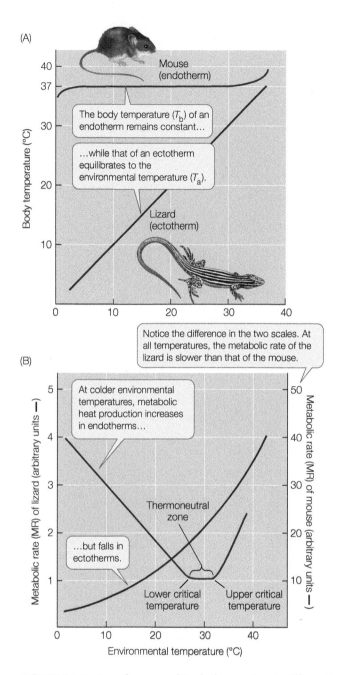

(A)

The body temperature (T_b) of an endotherm remains constant...

...while that of an ectotherm equilibrates to the environmental temperature (T_a).

Notice the difference in the two scales. At all temperatures, the metabolic rate of the lizard is slower than that of the mouse.

At colder environmental temperatures, metabolic heat production increases in endotherms...

...but falls in ectotherms.

Thermoneutral zone

Lower critical temperature

Upper critical temperature

FIGURE 29.5 Ectotherms and Endotherms React Differently to Environmental Temperatures (Page 593)

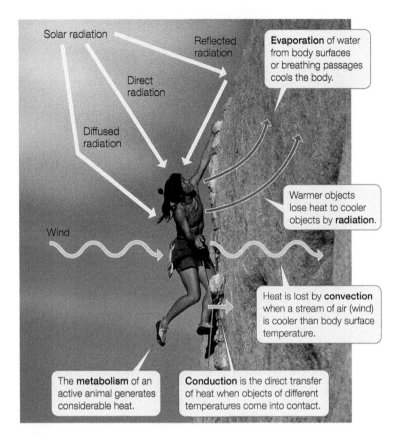

Solar radiation

Reflected radiation

Direct radiation

Diffused radiation

Wind

Evaporation of water from body surfaces or breathing passages cools the body.

Warmer objects lose heat to cooler objects by **radiation**.

Heat is lost by **convection** when a stream of air (wind) is cooler than body surface temperature.

The **metabolism** of an active animal generates considerable heat.

Conduction is the direct transfer of heat when objects of different temperatures come into contact.

FIGURE 29.6 Animals Exchange Heat with the Environment
(Page 595)

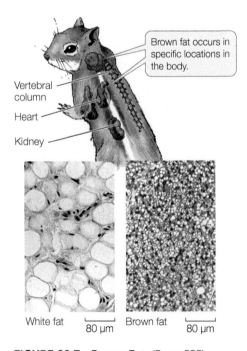

Brown fat occurs in specific locations in the body.

Vertebral column

Heart

Kidney

White fat | 80 µm | Brown fat | 80 µm

FIGURE 29.7 Brown Fat (Page 595)

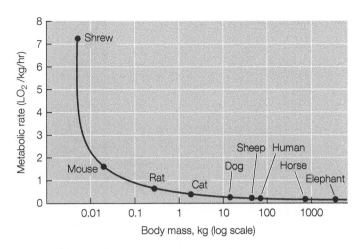

FIGURE 29.8   The Mouse-to-Elephant Curve *(Page 596)*

FIGURE 29.9   Anatomical Adaptations to Climate *(Page 596)*

(A) "Cold" fish

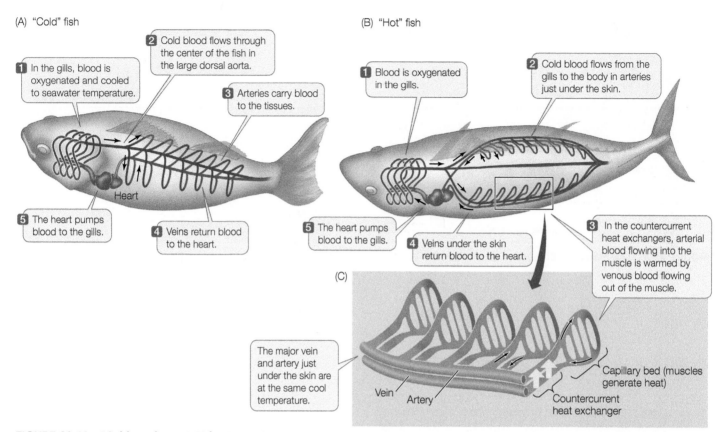

1 In the gills, blood is oxygenated and cooled to seawater temperature.

2 Cold blood flows through the center of the fish in the large dorsal aorta.

3 Arteries carry blood to the tissues.

Heart

5 The heart pumps blood to the gills.

4 Veins return blood to the heart.

(B) "Hot" fish

1 Blood is oxygenated in the gills.

2 Cold blood flows from the gills to the body in arteries just under the skin.

5 The heart pumps blood to the gills.

4 Veins under the skin return blood to the heart.

3 In the countercurrent heat exchangers, arterial blood flowing into the muscle is warmed by venous blood flowing out of the muscle.

(C)

The major vein and artery just under the skin are at the same cool temperature.

Vein   Artery

Capillary bed (muscles generate heat)

Countercurrent heat exchanger

FIGURE 29.10 *"Cold" and "Hot" Fish* (Page 597)

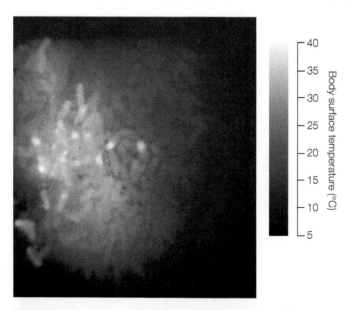

Body surface temperature (°C)

— 40
— 35
— 30
— 25
— 20
— 15
— 10
— 5

FIGURE 29.11 **Bees Keep Warm in Winter** (Page 598)

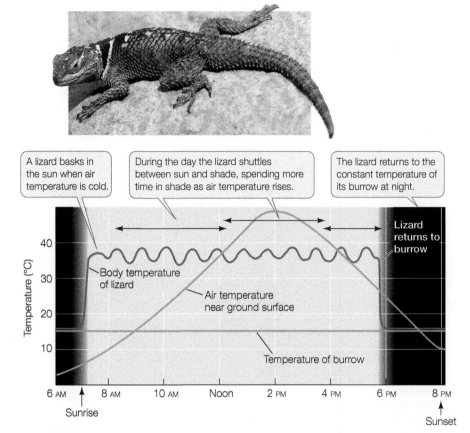

FIGURE 29.12   Ectotherms Can Use Behavior to Regulate Body Temperature
(Page 599)

INVESTIGATION

FIGURE 29.13   The Hypothalamus Regulates Body Temperature
A mammal's hypothalamus was subjected directly to temperature manipulation. The body's responses to the manipulations were as expected if the hypothalamus is the mammalian "thermostat."

HYPOTHESIS

Heating or cooling the mammalian hypothalamus results in corresponding and predictable changes in body temperature.

METHOD

1. Implant a probe into the hypothalamus of a living ground squirrel's brain. Use the probe to heat or cool the hypothalamus directly (i.e., without affecting the ambient temperature).

2. Manipulate the hypothalamic temperature T_H.

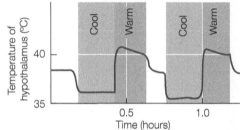

3. Measure the animal's metabolic rate and body temperature throughout the period of hypothalamic manipulation.

1 When the hypothalamus was cooled, metabolic heat production increased and the animal's body temperature rose.

RESULTS

2 When the hypothalamus was heated, the squirrel's metabolic rate and body temperature fell.

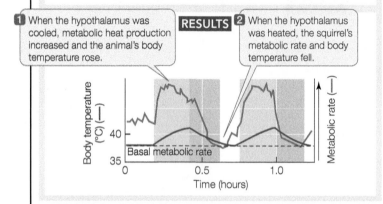

CONCLUSION

The ground squirrel's hypothalamus acts as a thermostat. When cooled it activates metabolic heat production; when warmed, it suppresses metabolic heat production and favors heat loss.

ANALYZE THE DATA

The data below were recorded from an experiment in which the hypothalamus of a ground squirrel was randomly cooled (T_H) while the animal's metabolic rate (MR) was measured. T_H is given in °C, MR is given in calories per gram of body mass per minute.

T_H	MR	T_H	MR	T_H	MR
39.5	0.040	36.5	0.038	37.5	0.041
39.0	0.041	36.0	0.040	37.0	0.039
38.5	0.040	35.5	0.060	34.5	0.110
38.0	0.038	35.0	0.080	34.0	0.140

A. Plot the data and describe what it tells you about the properties of the hypothalamic thermostat.

B. What is the threshold temperature for the metabolic heat production response?

For more, go to Working with Data 29.1 at **yourBioPortal.com**.

Go to **yourBioPortal.com** for original citations, discussions, and relevant links for all INVESTIGATION figures.

(A)

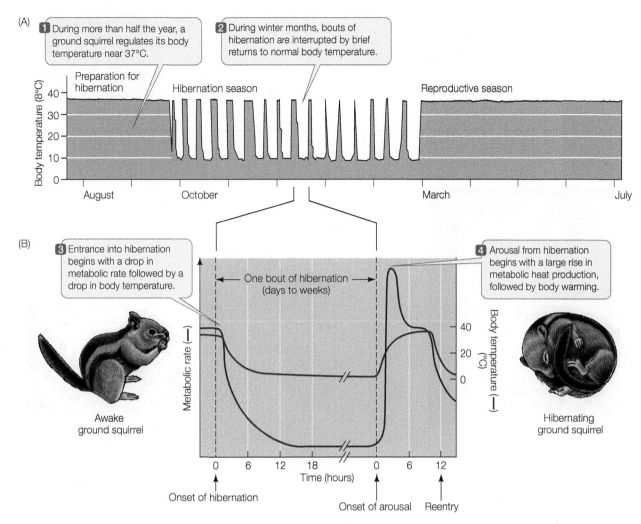

1 During more than half the year, a ground squirrel regulates its body temperature near 37°C.

2 During winter months, bouts of hibernation are interrupted by brief returns to normal body temperature.

Body temperature (8°C)

Preparation for hibernation

Hibernation season

Reproductive season

August   October   March   July

(B)

3 Entrance into hibernation begins with a drop in metabolic rate followed by a drop in body temperature.

4 Arousal from hibernation begins with a large rise in metabolic heat production, followed by body warming.

One bout of hibernation (days to weeks)

Metabolic rate (—)

Body temperature (°C)

40

20

0

Awake ground squirrel

Hibernating ground squirrel

0   6   12   18   0   6   12
Time (hours)

Onset of hibernation

Onset of arousal   Reentry

FIGURE 29.14 Hibernation Patterns in a Ground Squirrel *(Page 601)*

Animal Hormones

(A) Protein hormones

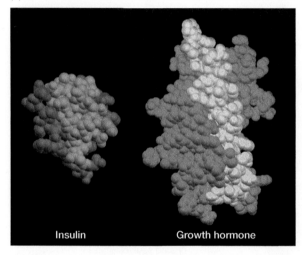

Insulin   Growth hormone

FIGURE 30.1 Three Classes of Hormones *(Page 605)*

(B) Steroid hormones

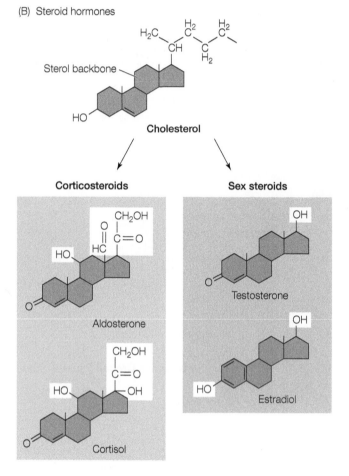

Sterol backbone

HO

Cholesterol

Corticosteroids

CH_2OH

$C=O$

HO

Aldosterone

CH_2OH

$C=O$

HO   OH

Cortisol

Sex steroids

OH

Testosterone

OH

HO

Estradiol

(C) Amine hormones

HO — C — C — NH_3^+
        COO^-

Tyrosine

HO

HO — C — C — N — CH_3
   OH

Epinephrine

HO — O — C — C — N

   C
  O   OH

Thyroxine

INVESTIGATION

FIGURE 30.2 **A Diffusible Substance Triggers Molting**
The bloodsucking bug *Rhodnius prolixus* develops from hatchling to adult in a series of five molts (instars) that are triggered by ingesting blood. Sir Vincent Wigglesworth's experiments demonstrated that a blood meal stimulates production of some molt-inducing substance in the insect's head.

HYPOTHESIS

The substance that controls molting in *R. prolixus* is produced in the head segment and diffuses slowly through the body.

OBSERVATION

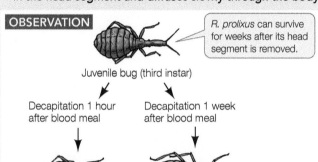

R. prolixus can survive for weeks after its head segment is removed.

Juvenile bug (third instar)

Decapitation 1 hour after blood meal

Decapitation 1 week after blood meal

Does not molt (remains a juvenile)

Molts into an adult

METHOD

1. Decapitate third-instar juveniles at different times after blood meal.

1 hour after blood meal   1 week after blood meal

2. Join bugs with glass tube

Tubing allows body fluids to pass from one bug to another

RESULTS

Both bugs molt into adults

CONCLUSION

A blood meal stimulates production of some substance within the insect's head that then diffuses slowly through the body, triggering a molt.

Go to **yourBioPortal.com** for original citations, discussions, and relevant links for all INVESTIGATION figures.

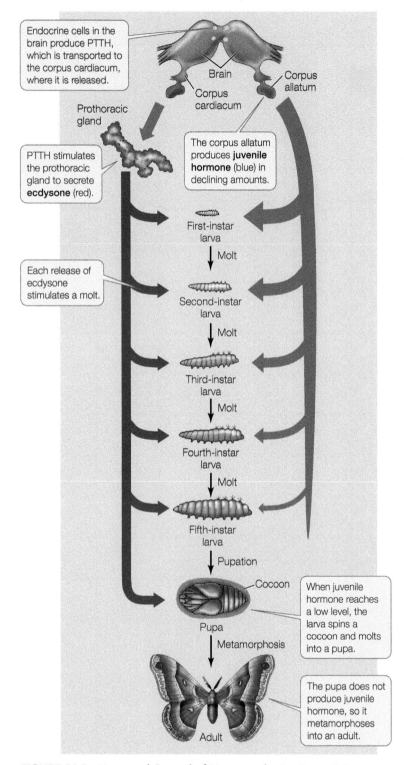

Endocrine cells in the brain produce PTTH, which is transported to the corpus cardiacum, where it is released.

Brain

Corpus cardiacum

Corpus allatum

Prothoracic gland

The corpus allatum produces **juvenile hormone** (blue) in declining amounts.

PTTH stimulates the prothoracic gland to secrete **ecdysone** (red).

First-instar larva

Molt

Each release of ecdysone stimulates a molt.

Second-instar larva

Molt

Third-instar larva

Molt

Fourth-instar larva

Molt

Fifth-instar larva

Pupation

Cocoon

When juvenile hormone reaches a low level, the larva spins a cocoon and molts into a pupa.

Pupa

Metamorphosis

The pupa does not produce juvenile hormone, so it metamorphoses into an adult.

Adult

FIGURE 30.3   Hormonal Control of Metamorphosis *(Page 607)*

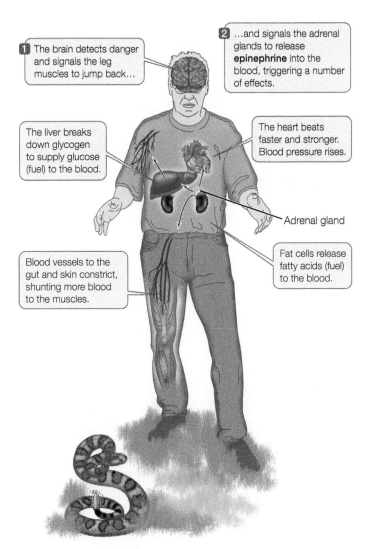

FIGURE 30.4 The Fight-or-Flight Response *(Page 608)*

β-Adrenergic receptors

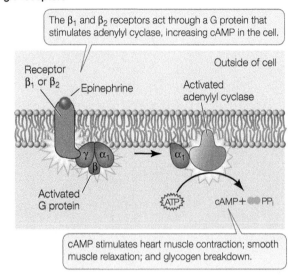

The β₁ and β₂ receptors act through a G protein that stimulates adenylyl cyclase, increasing cAMP in the cell.

Outside of cell

Receptor β₁ or β₂

Epinephrine

Activated adenylyl cyclase

Activated G protein

ATP

cAMP + PPᵢ

cAMP stimulates heart muscle contraction; smooth muscle relaxation; and glycogen breakdown.

FIGURE 30.5 Adrenergic Receptors (Page 609)

α-Adrenergic receptors

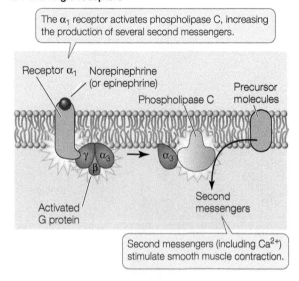

The α₁ receptor activates phospholipase C, increasing the production of several second messengers.

Receptor α₁

Norepinephrine (or epinephrine)

Precursor molecules

Phospholipase C

Activated G protein

Second messengers

Second messengers (including Ca^{2+}) stimulate smooth muscle contraction.

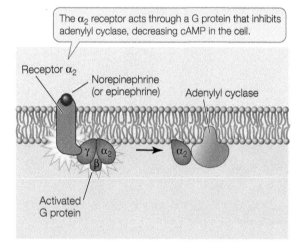

The α₂ receptor acts through a G protein that inhibits adenylyl cyclase, decreasing cAMP in the cell.

Receptor α₂

Norepinephrine (or epinephrine)

Adenylyl cyclase

Activated G protein

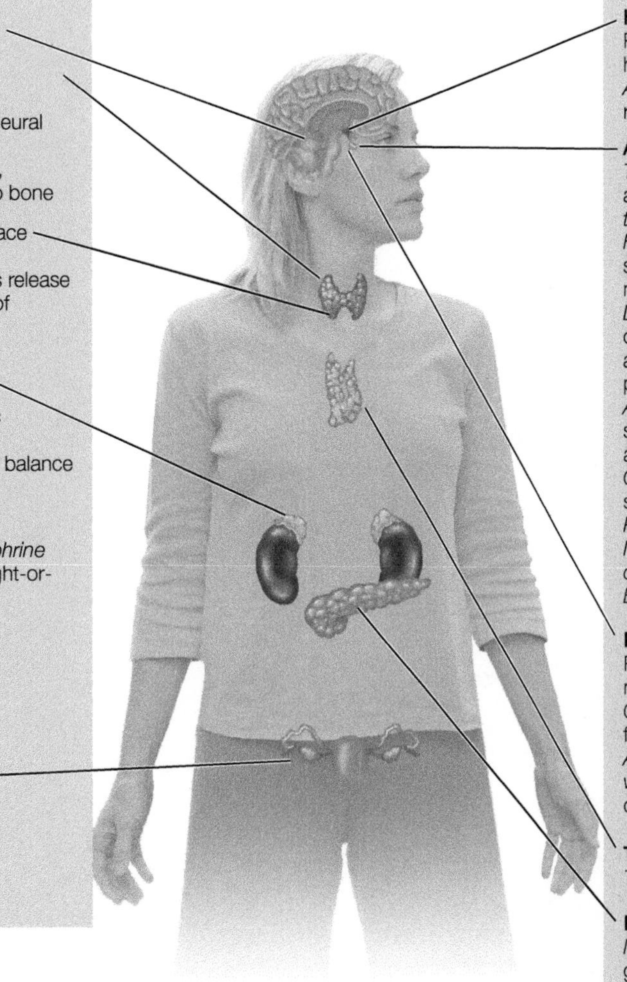

Pineal gland
Melatonin: regulates daily rhythms

Thyroid gland (see Figure 30.11)
Thyroxine (T₃ and T₄): increases cell metabolism; essential for growth and neural development
Calcitonin: lowers blood calcium levels, stimulates incorporation of calcium into bone

Parathyroid glands (on posterior surface of thyroid; see Figure 30.11)
Parathyroid hormone (PTH): stimulates release of calcium from bone and absorption of calcium by gut and kidney

Adrenal gland (see Figure 30.12)
Cortex
Cortisol: mediates long-term metabolic responses to stress
Aldosterone: involved in salt and water balance
Sex steroids

Medulla
Epinephrine (adrenaline) and *norepinephrine* (noradrenaline): stimulate immediate fight-or-flight reactions

Gonads (see Chapter 32)
Testes (male)
Androgens (esp. testosterone): development and maintenance of male sexual characteristics
Ovaries (female)
Estrogens: development and maintenance of female sexual characteristics
Progesterone: supports pregnancy

Hypothalamus (see Figure 30.7)
Releasing and release-inhibiting neuro-hormones control the anterior pituitary; *ADH* and *oxytocin* are transported to and released from the posterior pituitary

Anterior pituitary (see Figure 30.8)
Thyroid-stimulating hormone (TSH): activates the thyroid gland; also called *thyrotropin*
Follicle-stimulating hormone (FSH): in females, stimulates maturation of ovarian follicles; in males, stimulates spermatogenesis
Luteinizing hormone (LH): in females, triggers ovulation and ovarian production of estrogens and progesterone; in males, stimulates production of testosterone
Adrenocorticotropic hormone (ACTH): stimulates growth and secretory activity of the adrenal cortex; also called corticotropin
Growth hormone (GH): stimulates protein synthesis and growth
Prolactin: stimulates milk production
Melanocyte-stimulating hormone (MSH): controls skin pigmentation
Endorphins and *enkephalins*: pain control

Posterior pituitary (see Figure 30.7)
Receives and releases two hypothalamic neurohormones:
Oxytocin: stimulates contraction of uterus, flow of milk, interindividual bonding
Antidiuretic hormone (ADH; also known as vasopressin): promotes water conservation by kidneys

Thymus (diminishes in adults)
Thymosin: activates immune system T cells

Pancreas (islets of Langerhans)
Insulin: stimulates cells to take up and use glucose
Glucagon: stimulates liver to release glucose
Somatostatin: slows release of insulin and glucagon and digestive tract functions

Other organs include cells that produce and secrete hormones:

Organ	Hormone
Adipose tissue	Leptin
Heart	Atrial natriuretic peptide
Kidney	Erythropoietin
Stomach	Gastrin
Intestine	Secretin, cholecystokinin
Skin	Vitamin D (calciferol)
Liver	Somatomedins, insulin-like growth factors

FIGURE 30.6 The Human Endocrine System *(Page 610)*

(A)

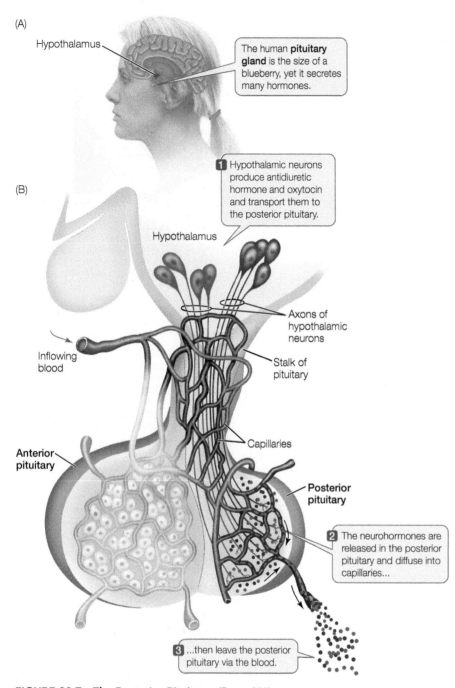

Hypothalamus

The human **pituitary gland** is the size of a blueberry, yet it secretes many hormones.

(B)

1 Hypothalamic neurons produce antidiuretic hormone and oxytocin and transport them to the posterior pituitary.

Hypothalamus

Axons of hypothalamic neurons

Inflowing blood

Stalk of pituitary

Capillaries

Anterior pituitary

Posterior pituitary

2 The neurohormones are released in the posterior pituitary and diffuse into capillaries...

3 ...then leave the posterior pituitary via the blood.

FIGURE 30.7 The Posterior Pituitary *(Page 611)*

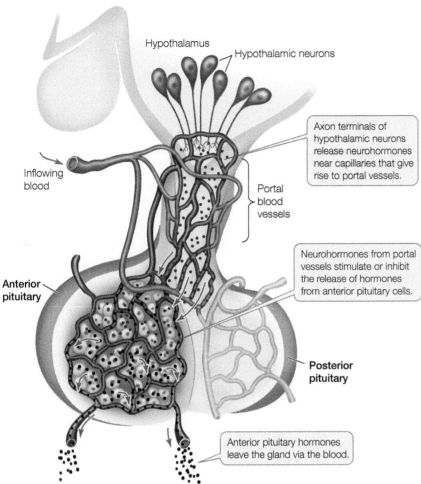

Hypothalamus

Hypothalamic neurons

Axon terminals of hypothalamic neurons release neurohormones near capillaries that give rise to portal vessels.

Inflowing blood

Portal blood vessels

Neurohormones from portal vessels stimulate or inhibit the release of hormones from anterior pituitary cells.

Anterior pituitary

Posterior pituitary

Anterior pituitary hormones leave the gland via the blood.

FIGURE 30.8   The Anterior Pituitary *(Page 612)*

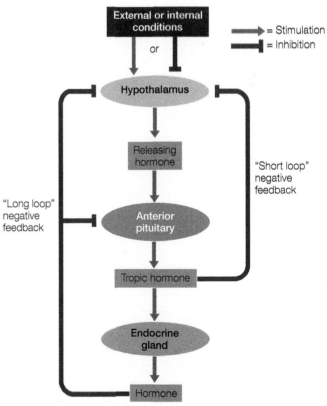

External or internal conditions

or

= Stimulation

= Inhibition

Hypothalamus

"Long loop" negative feedback

Releasing hormone

"Short loop" negative feedback

Anterior pituitary

Tropic hormone

Endocrine gland

Hormone

FIGURE 30.9   Multiple Feedback Loops Control Hormone Secretion *(Page 613)*

IN-TEXT ART *(Page 614)*

IN-TEXT ART *(Page 614)*

FIGURE 30.10 Goiter *(Page 614)*

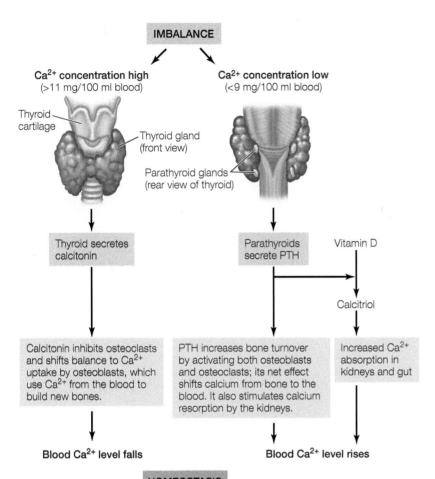

IMBALANCE

Ca²⁺ concentration high
(>11 mg/100 ml blood)

Thyroid cartilage

Thyroid gland (front view)

Parathyroid glands (rear view of thyroid)

Ca²⁺ concentration low
(<9 mg/100 ml blood)

Thyroid secretes calcitonin

Parathyroids secrete PTH

Vitamin D

Calcitriol

Calcitonin inhibits osteoclasts and shifts balance to Ca²⁺ uptake by osteoblasts, which use Ca²⁺ from the blood to build new bones.

PTH increases bone turnover by activating both osteoblasts and osteoclasts; its net effect shifts calcium from bone to the blood. It also stimulates calcium resorption by the kidneys.

Increased Ca²⁺ absorption in kidneys and gut

Blood Ca²⁺ level falls

Blood Ca²⁺ level rises

HOMEOSTASIS

Ca²⁺ concentration between 9 and 11 mg/100 ml blood

FIGURE 30.11   Hormonal Regulation of Calcium *(Page 615)*

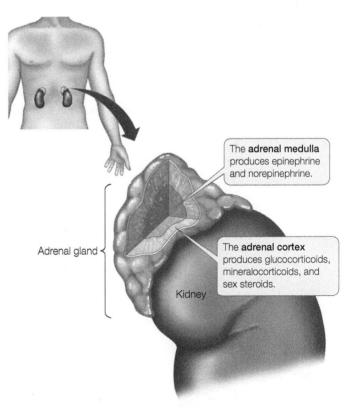

The **adrenal medulla** produces epinephrine and norepinephrine.

Adrenal gland

The **adrenal cortex** produces glucocorticoids, mineralocorticoids, and sex steroids.

Kidney

FIGURE 30.12   The Adrenal Is a Gland within a Gland *(Page 616)*

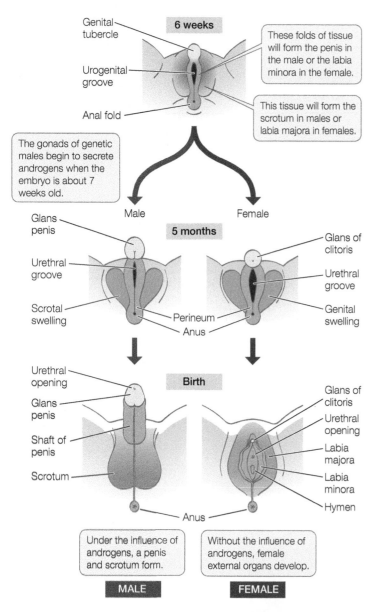

FIGURE 30.13 Sex Steroids Direct the Development of Human Sex Organs *(Page 617)*

FIGURE 30.14 Real People, Real Lives *(Page 618)*

Immunology: Animal Defense Systems

TABLE 31.1	Innate and Adaptive Immune Responses to an Infection	
RESPONSE (TIME AFTER INFECTION BY A PATHOGEN)	**SYSTEM**	**MECHANISMS**
Early (0–4 hr)	Innate, nonspecific (first line)	Barrier (skin and lining of organs)
		Dryness, low pH
		Mucus
		Lysozyme, defensins
Middle (4–96 hr)	Innate, nonspecific (second line)	Inflammation
		Phagocytosis
		Natural killer cells
		Complement system
		Interferons
Late (>96 hr)	Adaptive, specific	Humoral immunity (B cells, antibodies)
		Cellular immunity (T cells)

(Page 621)

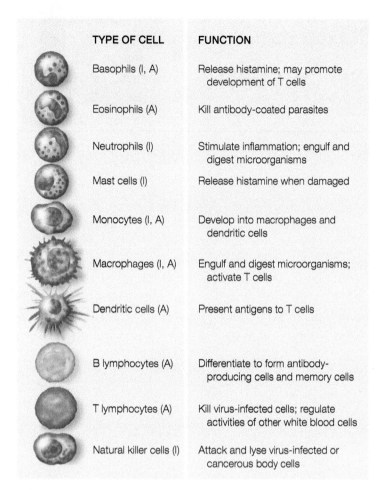

	TYPE OF CELL	FUNCTION
	Basophils (I, A)	Release histamine; may promote development of T cells
	Eosinophils (A)	Kill antibody-coated parasites
	Neutrophils (I)	Stimulate inflammation; engulf and digest microorganisms
	Mast cells (I)	Release histamine when damaged
	Monocytes (I, A)	Develop into macrophages and dendritic cells
	Macrophages (I, A)	Engulf and digest microorganisms; activate T cells
	Dendritic cells (A)	Present antigens to T cells
	B lymphocytes (A)	Differentiate to form antibody-producing cells and memory cells
	T lymphocytes (A)	Kill virus-infected cells; regulate activities of other white blood cells
	Natural killer cells (I)	Attack and lyse virus-infected or cancerous body cells

FIGURE 31.1   White Blood Cells *(Page 622)*

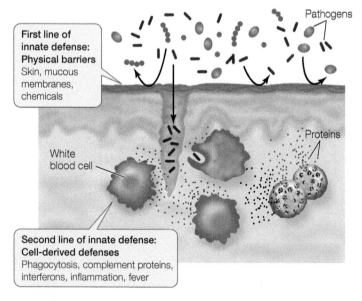

First line of innate defense:
Physical barriers
Skin, mucous membranes, chemicals

Pathogens

White blood cell

Proteins

Second line of innate defense:
Cell-derived defenses
Phagocytosis, complement proteins, interferons, inflammation, fever

FIGURE 31.2   Innate Immunity *(Page 622)*

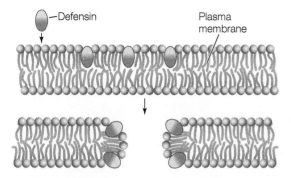

IN-TEXT ART *(Page 623)*

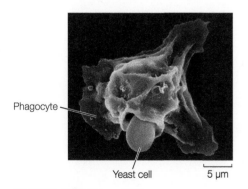

IN-TEXT ART *(Page 623)*

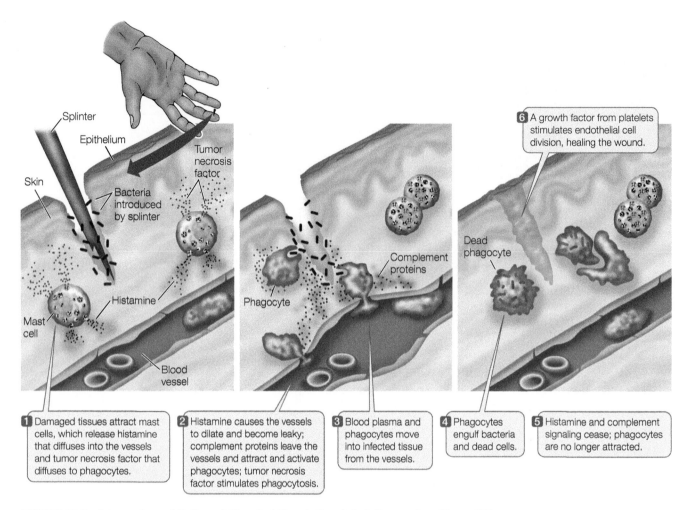

1 Damaged tissues attract mast cells, which release histamine that diffuses into the vessels and tumor necrosis factor that diffuses to phagocytes.

2 Histamine causes the vessels to dilate and become leaky; complement proteins leave the vessels and attract and activate phagocytes; tumor necrosis factor stimulates phagocytosis.

3 Blood plasma and phagocytes move into infected tissue from the vessels.

4 Phagocytes engulf bacteria and dead cells.

5 Histamine and complement signaling cease; phagocytes are no longer attracted.

6 A growth factor from platelets stimulates endothelial cell division, healing the wound.

FIGURE 31.3 Interactions of Cells and Chemical Signals Result in Inflammation (Page 624)

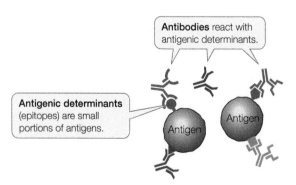

Antibodies react with antigenic determinants.

Antigenic determinants (epitopes) are small portions of antigens.

Antigen

Antigen

IN-TEXT ART (Page 625)

INVESTIGATION

FIGURE 31.4   The Discovery of Specific Immunity   Until the twentieth century, most people did not survive an attack of diphtheria, but a few did. Emil von Behring and Shibasaburo Kitasato performed a key experiment using an animal model. They demonstrated that the factor(s) responsible for immunity against diphtheria was in the blood serum.

HYPOTHESIS

Serum from guinea pigs injected with a sublethal dose of diphtheria toxin protects other guinea pigs that are exposed to a lethal dose of the same toxin.

METHOD

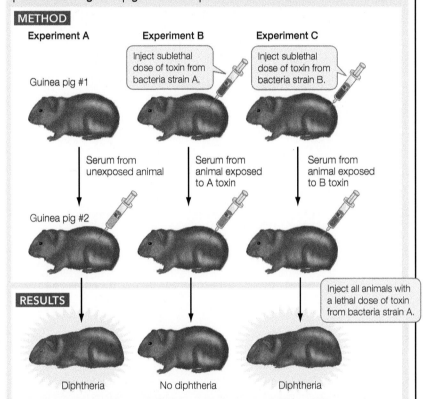

Experiment A   **Experiment B**   **Experiment C**

Inject sublethal dose of toxin from bacteria strain A.

Inject sublethal dose of toxin from bacteria strain B.

Guinea pig #1

Serum from unexposed animal

Serum from animal exposed to A toxin

Serum from animal exposed to B toxin

Guinea pig #2

Inject all animals with a lethal dose of toxin from bacteria strain A.

RESULTS

Diphtheria   No diphtheria   Diphtheria

CONCLUSION

Serum of toxin-exposed guinea pigs is protective against later exposure to a lethal dose of toxin from the same genetic strain of bacteria, but not a different strain.

ANALYZE THE DATA

In their experiments, Behring and Kitasato used different doses of toxin to test the immunity of guinea pig #2 in each experiment. These are the results:

	Symptoms	
Experiment	0.5 ml dose	10 ml dose
A	Diphtheria	Diphtheria
B	No diphtheria	No diphtheria
C	Diphtheria	Diphtheria

A. Explain these data in terms of the level of protection afforded by the serum.

B. These experiments could be performed with either intact bacteria that cause diphtheria, or a bacteria-free filtrate of a 10-day-old culture of the bacteria. Explain.

Go to **yourBioPortal.com** for original citations, discussions, and relevant links for all INVESTIGATION figures.

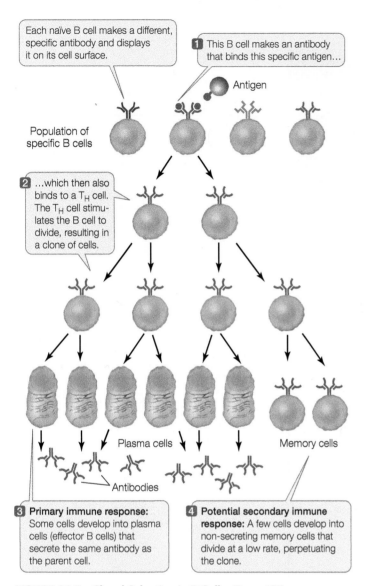

Each naïve B cell makes a different, specific antibody and displays it on its cell surface.

1 This B cell makes an antibody that binds this specific antigen...

Antigen

Population of specific B cells

2 ...which then also binds to a T_H cell. The T_H cell stimulates the B cell to divide, resulting in a clone of cells.

Plasma cells

Memory cells

Antibodies

3 **Primary immune response:** Some cells develop into plasma cells (effector B cells) that secrete the same antibody as the parent cell.

4 **Potential secondary immune response:** A few cells develop into non-secreting memory cells that divide at a low rate, perpetuating the clone.

FIGURE 31.5   Clonal Selection in B Cells *(Page 627)*

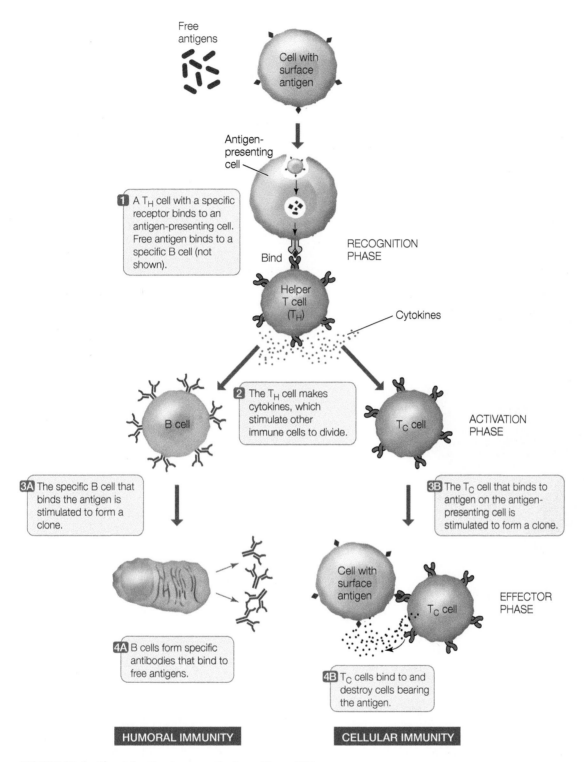

Free
antigens

Cell with
surface
antigen

Antigen-
presenting
cell

1 A T$_H$ cell with a specific
receptor binds to an
antigen-presenting cell.
Free antigen binds to a
specific B cell (not
shown).

Bind

RECOGNITION
PHASE

Helper
T cell
(T$_H$)

Cytokines

B cell

2 The T$_H$ cell makes
cytokines, which
stimulate other
immune cells to divide.

T$_C$ cell

ACTIVATION
PHASE

3A The specific B cell that
binds the antigen is
stimulated to form a
clone.

3B The T$_C$ cell that binds to
antigen on the antigen-
presenting cell is
stimulated to form a clone.

Cell with
surface
antigen

T$_C$ cell

EFFECTOR
PHASE

4A B cells form specific
antibodies that bind to
free antigens.

4B T$_C$ cells bind to and
destroy cells bearing
the antigen.

HUMORAL IMMUNITY

CELLULAR IMMUNITY

FIGURE 31.6   The Adaptive Immune System *(Page 628)*

(A)

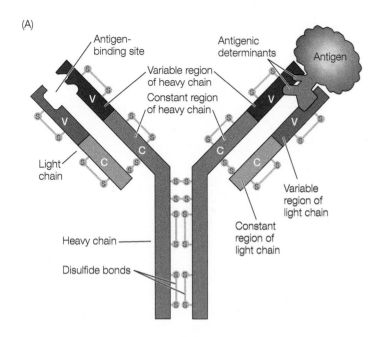

(B)

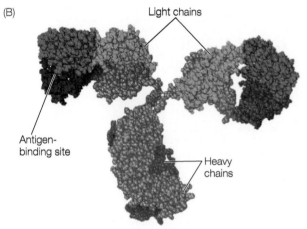

FIGURE 31.7   The Structure of an Immunoglobulin *(Page 630)*

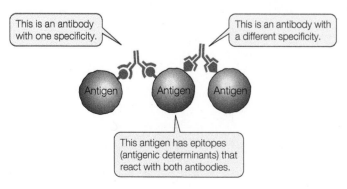

IN-TEXT ART *(Page 630)*

The **variable region** for the heavy chain of a specific antibody is encoded by one *V* gene, one *D* gene, and one *J* gene. Each of these genes is taken from a pool of like genes.

The **constant region** (C) is selected from another pool of genes. The number of possible combinations to make an immunoglobulin heavy chain from these pools of genes is $(100\ V)(30\ D)(6\ J)(8\ C) = 144{,}000$.

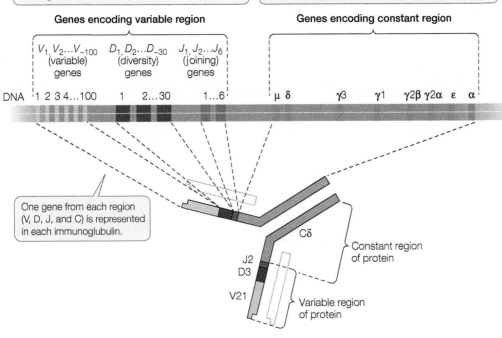

Genes encoding variable region

Genes encoding constant region

$V_1, V_2...V_{\sim100}$ (variable) genes $D_1, D_2...D_{\sim30}$ (diversity) genes $J_1, J_2...J_6$ (joining) genes

DNA   1 2 3 4...100   1   2...30   1...6   μ δ   γ3   γ1   γ2β γ2α ε α

One gene from each region (V, D, J, and C) is represented in each immunoglubulin.

Cδ

Constant region of protein

J2
D3
V21

Variable region of protein

FIGURE 31.8 Heavy-Chain Genes *(Page 631)*

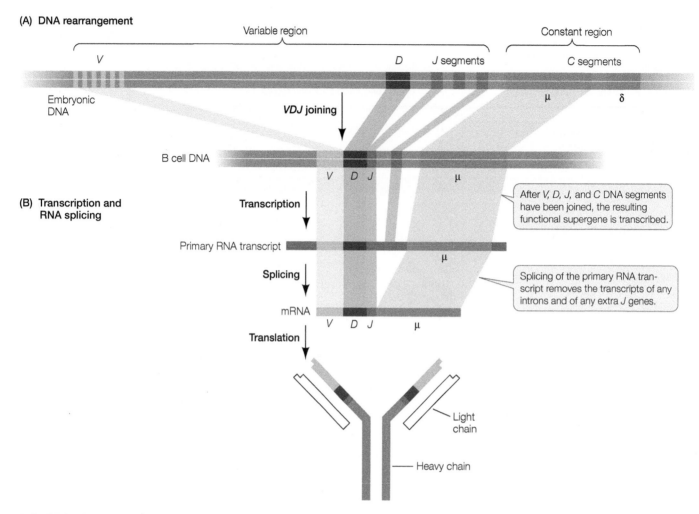

(A) DNA rearrangement

Variable region

Constant region

V

D *J* segments

C segments

Embryonic DNA

VDJ joining

μ δ

B cell DNA

V *D* *J* μ

(B) Transcription and RNA splicing

Transcription

After *V, D, J,* and *C* DNA segments have been joined, the resulting functional supergene is transcribed.

Primary RNA transcript

μ

Splicing

Splicing of the primary RNA transcript removes the transcripts of any introns and of any extra *J* genes.

mRNA

V *D* *J* μ

Translation

Light chain

Heavy chain

FIGURE 31.9 Heavy-Chain Gene Recombination and RNA Splicing *(Page 632)*

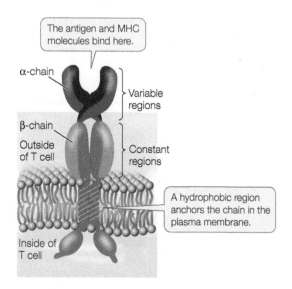

The antigen and MHC molecules bind here.

α-chain

Variable regions

β-chain

Outside of T cell

Constant regions

A hydrophobic region anchors the chain in the plasma membrane.

Inside of T cell

FIGURE 31.10 A T Cell Receptor *(Page 633)*

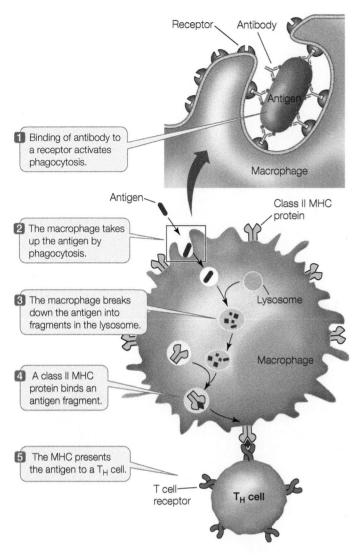

FIGURE 31.11   Macrophages Are Antigen-Presenting Cells
(Page 634)

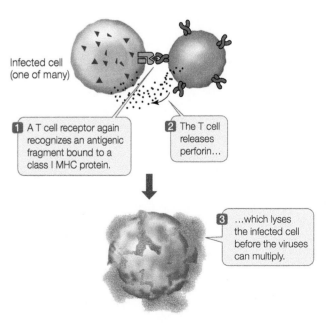

IN-TEXT ART *(Page 634)*

TABLE 31.2	The Interaction between T Cells and Antigen-Presenting Cells		
PRESENTING CELL TYPE	ANTIGEN PRESENTED	MHC CLASS	T CELL TYPE
Any cell	Intracellular protein fragment	Class I	Cytotoxic T cell (T_C)
Macrophages and B cells	Fragments from extracellular proteins	Class II	Helper T cell (T_H)

(Page 635)

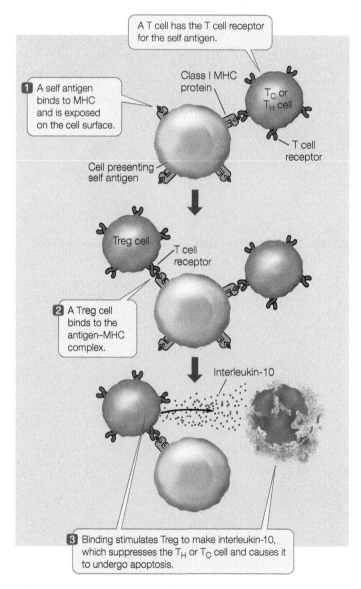

FIGURE 31.12 Tregs and Tolerance *(Page 635)*

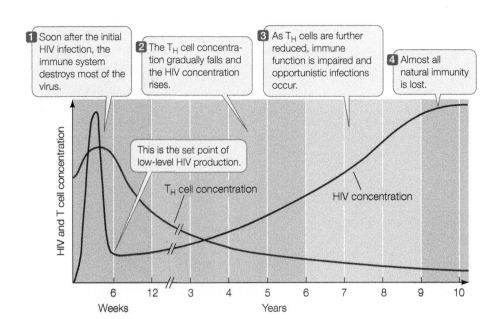

FIGURE 31.13 The Course of an HIV Infection *(Page 636)*

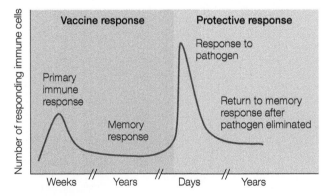

FIGURE 31.14 Vaccination *(Page 637)*

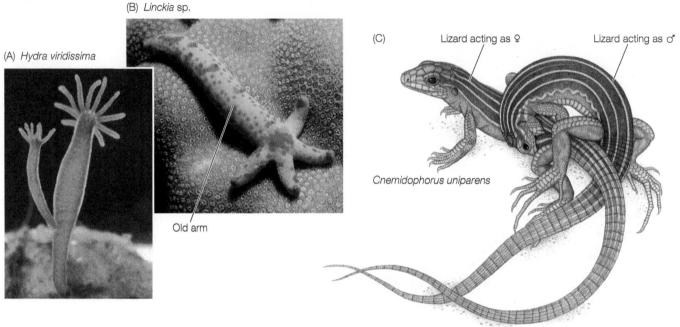

(A) *Hydra viridissima*

(B) *Linckia* sp.

Old arm

(C)

Lizard acting as ♀

Lizard acting as ♂

Cnemidophorus uniparens

FIGURE 32.1 Three Forms of Asexual Reproduction *(Page 639)*

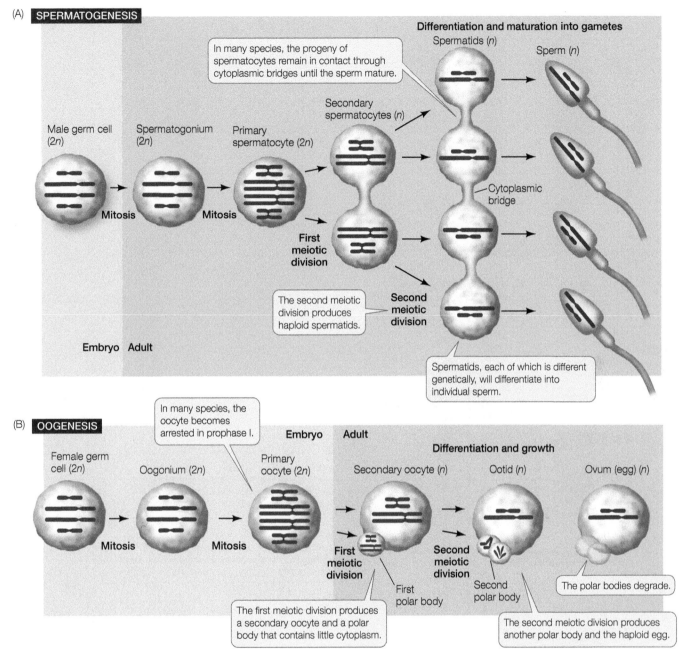

FIGURE 32.2 Gametogenesis *(Page 641)*

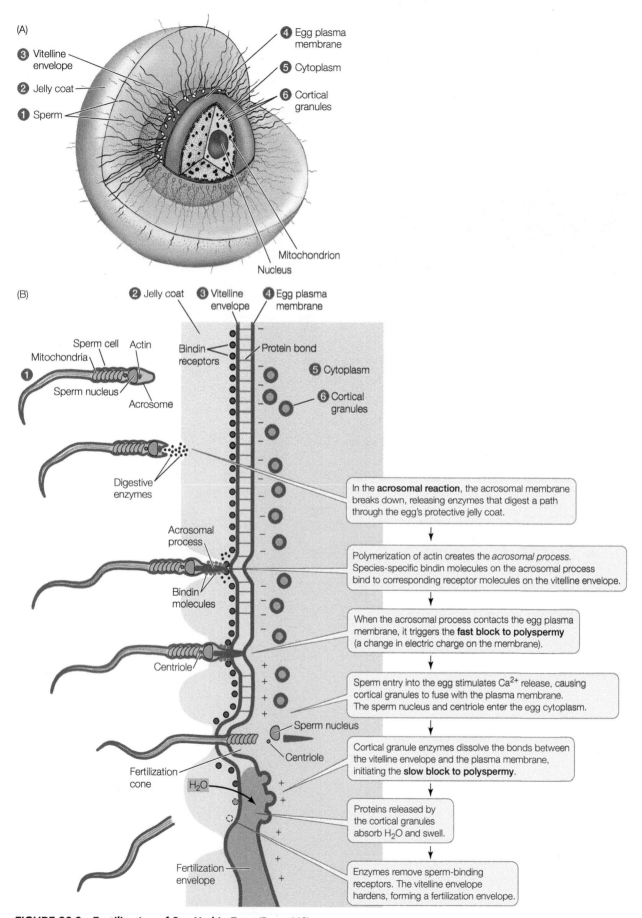

(A)

❸ Vitelline envelope

❷ Jelly coat

❶ Sperm

❹ Egg plasma membrane

❺ Cytoplasm

❻ Cortical granules

Mitochondrion

Nucleus

(B)

❷ Jelly coat ❸ Vitelline envelope ❹ Egg plasma membrane

Sperm cell   Actin

Mitochondria

Sperm nucleus   Acrosome

❶

Bindin receptors

Protein bond

❺ Cytoplasm

❻ Cortical granules

Digestive enzymes

Acrosomal process

Bindin molecules

Centriole

Sperm nucleus

Centriole

Fertilization cone

H_2O

Fertilization envelope

In the **acrosomal reaction**, the acrosomal membrane breaks down, releasing enzymes that digest a path through the egg's protective jelly coat.

Polymerization of actin creates the *acrosomal process*. Species-specific bindin molecules on the acrosomal process bind to corresponding receptor molecules on the vitelline envelope.

When the acrosomal process contacts the egg plasma membrane, it triggers the **fast block to polyspermy** (a change in electric charge on the membrane).

Sperm entry into the egg stimulates Ca^{2+} release, causing cortical granules to fuse with the plasma membrane. The sperm nucleus and centriole enter the egg cytoplasm.

Cortical granule enzymes dissolve the bonds between the vitelline envelope and the plasma membrane, initiating the **slow block to polyspermy**.

Proteins released by the cortical granules absorb H_2O and swell.

Enzymes remove sperm-binding receptors. The vitelline envelope hardens, forming a fertilization envelope.

FIGURE 32.3 Fertilization of Sea Urchin Egg *(Page 643)*

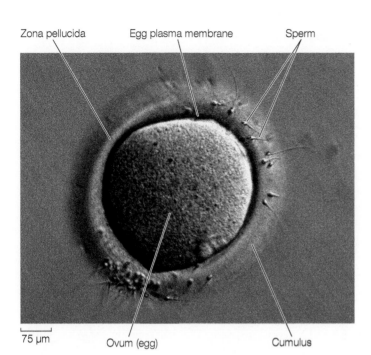

Zona pellucida   Egg plasma membrane   Sperm

75 μm

Ovum (egg)   Cumulus

FIGURE 32.4   Barriers to Mammalian Sperm *(Page 644)*

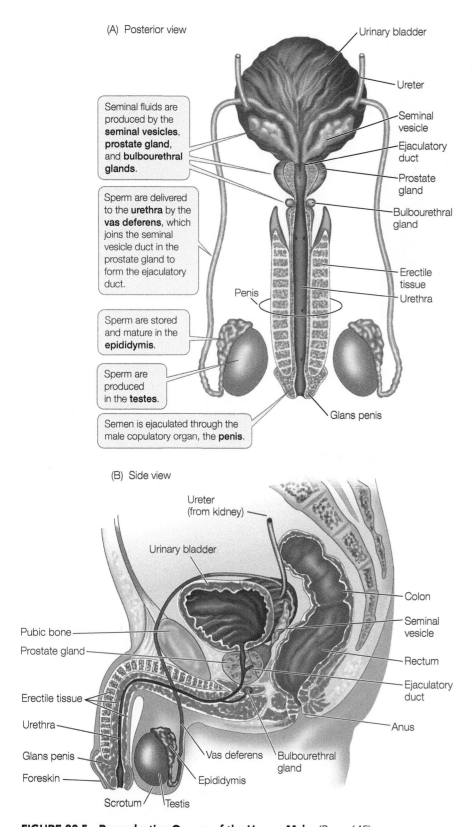

(A) Posterior view

Urinary bladder

Ureter

Seminal fluids are produced by the **seminal vesicles**, **prostate gland**, and **bulbourethral glands**.

Seminal vesicle

Ejaculatory duct

Prostate gland

Sperm are delivered to the **urethra** by the **vas deferens**, which joins the seminal vesicle duct in the prostate gland to form the ejaculatory duct.

Bulbourethral gland

Penis

Erectile tissue

Urethra

Sperm are stored and mature in the **epididymis**.

Sperm are produced in the **testes**.

Semen is ejaculated through the male copulatory organ, the **penis**.

Glans penis

(B) Side view

Ureter (from kidney)

Urinary bladder

Colon

Seminal vesicle

Pubic bone

Prostate gland

Rectum

Ejaculatory duct

Erectile tissue

Urethra

Anus

Glans penis

Foreskin

Vas deferens

Bulbourethral gland

Epididymis

Scrotum

Testis

FIGURE 32.5 Reproductive Organs of the Human Male *(Page 645)*

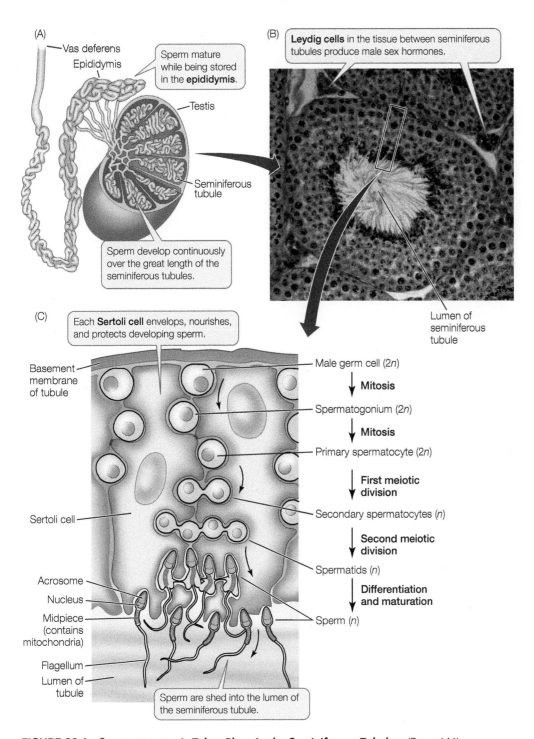

(A)

Vas deferens
Epididymis

Sperm mature while being stored in the **epididymis**.

Testis

Seminiferous tubule

Sperm develop continuously over the great length of the seminiferous tubules.

(B) **Leydig cells** in the tissue between seminiferous tubules produce male sex hormones.

Lumen of seminiferous tubule

(C) Each **Sertoli cell** envelops, nourishes, and protects developing sperm.

Basement membrane of tubule

Sertoli cell

Acrosome
Nucleus
Midpiece (contains mitochondria)
Flagellum
Lumen of tubule

Sperm are shed into the lumen of the seminiferous tubule.

Male germ cell ($2n$)

⬇ **Mitosis**

Spermatogonium ($2n$)

⬇ **Mitosis**

Primary spermatocyte ($2n$)

⬇ **First meiotic division**

Secondary spermatocytes (n)

⬇ **Second meiotic division**

Spermatids (n)

⬇ **Differentiation and maturation**

Sperm (n)

FIGURE 32.6 Spermatogenesis Takes Place in the Seminiferous Tubules *(Page 646)*

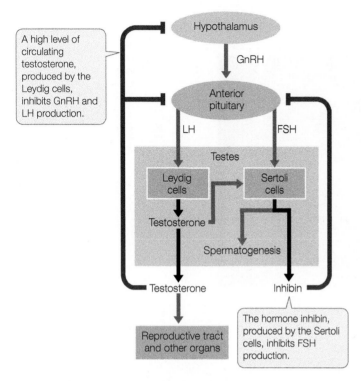

A high level of circulating testosterone, produced by the Leydig cells, inhibits GnRH and LH production.

Hypothalamus

GnRH

Anterior pituitary

LH   FSH

Testes

Leydig cells   Sertoli cells

Testosterone

Spermatogenesis

Testosterone   Inhibin

Reproductive tract and other organs

The hormone inhibin, produced by the Sertoli cells, inhibits FSH production.

FIGURE 32.7   Male Reproductive Hormones *(Page 647)*

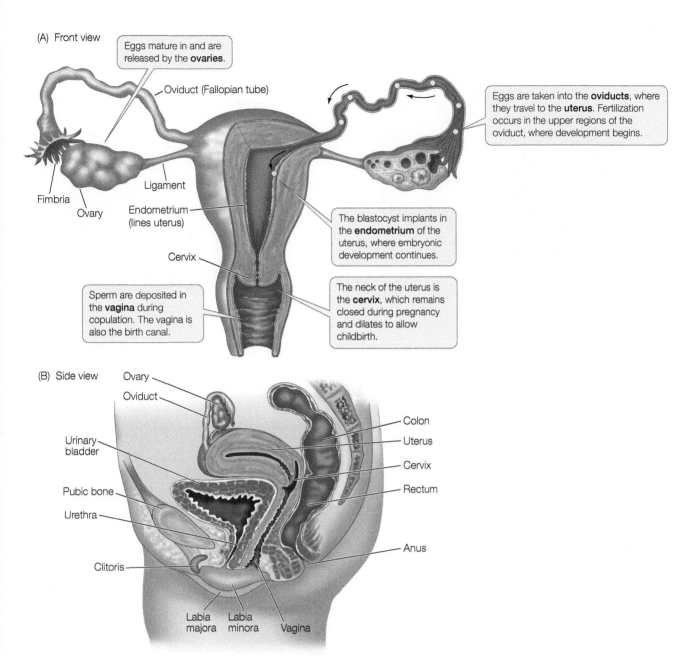

(A) Front view

Eggs mature in and are released by the **ovaries**.

Oviduct (Fallopian tube)

Eggs are taken into the **oviducts**, where they travel to the **uterus**. Fertilization occurs in the upper regions of the oviduct, where development begins.

Fimbria

Ovary

Ligament

Endometrium (lines uterus)

The blastocyst implants in the **endometrium** of the uterus, where embryonic development continues.

Cervix

Sperm are deposited in the **vagina** during copulation. The vagina is also the birth canal.

The neck of the uterus is the **cervix**, which remains closed during pregnancy and dilates to allow childbirth.

(B) Side view

Ovary

Oviduct

Urinary bladder

Pubic bone

Urethra

Clitoris

Labia majora

Labia minora

Vagina

Colon

Uterus

Cervix

Rectum

Anus

FIGURE 32.8 Reproductive Organs of the Human Female (Page 649)

(A)

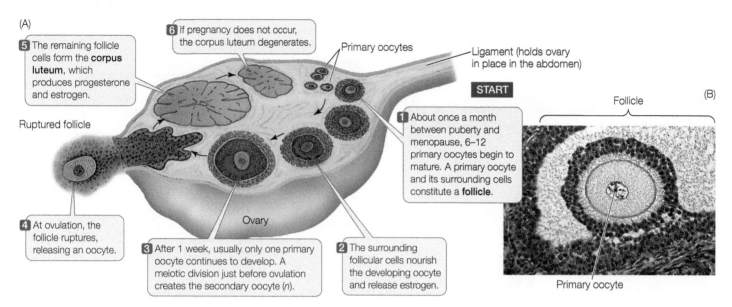

5 The remaining follicle cells form the **corpus luteum**, which produces progesterone and estrogen.

6 If pregnancy does not occur, the corpus luteum degenerates.

Primary oocytes

Ligament (holds ovary in place in the abdomen)

START

Ruptured follicle

4 At ovulation, the follicle ruptures, releasing an oocyte.

Ovary

3 After 1 week, usually only one primary oocyte continues to develop. A meiotic division just before ovulation creates the secondary oocyte (*n*).

2 The surrounding follicular cells nourish the developing oocyte and release estrogen.

1 About once a month between puberty and menopause, 6–12 primary oocytes begin to mature. A primary oocyte and its surrounding cells constitute a **follicle**.

Follicle

(B)

Primary oocyte

FIGURE 32.9 The Ovarian Cycle *(Page 649)*

(A) Gonadotropins (from anterior pituitary)

FSH and LH secretion are under control of GnRH from the hypo-thalamus and the ovarian hormones estrogen and proges-terone (part C).

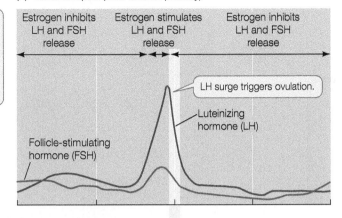

(B) Events in ovary (ovarian cycle)

FSH stimulates the development of follicles; the LH surge causes ovulation and then the development of the corpus luteum.

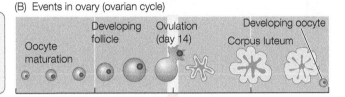

(C) Ovarian hormones and the uterine cycle

Estrogen and proges-terone stimulate the development of the endometrium in preparation for pregnancy.

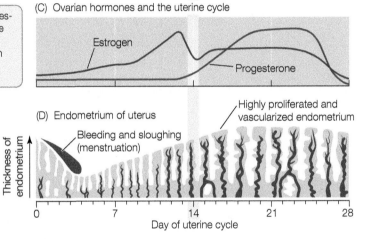

FIGURE 32.10 **The Ovarian and Uterine Cycles** *(Page 650)*

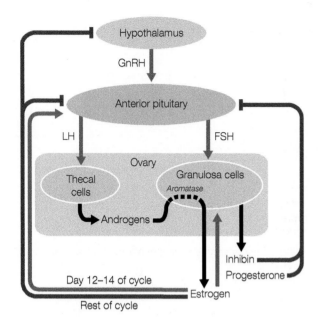

FIGURE 32.11 Hormones Control the Female Reproductive Cycles *(Page 650)*

TABLE 32.1   Methods of Contraception

METHOD	MODE OF ACTION	FAILURE RATE[a]	COMMENTS
Unprotected	No form of birth control	85	High risk of pregnancy, especially for women 15–30.
Nontechnological methods			
Rhythm method	The couple abstains from intercourse between days 10 and 20 of the ovarian cycle (peak fertility).	15–35	High failure rate due to miscalculation and/or variation of individual cycles.
Coitus interruptus	The man withdraws his penis prior to ejaculation with the intention of not depositing sperm into the vagina.	20–40	Requires self-control, especially by the man. Very high failure rate.
Barrier methods[b]			
Condom	A sheath of impermeable material (often latex) is fitted over the erect penis. Semen is trapped in the condom, so no sperm are deposited in the vagina.	15	If fitted correctly, an intact condom can prevent pregnancy and provide protection against sexually transmitted diseases (STDs), including HIV (AIDS).
Spermicidal jellies	Applied inside the vagina, these chemical compounds kill or immobilize sperm.	25	Used alone, spermicidal compounds have a fairly high failure rate.
Diaphragms, cervical caps	Inserted by the woman prior to intercourse, these devices work by blocking the cervix so that sperm cannot pass into the uterus.	10–15	Approximately the same failure rate as condom use by men, but do not protect against STDs. Can be used in conjunction with spermicidal jelly for extra protection.
Hormone-based contraceptives			
Oral hormones ("the pill")	A daily pill for women containing a combination of synthetic estrogens and progesterone (progestin). These hormones mimic pregnancy to the extent that the ovarian cycle and ovulation are suspended. The uterine cycle is allowed to continue by including a week of non-hormone administration every 21–28 days.	0–3	Requires medical consultation and prescription. Taken correctly, oral contraceptives are extremely effective. In the U.S., more than 12 million women use them each year; they are sometimes prescribed to treat menstrual disorders.
Non-orally administered hormones	Making use of same hormonal actions as the pill, these methods include long-acting injections, patches that release hormones transdermally (through the skin), and a hormone-containing vaginal ring.	<1	Same as oral hormones. A slightly lower failure rate because the woman does not have to remember to take a daily pill.
Progestin-only pill	An oral contraceptive meant to be taken within 72 hours after unprotected sex. A high dose of progestin in two pills prevents ovulation in the same manner birth control pills do.	5–40[c]	Not an "abortion pill," this drug will not terminate an existing pregnancy. Currently available to women over 17 without a prescription.
Implantation blockers			
Intrauterine device (IUD)	A medical professional inserts a small plastic or metal device into the uterus. The resulting inflammation reaction (see Chapter 31) releases prostaglandins, which prevent implantation of the fertilized egg.	0.5–5	A highly effective contraceptive, it is the most widely used birth control device in China (and hence the world). With medical monitoring, can remain in place for several years.
Mifepristone (RU-486)	This drug blocks progesterone receptors necessary to maintain the endometrium during implantation and pregnancy.	0.5–6	Prevents implantation when taken up to several days after unprotected intercourse. Can terminate a pregnancy up to the time of the first missed menstrual period. In the U.S., available from specialized providers.
Sterilization			
Vasectomy	The vasa deferentia (see Figure 32.5A) are cut and tied off so that sperm can no longer pass into the urethra. Sperm continue to be produced but are reabsorbed by the man's body. Male hormone levels and sexual responses are not affected.	0–0.15	A simple surgical procedure performed under local anesthetic in a doctor's office. Although it can theoretically be reversed, vasectomy should be considered permanent.
Tubal ligation	The oviducts (see Figure 32.8A) are tied off so that eggs cannot reach the uterus and sperm cannot reach the egg. As with vasectomy, hormone levels and sexual responses are not affected.	0–0.05	This surgical procedure is somewhat more complex than vasectomy. It is often performed in conjunction with childbirth when a woman has decided that her family is complete.

[a] "Failure rate" refers to the number of pregnancies per 100 women per year.

[b] All of these barrier methods are routinely available without medical prescription.

[c] Failure rate varies widely depending on when taken.

(Page 652)

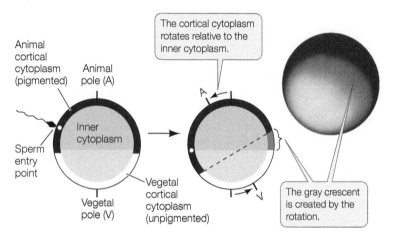

FIGURE 33.1 The Gray Crescent *(Page 656)*

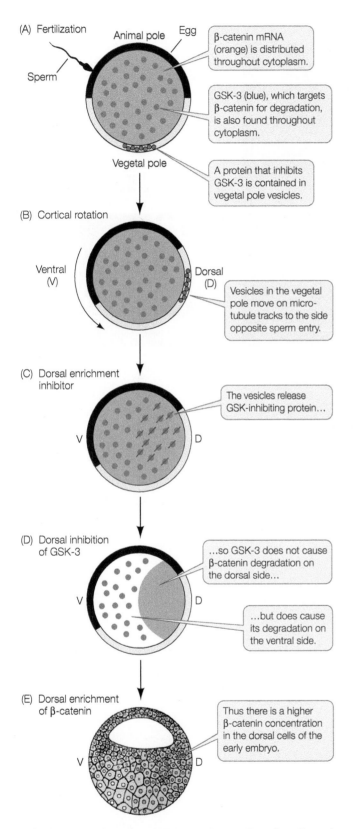

(A) Fertilization

Animal pole

Egg

Sperm

β-catenin mRNA (orange) is distributed throughout cytoplasm.

GSK-3 (blue), which targets β-catenin for degradation, is also found throughout cytoplasm.

Vegetal pole

A protein that inhibits GSK-3 is contained in vegetal pole vesicles.

(B) Cortical rotation

Ventral (V)

Dorsal (D)

Vesicles in the vegetal pole move on micro-tubule tracks to the side opposite sperm entry.

(C) Dorsal enrichment inhibitor

The vesicles release GSK-inhibiting protein...

V

D

(D) Dorsal inhibition of GSK-3

...so GSK-3 does not cause β-catenin degradation on the dorsal side...

V

D

...but does cause its degradation on the ventral side.

(E) Dorsal enrichment of β-catenin

Thus there is a higher β-catenin concentration in the dorsal cells of the early embryo.

V

D

FIGURE 33.2 Cytoplasmic Factors Set Up Signaling Cascades
(Page 657)

(A) Complete cleavage (frog)

Animal pole

Vegetal cells have incorporated yolk and are thus larger than the animal cells in the 16-cell embryo.

The planes of the second cleavage are displaced only slightly by yolk in the cytoplasm.

(B) Incomplete cleavage (zebrafish)

The embryo forms as a blastodisc that sits on top of the yolk mass.

In birds and fishes, cleavage furrows do not penetrate the large yolk mass.

(C) Superficial cleavage (*Drosophila*)

Nucleus

1 Mitosis (nuclear division) occurs without cell division.

3 The nuclei migrate to the inner edge of the plasma membrane.

2 A syncytium—a single cell with many nuclei—is produced.

4 Cellularization occurs, creating a blastoderm.

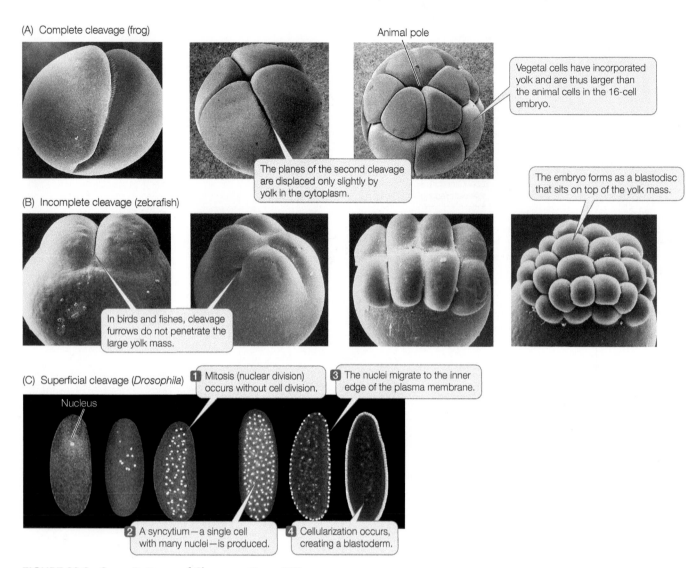

FIGURE 33.3 Some Patterns of Cleavage *(Page 658)*

(A)

The inner cell mass will form the embryo.

Trophoblast (outer cells)

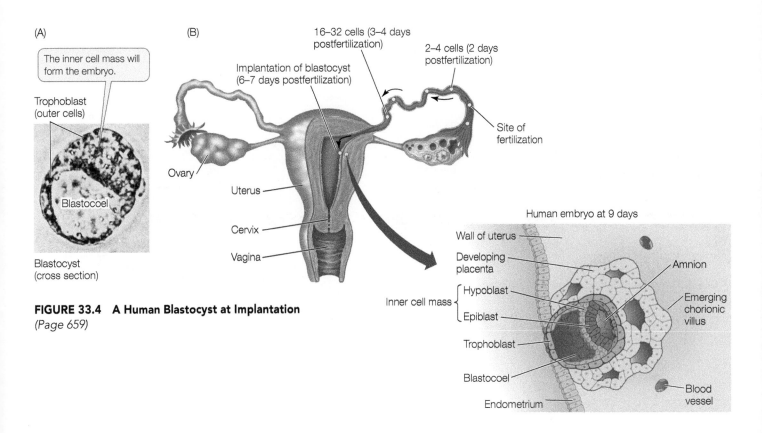

Blastocoel

Blastocyst (cross section)

FIGURE 33.4 A Human Blastocyst at Implantation
(Page 659)

(B)

16–32 cells (3–4 days postfertilization)

2–4 cells (2 days postfertilization)

Implantation of blastocyst (6–7 days postfertilization)

Site of fertilization

Ovary

Uterus

Cervix

Vagina

Human embryo at 9 days

Wall of uterus

Developing placenta

Amnion

Inner cell mass { Hypoblast / Epiblast

Emerging chorionic villus

Trophoblast

Blastocoel

Blood vessel

Endometrium

Animal pole

Ectoderm will form epidermal layer of skin.

The neural ectoderm (midline) will form the nervous system.

The gray crescent is the site where major cell movement will begin (see Figure 33.1).

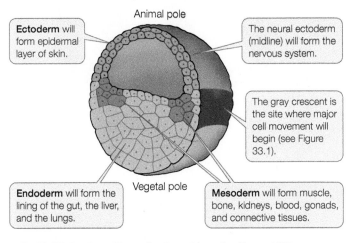

Vegetal pole

Endoderm will form the lining of the gut, the liver, and the lungs.

Mesoderm will form muscle, bone, kidneys, blood, gonads, and connective tissues.

FIGURE 33.5 Fate Map of a Frog Blastula (Page 659)

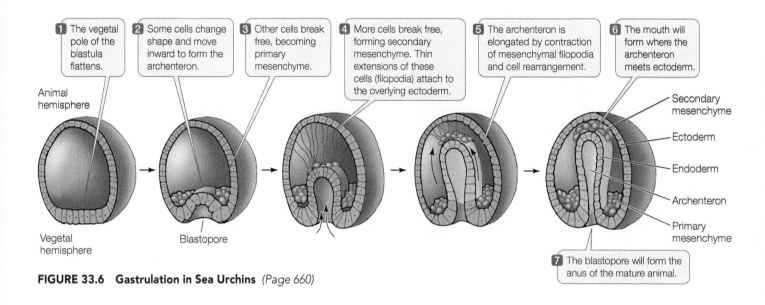

1 The vegetal pole of the blastula flattens.

2 Some cells change shape and move inward to form the archenteron.

3 Other cells break free, becoming primary mesenchyme.

4 More cells break free, forming secondary mesenchyme. Thin extensions of these cells (filopodia) attach to the overlying ectoderm.

5 The archenteron is elongated by contraction of mesenchymal filopodia and cell rearrangement.

6 The mouth will form where the archenteron meets ectoderm.

Animal hemisphere

Vegetal hemisphere

Blastopore

Secondary mesenchyme
Ectoderm
Endoderm
Archenteron
Primary mesenchyme

7 The blastopore will form the anus of the mature animal.

FIGURE 33.6 Gastrulation in Sea Urchins *(Page 660)*

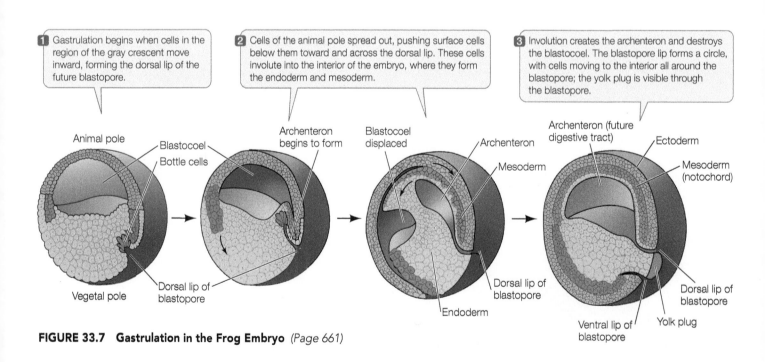

1 Gastrulation begins when cells in the region of the gray crescent move inward, forming the dorsal lip of the future blastopore.

2 Cells of the animal pole spread out, pushing surface cells below them toward and across the dorsal lip. These cells involute into the interior of the embryo, where they form the endoderm and mesoderm.

3 Involution creates the archenteron and destroys the blastocoel. The blastopore lip forms a circle, with cells moving to the interior all around the blastopore; the yolk plug is visible through the blastopore.

Animal pole
Blastocoel
Bottle cells

Archenteron begins to form

Blastocoel displaced
Archenteron
Mesoderm

Archenteron (future digestive tract)
Ectoderm
Mesoderm (notochord)

Vegetal pole

Dorsal lip of blastopore

Dorsal lip of blastopore

Endoderm

Dorsal lip of blastopore

Ventral lip of blastopore
Yolk plug

FIGURE 33.7 Gastrulation in the Frog Embryo *(Page 661)*

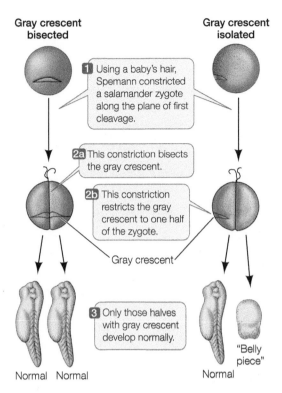

Gray crescent bisected

Gray crescent isolated

1 Using a baby's hair, Spemann constricted a salamander zygote along the plane of first cleavage.

2a This constriction bisects the gray crescent.

2b This constriction restricts the gray crescent to one half of the zygote.

Gray crescent

3 Only those halves with gray crescent develop normally.

"Belly piece"

Normal   Normal

Normal

FIGURE 33.8   Gastrulation and the Gray Crescent
(Page 662)

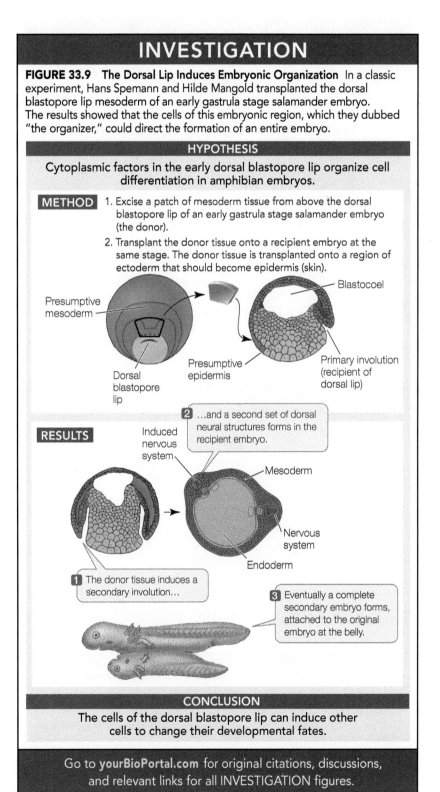

INVESTIGATION

FIGURE 33.9   The Dorsal Lip Induces Embryonic Organization In a classic experiment, Hans Spemann and Hilde Mangold transplanted the dorsal blastopore lip mesoderm of an early gastrula stage salamander embryo. The results showed that the cells of this embryonic region, which they dubbed "the organizer," could direct the formation of an entire embryo.

HYPOTHESIS

Cytoplasmic factors in the early dorsal blastopore lip organize cell differentiation in amphibian embryos.

METHOD
1. Excise a patch of mesoderm tissue from above the dorsal blastopore lip of an early gastrula stage salamander embryo (the donor).
2. Transplant the donor tissue onto a recipient embryo at the same stage. The donor tissue is transplanted onto a region of ectoderm that should become epidermis (skin).

Presumptive mesoderm

Blastocoel

Dorsal blastopore lip

Presumptive epidermis

Primary involution (recipient of dorsal lip)

RESULTS

2 ...and a second set of dorsal neural structures forms in the recipient embryo.

Induced nervous system

Mesoderm

Nervous system

Endoderm

1 The donor tissue induces a secondary involution...

3 Eventually a complete secondary embryo forms, attached to the original embryo at the belly.

CONCLUSION

The cells of the dorsal blastopore lip can induce other cells to change their developmental fates.

Go to **yourBioPortal.com** for original citations, discussions, and relevant links for all INVESTIGATION figures.

INVESTIGATION

FIGURE 33.10 Differentiation Can Be Due to Inhibition of Transcription Factors When organizer cells involute to underlie dorsal ectoderm along the embryo midline, that overlying ectoderm becomes neural tissue rather than skin (epidermis). But do the organizer cells *cause* dorsal ectoderm to become neural tissue, or do they *prevent* this ectoderm from becoming skin?

HYPOTHESIS

The default state of amphibian dorsal ectoderm is neural; it is induced by underlying mesoderm to become epidermis.

METHOD

1. Excise animal caps (presumptive ectoderm) from amphibian blastulas. Culture presumptive mesodermal cells from early gastrulas and extract BMP4. BMP4 is a growth factor released from the notochord that induces overlying ectoderm to become skin.

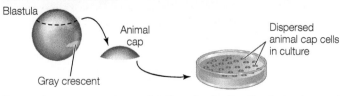

2. Prepare four separate cultures of embryonic ectodermal cells. Incubate with no additions (control); with BMP4 from step 1; with a BMP4 inhibitor; and with both molecules.

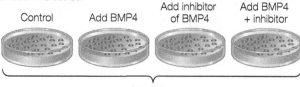

3. After incubation, extract mRNAs from the cultured ectodermal cells and run on gels to reveal expression of NCAM (a neural tissue marker) and keratin (an epidermal tissue marker).

RESULTS

Gels reveal that different treatments with BMP4 and its inhibitor alter patterns of gene expression in cultured ectodermal cells.

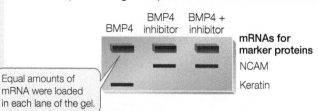

CONCLUSION

The organizer cells secrete an inhibitor of BMP4.

ANALYZE THE DATA

Use the gel results shown above to answer the questions.

A. Does BMP4 induce expression of neural specific or epidermal specific genes?

B. Does BMP4 block any gene expression in the ectodermal cells?

C. What is the evidence that BMP4 has an inductive and/or an inhibitory effect on gene expression in ectodermal cells?

D. Do these results support the hypothesis?

Go to **yourBioPortal.com** for original citations, discussions, and relevant links for all INVESTIGATION figures.

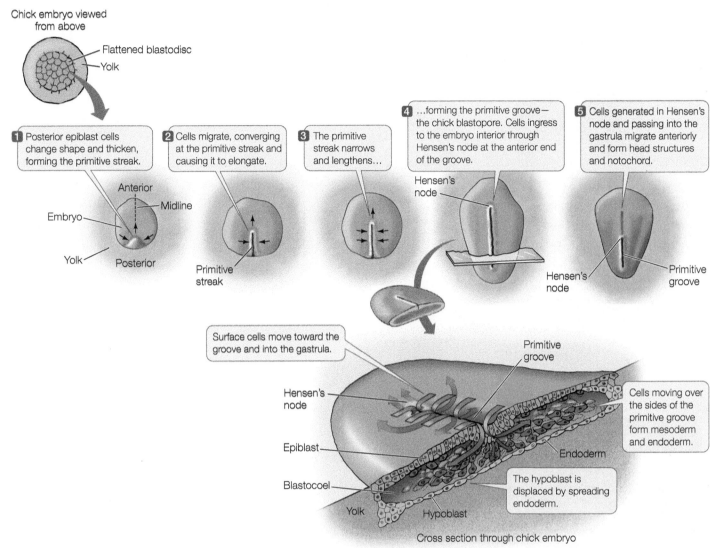

Chick embryo viewed from above

Flattened blastodisc
Yolk

1 Posterior epiblast cells change shape and thicken, forming the primitive streak.

Anterior
Midline
Embryo
Yolk
Posterior

2 Cells migrate, converging at the primitive streak and causing it to elongate.

Primitive streak

3 The primitive streak narrows and lengthens…

4 …forming the primitive groove—the chick blastopore. Cells ingress to the embryo interior through Hensen's node at the anterior end of the groove.

Hensen's node

5 Cells generated in Hensen's node and passing into the gastrula migrate anteriorly and form head structures and notochord.

Hensen's node
Primitive groove

Surface cells move toward the groove and into the gastrula.

Primitive groove

Hensen's node

Cells moving over the sides of the primitive groove form mesoderm and endoderm.

Epiblast

Endoderm

Blastocoel

The hypoblast is displaced by spreading endoderm.

Yolk
Hypoblast

Cross section through chick embryo

FIGURE 33.11 Gastrulation in Birds *(Page 665)*

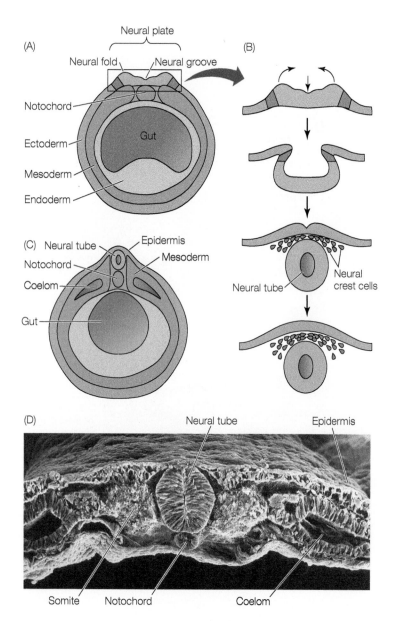

FIGURE 33.12   Neurulation in a Vertebrate *(Page 666)*

(A)

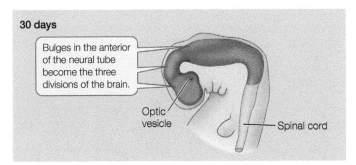

30 days

Bulges in the anterior of the neural tube become the three divisions of the brain.

Optic vesicle

Spinal cord

(B)

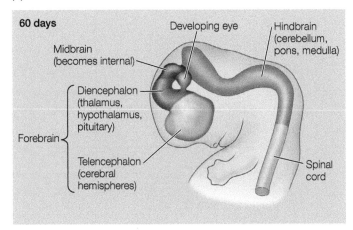

60 days

Developing eye

Hindbrain (cerebellum, pons, medulla)

Midbrain (becomes internal)

Diencephalon (thalamus, hypothalamus, pituitary)

Forebrain

Telencephalon (cerebral hemispheres)

Spinal cord

(C)

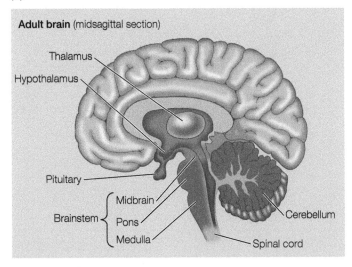

Adult brain (midsagittal section)

Thalamus

Hypothalamus

Pituitary

Brainstem

Midbrain

Pons

Medulla

Cerebellum

Spinal cord

FIGURE 33.13 Development of the Central Nervous System
(Page 667)

(A)

2-day chick embryo

Neural crest

Epidermis

Somites

Neural tube

Notochord

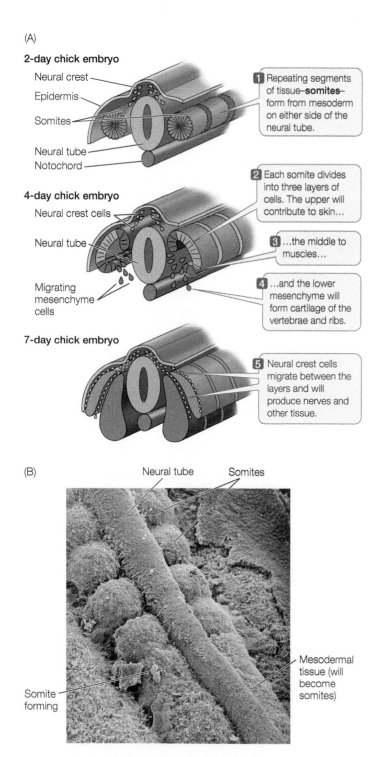

1 Repeating segments of tissue—**somites**—form from mesoderm on either side of the neural tube.

4-day chick embryo

Neural crest cells

Neural tube

Migrating mesenchyme cells

2 Each somite divides into three layers of cells. The upper will contribute to skin...

3 ...the middle to muscles...

4 ...and the lower mesenchyme will form cartilage of the vertebrae and ribs.

7-day chick embryo

5 Neural crest cells migrate between the layers and will produce nerves and other tissue.

(B)

Neural tube   Somites

Somite forming

Mesodermal tissue (will become somites)

FIGURE 33.14 Body Segmentation *(Page 667)*

5-day chick embryo

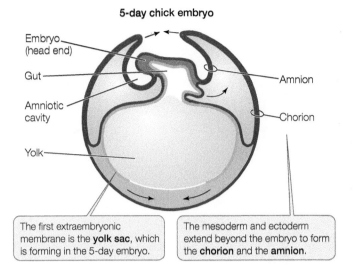

Embryo (head end)

Gut

Amniotic cavity

Yolk

Amnion

Chorion

The first extraembryonic membrane is the **yolk sac**, which is forming in the 5-day embryo.

The mesoderm and ectoderm extend beyond the embryo to form the **chorion** and the **amnion**.

9-day chick embryo

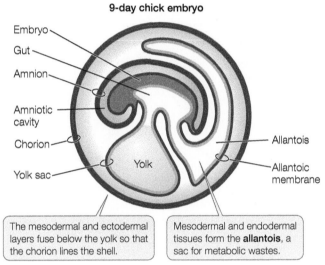

Embryo

Gut

Amnion

Amniotic cavity

Chorion

Yolk sac

Yolk

Allantois

Allantoic membrane

The mesodermal and ectodermal layers fuse below the yolk so that the chorion lines the shell.

Mesodermal and endodermal tissues form the **allantois**, a sac for metabolic wastes.

FIGURE 33.15   The Extraembryonic Membranes of Amniotes (Page 668)

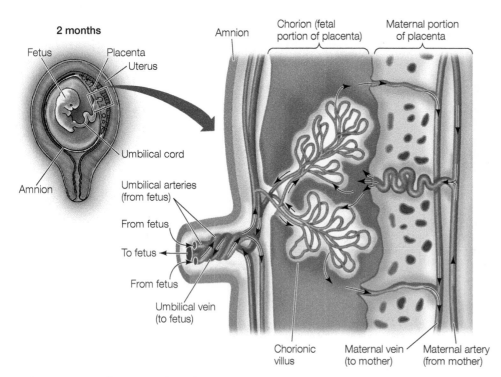

FIGURE 33.16 The Mammalian Placenta *(Page 669)*

FIGURE 33.17 Environmentally Induced Holoprosencephaly *(Page 670)*

Neurons and Nervous Systems

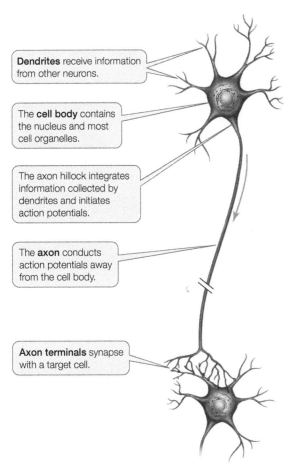

Dendrites receive information from other neurons.

The **cell body** contains the nucleus and most cell organelles.

The axon hillock integrates information collected by dendrites and initiates action potentials.

The **axon** conducts action potentials away from the cell body.

Axon terminals synapse with a target cell.

FIGURE 34.1   A Generalized Neuron *(Page 673)*

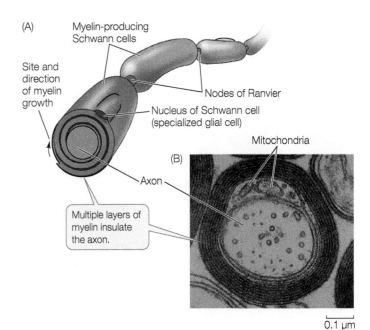

(A)

Myelin-producing Schwann cells

Site and direction of myelin growth

Nodes of Ranvier

Nucleus of Schwann cell (specialized glial cell)

Mitochondria

(B)

Axon

Multiple layers of myelin insulate the axon.

0.1 μm

FIGURE 34.2   Wrapping Up an Axon *(Page 674)*

(A) Sea anemone

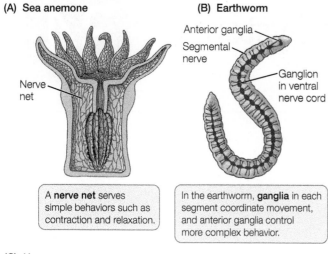

Nerve
net

A **nerve net** serves
simple behaviors such as
contraction and relaxation.

(B) Earthworm

Anterior ganglia

Segmental
nerve

Ganglion
in ventral
nerve cord

In the earthworm, **ganglia** in each
segment coordinate movement,
and anterior ganglia control
more complex behavior.

(C) Human

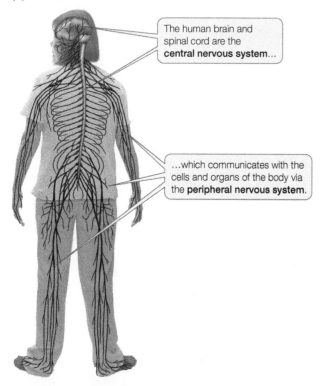

The human brain and
spinal cord are the
central nervous system...

...which communicates with the
cells and organs of the body via
the **peripheral nervous system**.

**FIGURE 34.3   Nervous Systems Vary in
Size and Complexity** *(Page 674)*

RESEARCH TOOLS

FIGURE 34.4 Measuring the Membrane Potential
An electrode can be made from a glass pipette with a very sharp tip filled with a solution that conducts electric charges. If one electrode is placed inside the plasma membrane of an axon and another is placed just outside the axon, the difference in voltage can be measured.

1 An electrode made from a glass pipette (pulled to a sharp tip and open at the end) is filled with an electrically conducting solution…

Outside axon

Inside axon

Plasma membrane

Axon

2 …and connected with a wire to an amplifier.

3 The voltage difference between an electrode placed inside the axon and a reference electrode outside the axon is detected…

Outside axon
+ + + + + + + + + +
– – – – – – – – – –
Inside axon
– – – – – – – – – –
+ + + + + + + + + +
Outside axon

Amplifier

4 …and this small potential difference displayed on a computer screen.

mV

0

–60

Time →

5 In an unstimulated neuron, the constant difference of –60 mV between outside and inside is the **resting potential**.

(Page 675)

(A) Na$^+$–K$^+$ pump (ATPase)

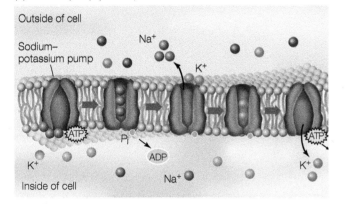

(B) Na$^+$–K$^+$ channels

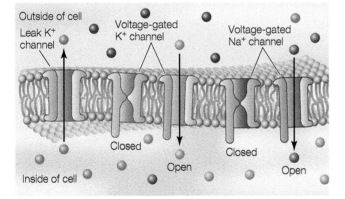

FIGURE 34.5 Ion Transporters and Channels (Page 676)

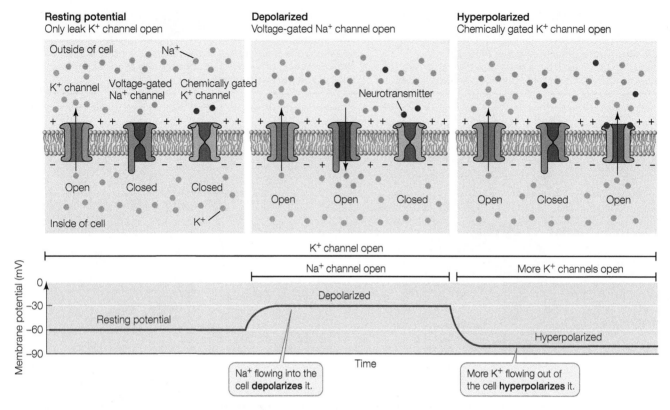

Resting potential
Only leak K⁺ channel open

Outside of cell
Na⁺
K⁺ channel   Voltage-gated   Chemically gated
Na⁺ channel   K⁺ channel
+ + + + +
Open   Closed   Closed
Inside of cell   K⁺

Depolarized
Voltage-gated Na⁺ channel open

Neurotransmitter
+ + + +
+ + +
Open   Open   Closed

Hyperpolarized
Chemically gated K⁺ channel open

+ + + + +
Open   Closed   Open

K⁺ channel open

Na⁺ channel open

More K⁺ channels open

Membrane potential (mV)

0
−30
−60
−90

Resting potential

Depolarized

Hyperpolarized

Time

Na⁺ flowing into the cell **depolarizes** it.

More K⁺ flowing out of the cell **hyperpolarizes** it.

FIGURE 34.6   Membranes Can Be Depolarized or Hyperpolarized *(Page 678)*

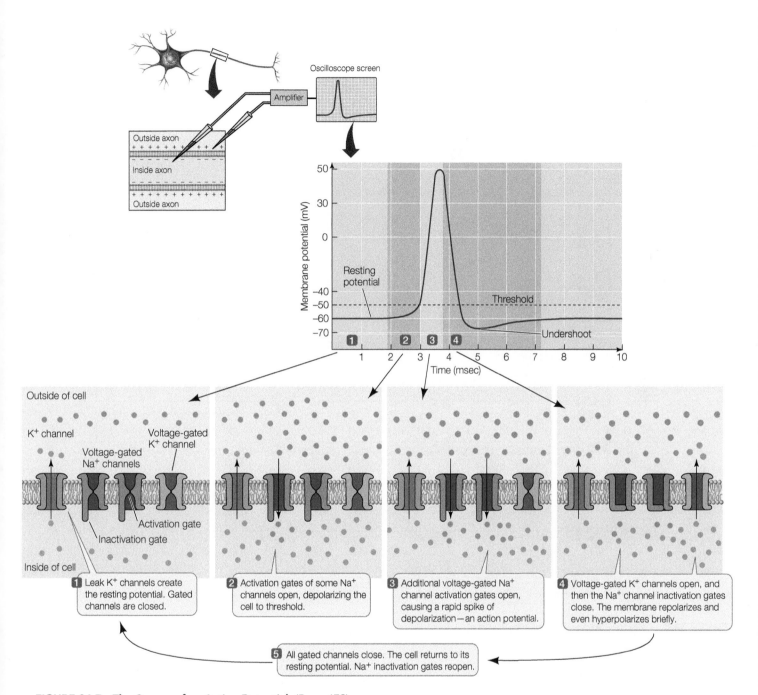

FIGURE 34.7 The Course of an Action Potential *(Page 679)*

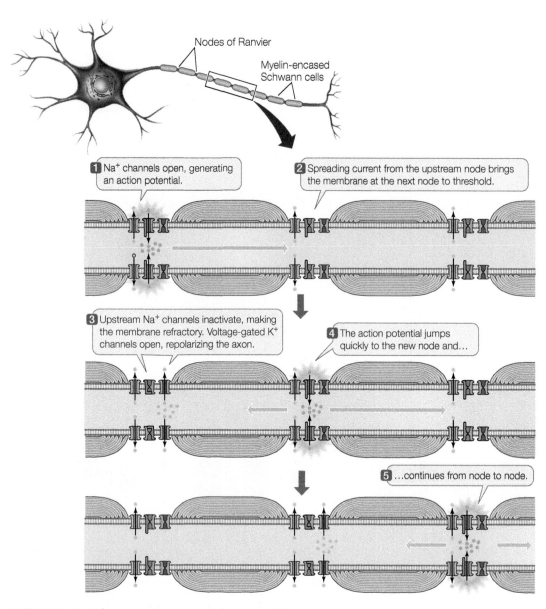

Nodes of Ranvier

Myelin-encased
Schwann cells

1 Na⁺ channels open, generating an action potential.

2 Spreading current from the upstream node brings the membrane at the next node to threshold.

3 Upstream Na⁺ channels inactivate, making the membrane refractory. Voltage-gated K⁺ channels open, repolarizing the axon.

4 The action potential jumps quickly to the new node and...

5 ...continues from node to node.

FIGURE 34.8 Saltatory Action Potentials *(Page 680)*

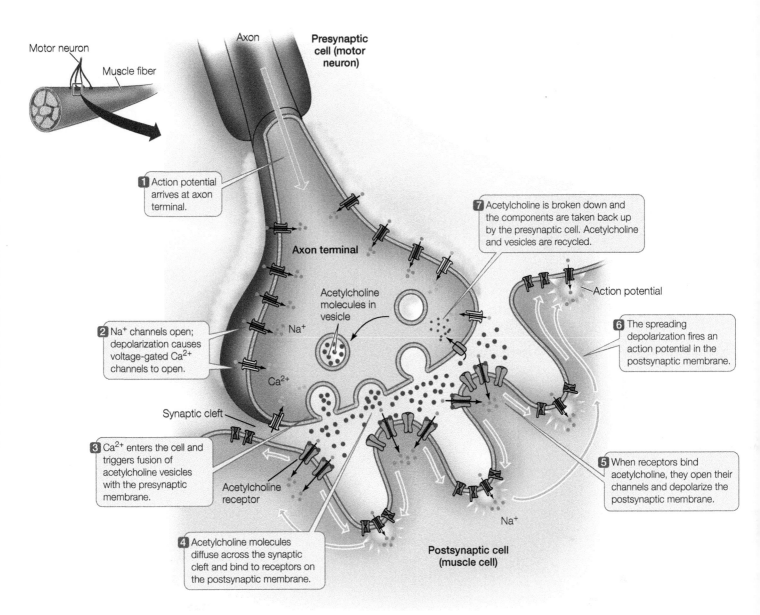

FIGURE 34.9 Chemical Synaptic Transmission *(Page 681)*

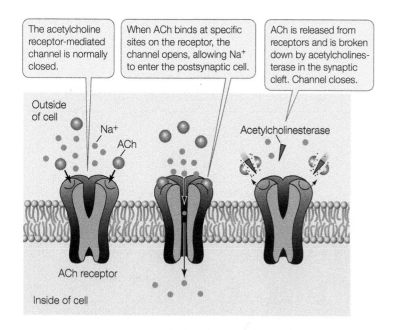

The acetylcholine receptor-mediated channel is normally closed.

When ACh binds at specific sites on the receptor, the channel opens, allowing Na$^+$ to enter the postsynaptic cell.

ACh is released from receptors and is broken down by acetylcholinesterase in the synaptic cleft. Channel closes.

Outside of cell

Na$^+$

ACh

Acetylcholinesterase

ACh receptor

Inside of cell

FIGURE 34.10   Chemically Gated Channels *(Page 682)*

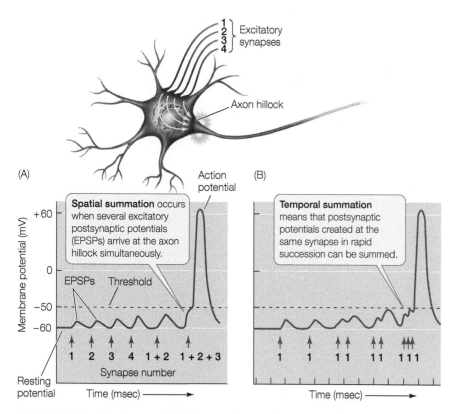

1
2   Excitatory
3   synapses
4

Axon hillock

(A)

Action potential

(B)

Membrane potential (mV)

+60

0

−50

−60

Spatial summation occurs when several excitatory postsynaptic potentials (EPSPs) arrive at the axon hillock simultaneously.

EPSPs   Threshold

1   2   3   4   1 + 2   1 + 2 + 3

Synapse number

Resting potential

Time (msec) ⟶

Temporal summation means that postsynaptic potentials created at the same synapse in rapid succession can be summed.

1   1   1 1   1 1   1 1 1

Time (msec) ⟶

FIGURE 34.11   The Postsynaptic Neuron Sums Information *(Page 683)*

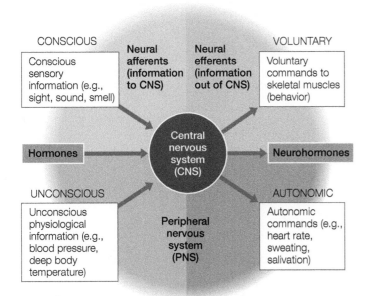

FIGURE 34.12   Organization of the Nervous System *(Page 685)*

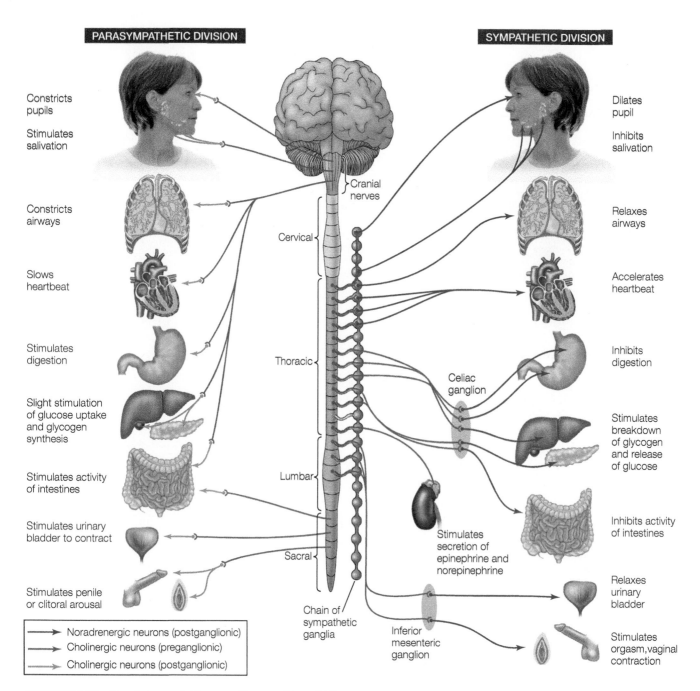

PARASYMPATHETIC DIVISION

SYMPATHETIC DIVISION

Constricts
pupils

Stimulates
salivation

Constricts
airways

Slows
heartbeat

Stimulates
digestion

Slight stimulation
of glucose uptake
and glycogen
synthesis

Stimulates activity
of intestines

Stimulates urinary
bladder to contract

Stimulates penile
or clitoral arousal

Cranial
nerves

Cervical

Thoracic

Lumbar

Sacral

Chain of
sympathetic
ganglia

Celiac
ganglion

Stimulates
secretion of
epinephrine and
norepinephrine

Inferior
mesenteric
ganglion

Dilates
pupil

Inhibits
salivation

Relaxes
airways

Accelerates
heartbeat

Inhibits
digestion

Stimulates
breakdown
of glycogen
and release
of glucose

Inhibits activity
of intestines

Relaxes
urinary
bladder

Stimulates
orgasm, vaginal
contraction

→ Noradrenergic neurons (postganglionic)
→ Cholinergic neurons (preganglionic)
→ Cholinergic neurons (postganglionic)

FIGURE 34.13 The Autonomic Nervous System *(Page 686)*

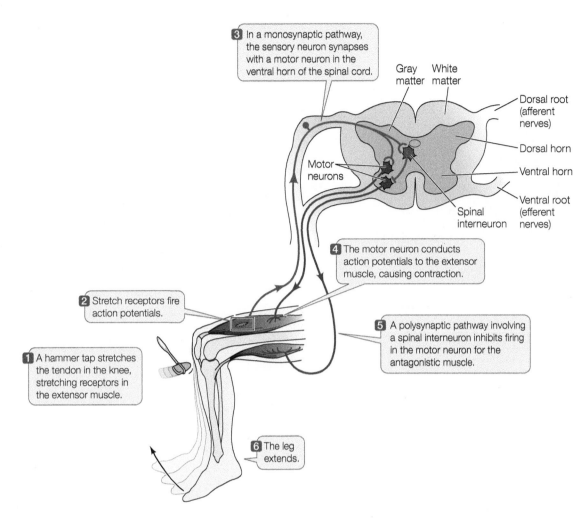

FIGURE 34.14   The Spinal Cord Coordinates the Knee-jerk Reflex *(Page 687)*

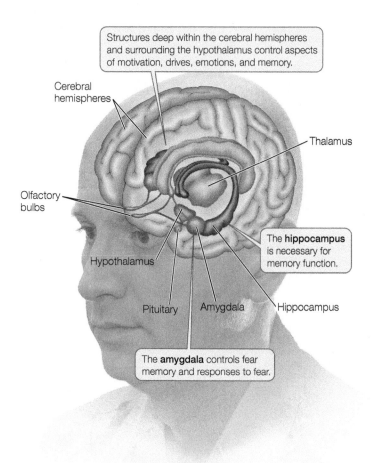

Structures deep within the cerebral hemispheres and surrounding the hypothalamus control aspects of motivation, drives, emotions, and memory.

Cerebral hemispheres

Thalamus

Olfactory bulbs

The **hippocampus** is necessary for memory function.

Hypothalamus

Pituitary   Amygdala   Hippocampus

The **amygdala** controls fear memory and responses to fear.

FIGURE 34.15 The Limbic System *(Page 688)*

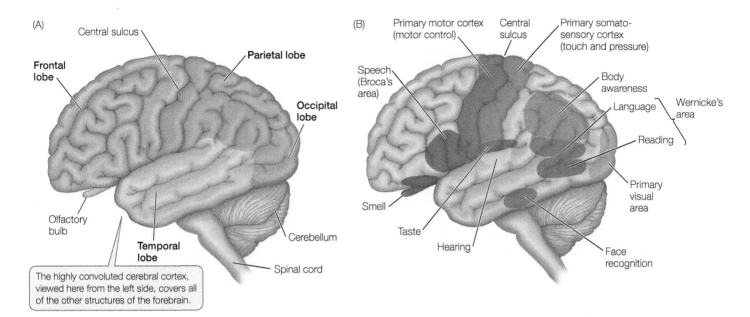

FIGURE 34.16 The Human Cerebrum *(Page 688)*

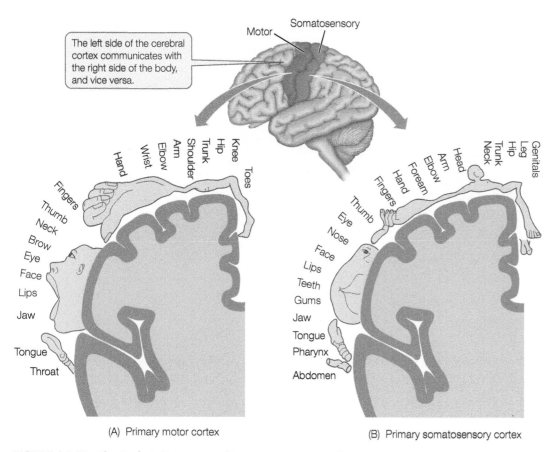

FIGURE 34.17 **The Body Is Represented in Primary Motor and Primary Somatosensory Cortexes** (Page 689)

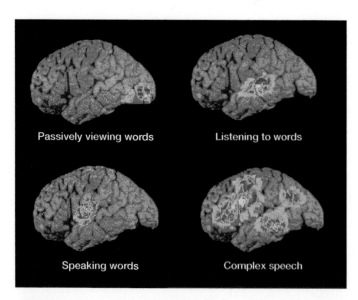

FIGURE 34.18 **Imaging Techniques Reveal Active Parts of the Brain** (Page 690)

(A)

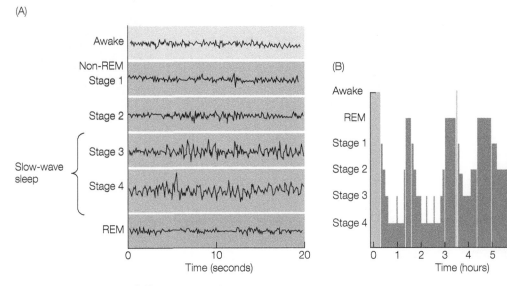

(B)

Figure 34.19 **Stages of Sleep** *(Page 692)*

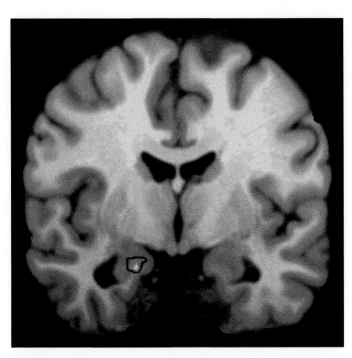

FIGURE 34.20 Source of the Fear Response *(Page 693)*

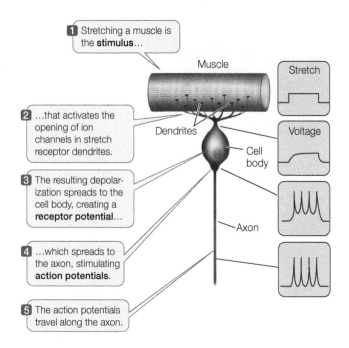

FIGURE 35.1   Stimulating a Sensory Cell Produces a Receptor Potential *(Page 696)*

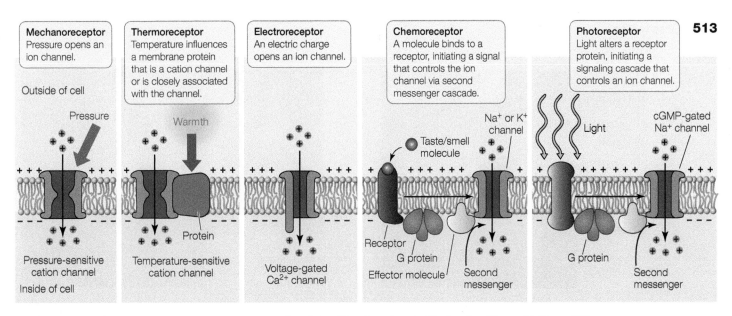

Mechanoreceptor
Pressure opens an ion channel.

Outside of cell

Pressure

Pressure-sensitive cation channel

Inside of cell

Thermoreceptor
Temperature influences a membrane protein that is a cation channel or is closely associated with the channel.

Warmth

Protein

Temperature-sensitive cation channel

Electroreceptor
An electric charge opens an ion channel.

Voltage-gated Ca^{2+} channel

Chemoreceptor
A molecule binds to a receptor, initiating a signal that controls the ion channel via second messenger cascade.

Taste/smell molecule

Na^+ or K^+ channel

Receptor

G protein

Effector molecule

Second messenger

Photoreceptor
Light alters a receptor protein, initiating a signaling cascade that controls an ion channel.

Light

cGMP-gated Na^+ channel

G protein

Second messenger

FIGURE 35.2 Sensory Receptor Proteins Respond to Stimuli by Opening or Closing Ion Channels *(Page 697)*

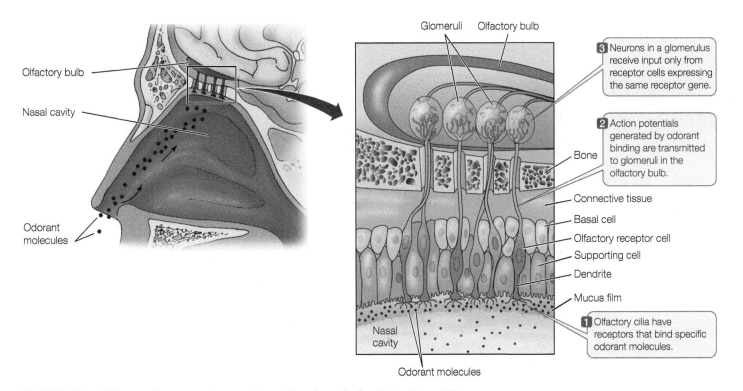

Olfactory bulb

Nasal cavity

Odorant molecules

Glomeruli   Olfactory bulb

3 Neurons in a glomerulus receive input only from receptor cells expressing the same receptor gene.

2 Action potentials generated by odorant binding are transmitted to glomeruli in the olfactory bulb.

Bone

Connective tissue

Basal cell

Olfactory receptor cell

Supporting cell

Dendrite

Mucus film

1 Olfactory cilia have receptors that bind specific odorant molecules.

Nasal cavity

Odorant molecules

FIGURE 35.3 Olfactory Receptors Communicate Directly with the Brain *(Page 698)*

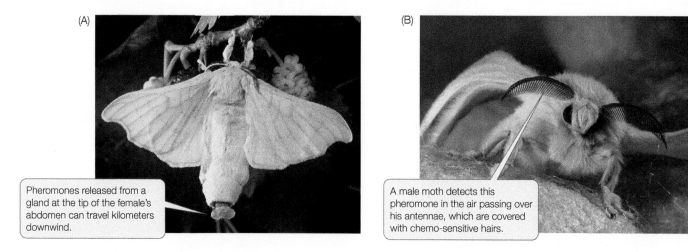

(A) Pheromones released from a gland at the tip of the female's abdomen can travel kilometers downwind.

(B) A male moth detects this pheromone in the air passing over his antennae, which are covered with chemo-sensitive hairs.

FIGURE 35.4   Some Scents Travel Great Distances *(Page 699)*

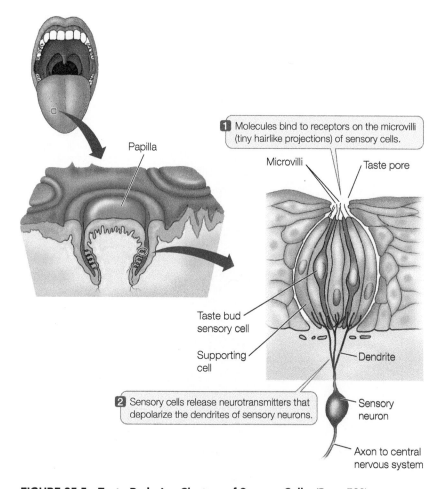

Papilla

1 Molecules bind to receptors on the microvilli (tiny hairlike projections) of sensory cells.

Microvilli

Taste pore

Taste bud sensory cell

Supporting cell

Dendrite

2 Sensory cells release neurotransmitters that depolarize the dendrites of sensory neurons.

Sensory neuron

Axon to central nervous system

FIGURE 35.5   Taste Buds Are Clusters of Sensory Cells *(Page 700)*

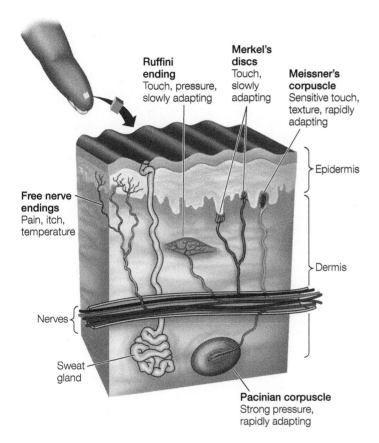

Free nerve endings
Pain, itch, temperature

Ruffini ending
Touch, pressure, slowly adapting

Merkel's discs
Touch, slowly adapting

Meissner's corpuscle
Sensitive touch, texture, rapidly adapting

Epidermis

Dermis

Nerves

Sweat gland

Pacinian corpuscle
Strong pressure, rapidly adapting

FIGURE 35.6 The Skin Feels Many Sensations *(Page 701)*

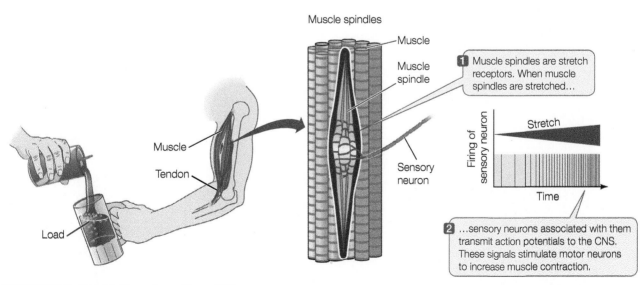

Muscle spindles

Muscle

Muscle spindle

Muscle

Tendon

Load

Sensory neuron

1 Muscle spindles are stretch receptors. When muscle spindles are stretched…

Stretch

Firing of sensory neuron

Time

2 …sensory neurons associated with them transmit action potentials to the CNS. These signals stimulate motor neurons to increase muscle contraction.

FIGURE 35.7 Stretch Receptors *(Page 701)*

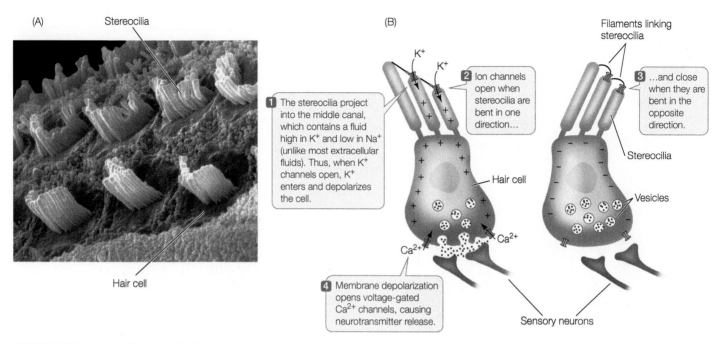

FIGURE 35.8 Hair Cells Have Mechanosensors on Their Stereocilia *(Page 702)*

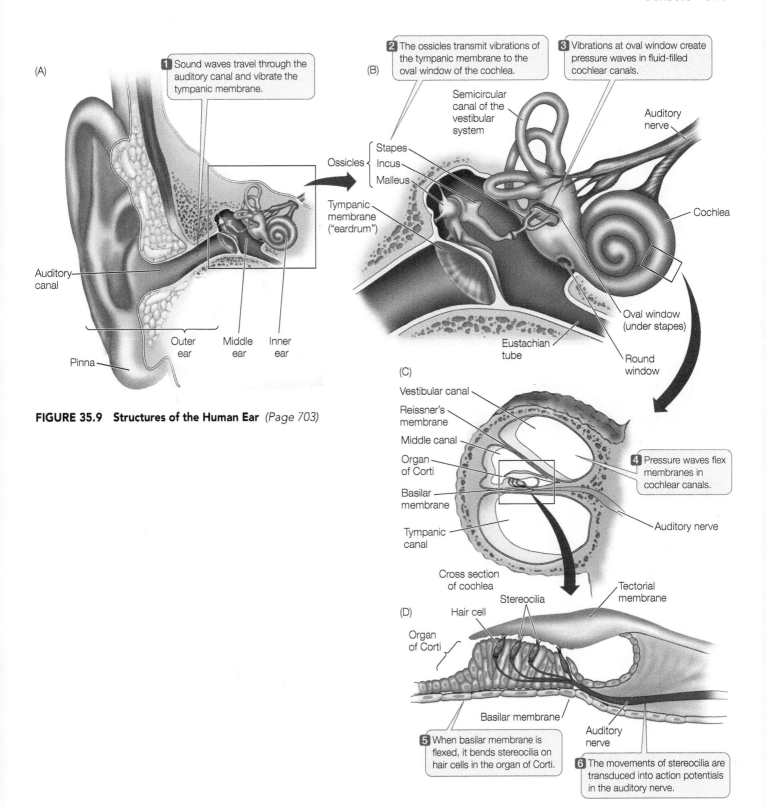

FIGURE 35.9 Structures of the Human Ear *(Page 703)*

(A)

1 Sound waves travel through the auditory canal and vibrate the tympanic membrane.

Auditory canal

Pinna

Outer ear

Middle ear

Inner ear

(B)

2 The ossicles transmit vibrations of the tympanic membrane to the oval window of the cochlea.

3 Vibrations at oval window create pressure waves in fluid-filled cochlear canals.

Semicircular canal of the vestibular system

Auditory nerve

Ossicles

Stapes

Incus

Malleus

Tympanic membrane ("eardrum")

Cochlea

Oval window (under stapes)

Eustachian tube

Round window

(C)

Vestibular canal

Reissner's membrane

Middle canal

Organ of Corti

Basilar membrane

Tympanic canal

4 Pressure waves flex membranes in cochlear canals.

Auditory nerve

Cross section of cochlea

(D)

Organ of Corti

Hair cell

Stereocilia

Tectorial membrane

Basilar membrane

Auditory nerve

5 When basilar membrane is flexed, it bends stereocilia on hair cells in the organ of Corti.

6 The movements of stereocilia are transduced into action potentials in the auditory nerve.

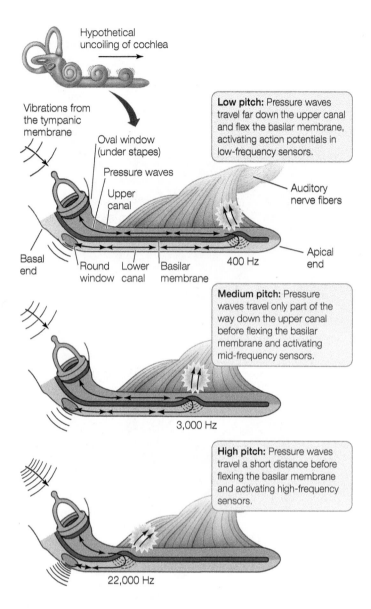

Hypothetical uncoiling of cochlea

Vibrations from the tympanic membrane

Oval window (under stapes)

Pressure waves

Upper canal

Low pitch: Pressure waves travel far down the upper canal and flex the basilar membrane, activating action potentials in low-frequency sensors.

Auditory nerve fibers

Basal end

Round window

Lower canal

Basilar membrane

400 Hz

Apical end

Medium pitch: Pressure waves travel only part of the way down the upper canal before flexing the basilar membrane and activating mid-frequency sensors.

3,000 Hz

High pitch: Pressure waves travel a short distance before flexing the basilar membrane and activating high-frequency sensors.

22,000 Hz

FIGURE 35.10 Sensing Pressure Waves in the Inner Ear *(Page 704)*

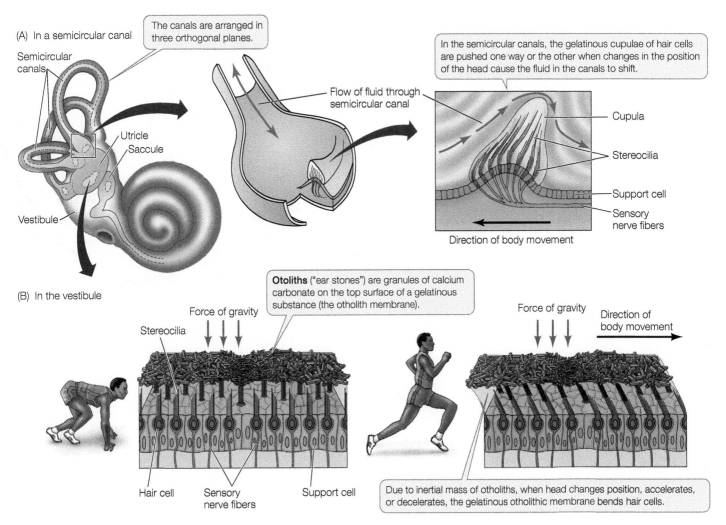

(A) In a semicircular canal

The canals are arranged in three orthogonal planes.

Semicircular canals

Utricle
Saccule

Vestibule

Flow of fluid through semicircular canal

In the semicircular canals, the gelatinous cupulae of hair cells are pushed one way or the other when changes in the position of the head cause the fluid in the canals to shift.

Cupula

Stereocilia

Support cell
Sensory nerve fibers

Direction of body movement

(B) In the vestibule

Stereocilia

Force of gravity

Otoliths ("ear stones") are granules of calcium carbonate on the top surface of a gelatinous substance (the otolith membrane).

Force of gravity

Direction of body movement

Hair cell

Sensory nerve fibers

Support cell

Due to inertial mass of otoliths, when head changes position, accelerates, or decelerates, the gelatinous otolithic membrane bends hair cells.

FIGURE 35.11 Organs of Equilibrium *(Page 705)*

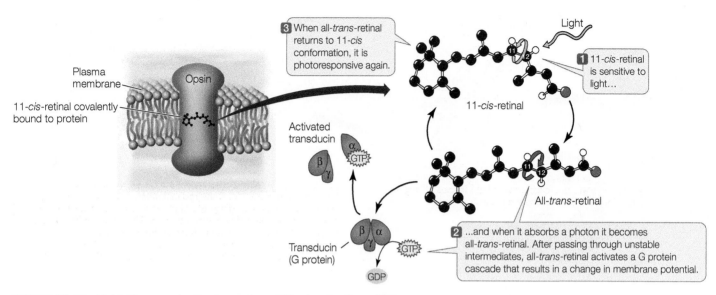

Plasma membrane

11-*cis*-retinal covalently bound to protein

Opsin

Activated transducin

Transducin (G protein)

3 When all-*trans*-retinal returns to 11-*cis* conformation, it is photoresponsive again.

Light

1 11-*cis*-retinal is sensitive to light…

11-*cis*-retinal

All-*trans*-retinal

2 …and when it absorbs a photon it becomes all-*trans*-retinal. After passing through unstable intermediates, all-*trans*-retinal activates a G protein cascade that results in a change in membrane potential.

FIGURE 35.12 Light Changes the Conformation of Rhodopsin *(Page 706)*

INVESTIGATION

FIGURE 35.13 A Rod Cell Responds to Light   The plasma membrane of a rod cell hyperpolarizes—becomes more negative—in response to a flash of light. Rod cells do not fire action potentials, but in response to the absorption of light energy, the neuron experiences a change in membrane potential.

HYPOTHESIS

When a rod cell absorbs photons (light energy), its membrane potential changes in proportion to the strength of the light stimulus.

METHOD

1. Record membrane potentials from the inner segment of a rod cell.
2. Stimulate the rod cells with light flashes of varying intensity and record the results.

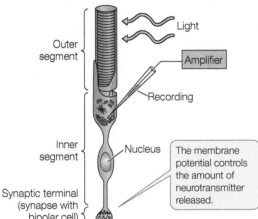

Outer segment

Light

Amplifier

Recording

Inner segment

Nucleus

The membrane potential controls the amount of neurotransmitter released.

Synaptic terminal (synapse with bipolar cell)

RESULTS

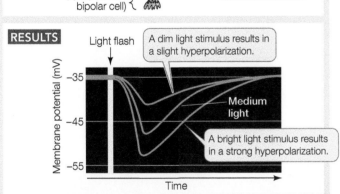

Light flash

A dim light stimulus results in a slight hyperpolarization.

Medium light

A bright light stimulus results in a strong hyperpolarization.

Membrane potential (mV)

Time

CONCLUSION

The membrane potential of rod cells is depolarized in the dark and hyperpolarizes (becomes more negative) in response to light.

ANALYZE THE DATA

In related experiments, researchers measured the effect of light on the current across the rod cell membrane. The figure shows a series of recordings of membrane currents (inward currents of positive ions) in rod cells when they are illuminated with lights of varying intensities. The initial values on the graph represent the condition of the cell when it is in total darkness. The light flash is given at time 0, and the intensity of the flashes is indicated on the right side of the response curves.

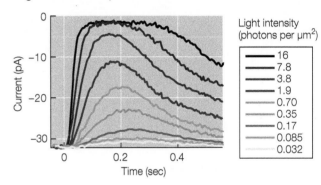

Light intensity (photons per μm²)

	16
	7.8
	3.8
	1.9
	0.70
	0.35
	0.17
	0.085
	0.032

A. If instead of an inward current, you measured membrane potential, how would the resulting recordings differ from this one?

B. Why is there no difference between the currents induced by flashes of light at 7.8 and 16 photons per square micrometer?

C. Why does a rod maintain its minimum current for longer in response to a flash of light at 16 photons per square micrometer than it does to one at 7.8 photons per square micrometer?

For more, go to Working with Data 35.1 at **yourBioPortal.com**.

Go to **yourBioPortal.com** for original citations, discussions, and relevant links for all INVESTIGATION figures.

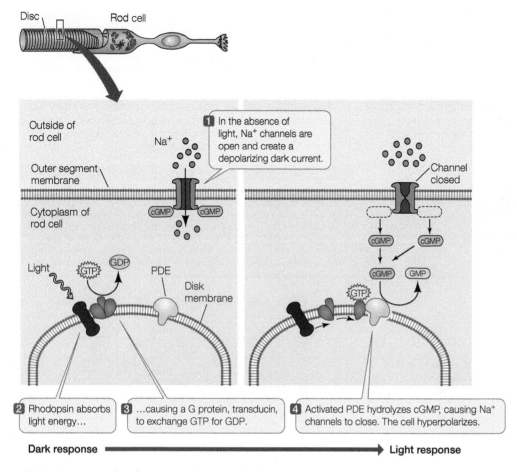

Disc | Rod cell

Outside of rod cell

Na+

1 In the absence of light, Na+ channels are open and create a depolarizing dark current.

Outer segment membrane

Cytoplasm of rod cell

cGMP cGMP

Channel closed

cGMP cGMP

cGMP GMP

Light

GTP GDP

PDE

GTP

Disk membrane

2 Rhodopsin absorbs light energy...

3 ...causing a G protein, transducin, to exchange GTP for GDP.

4 Activated PDE hydrolyzes cGMP, causing Na+ channels to close. The cell hyperpolarizes.

Dark response ⟶ Light response

FIGURE 35.14 Light Absorption Closes Sodium Channels *(Page 707)*

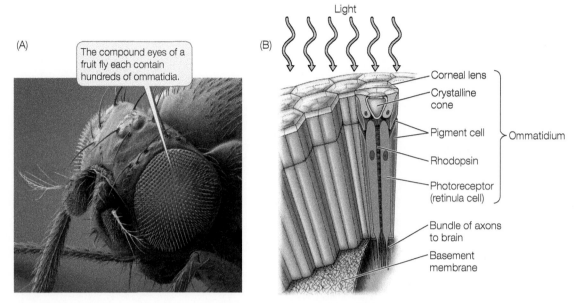

FIGURE 35.15 Ommatidia: The Functional Units of Insect Eyes *(Page 708)*

(A)

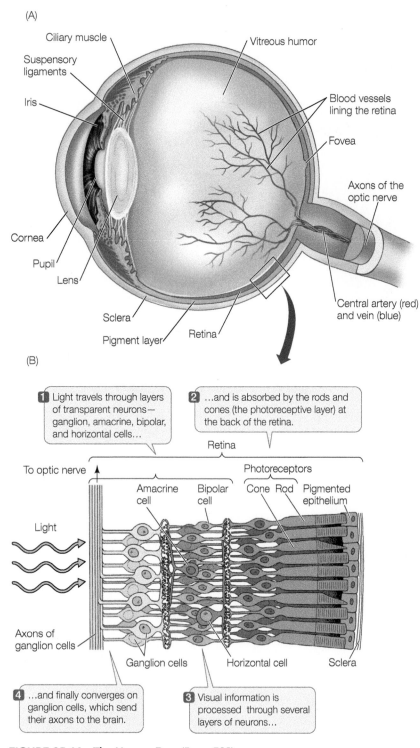

Ciliary muscle

Suspensory ligaments

Iris

Cornea

Pupil

Lens

Sclera

Pigment layer

Retina

Vitreous humor

Blood vessels lining the retina

Fovea

Axons of the optic nerve

Central artery (red) and vein (blue)

(B)

1 Light travels through layers of transparent neurons—ganglion, amacrine, bipolar, and horizontal cells...

2 ...and is absorbed by the rods and cones (the photoreceptive layer) at the back of the retina.

Retina

To optic nerve

Light

Amacrine cell

Bipolar cell

Photoreceptors

Cone Rod Pigmented epithelium

Axons of ganglion cells

Ganglion cells

Horizontal cell

Sclera

4 ...and finally converges on ganglion cells, which send their axons to the brain.

3 Visual information is processed through several layers of neurons...

FIGURE 35.16   The Human Eye *(Page 709)*

(A)

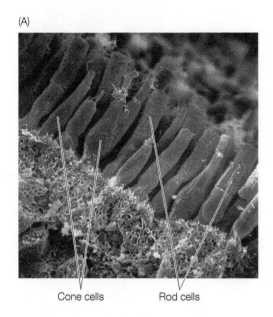

(B)

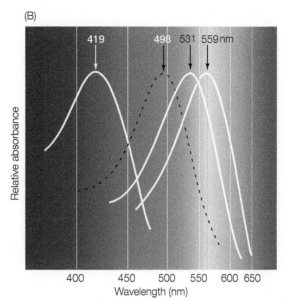

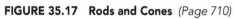

Cone cells   Rod cells

FIGURE 35.17 Rods and Cones *(Page 710)*

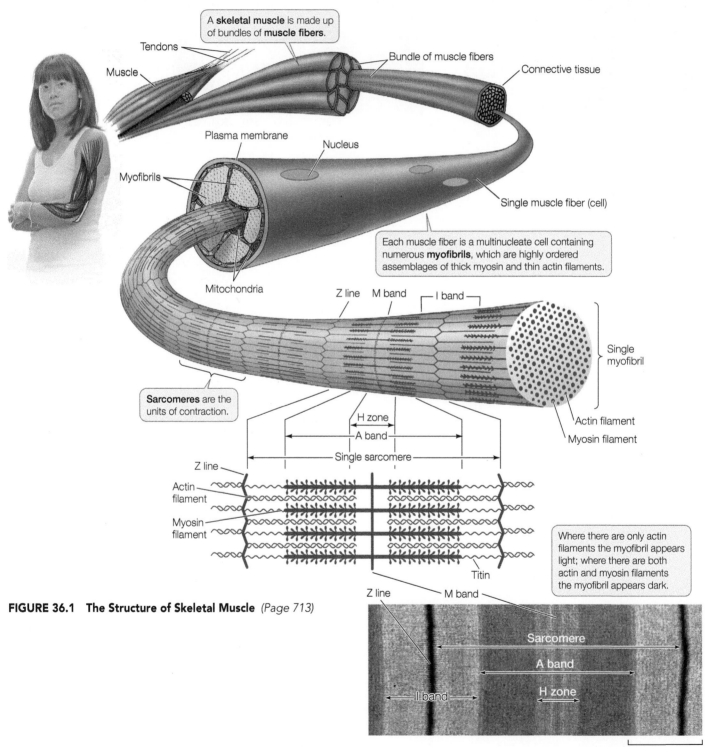

A **skeletal muscle** is made up of bundles of **muscle fibers**.

Tendons

Muscle

Bundle of muscle fibers

Connective tissue

Plasma membrane

Nucleus

Myofibrils

Single muscle fiber (cell)

Mitochondria

Each muscle fiber is a multinucleate cell containing numerous **myofibrils**, which are highly ordered assemblages of thick myosin and thin actin filaments.

Z line   M band   I band

Single myofibril

Actin filament

Myosin filament

Sarcomeres are the units of contraction.

H zone

A band

Single sarcomere

Z line

Actin filament

Myosin filament

Where there are only actin filaments the myofibril appears light; where there are both actin and myosin filaments the myofibril appears dark.

Titin

Z line   M band

FIGURE 36.1   The Structure of Skeletal Muscle *(Page 713)*

Z line   M band

Sarcomere

A band

I band   H zone

1 µm

526

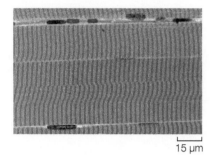

15 μm

IN-TEXT ART *(Page 714)*

Muscle relaxed

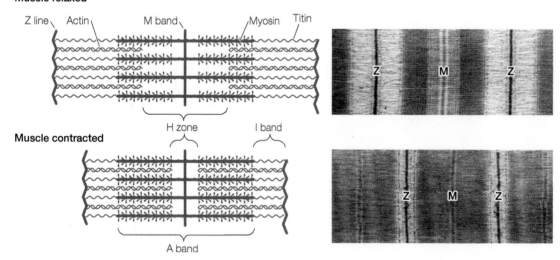

FIGURE 36.2 **Sliding Filaments** *(Page 714)*

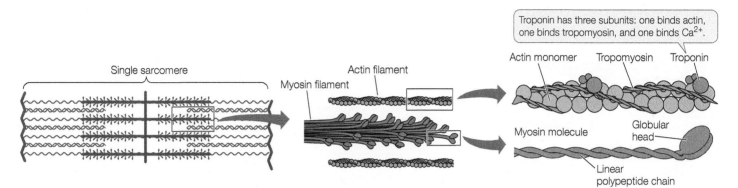

Troponin has three subunits: one binds actin, one binds tropomyosin, and one binds Ca^{2+}.

Single sarcomere

Actin filament

Myosin filament

Actin monomer   Tropomyosin   Troponin

Myosin molecule

Globular head

Linear polypeptide chain

FIGURE 36.3 Actin and Myosin Filaments Overlap in Myofibrils *(Page 715)*

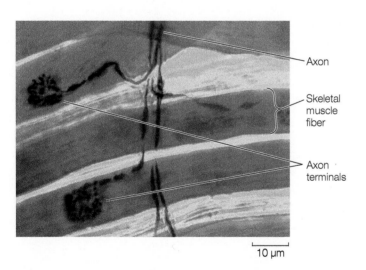

Axon

Skeletal muscle fiber

Axon terminals

10 µm

FIGURE 36.4 The Neuromuscular Junction *(Page 715)*

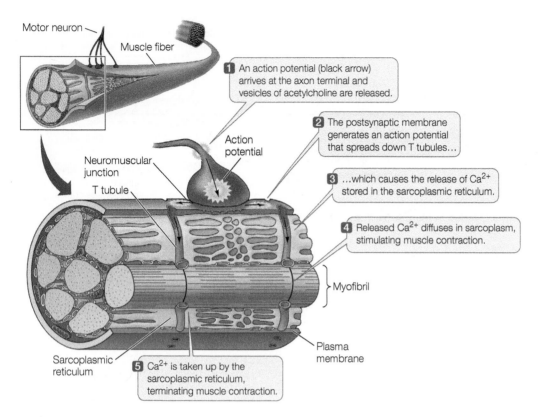

Motor neuron

Muscle fiber

1 An action potential (black arrow) arrives at the axon terminal and vesicles of acetylcholine are released.

2 The postsynaptic membrane generates an action potential that spreads down T tubules...

Action potential

3 ...which causes the release of Ca^{2+} stored in the sarcoplasmic reticulum.

Neuromuscular junction

T tubule

4 Released Ca^{2+} diffuses in sarcoplasm, stimulating muscle contraction.

Myofibril

Plasma membrane

Sarcoplasmic reticulum

5 Ca^{2+} is taken up by the sarcoplasmic reticulum, terminating muscle contraction.

FIGURE 36.5   T Tubules Spread Action Potentials into the Fiber *(Page 717)*

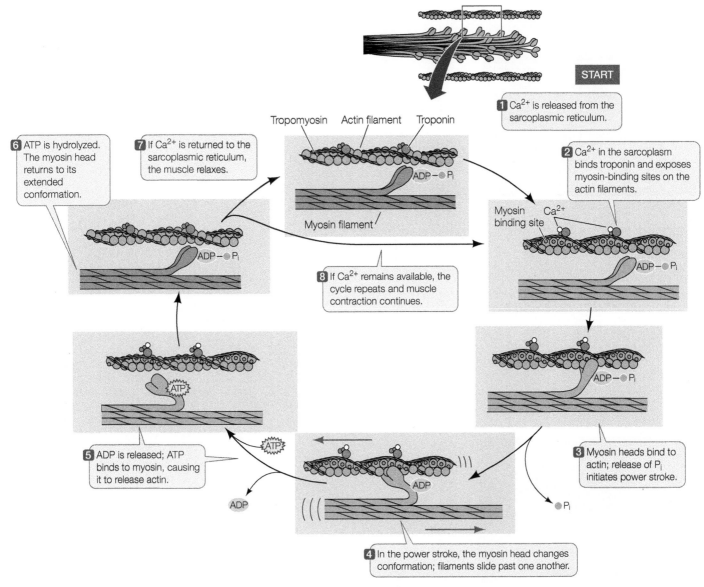

FIGURE 36.6   Release of Ca²⁺ from the Sarcoplasmic Reticulum Triggers Muscle Contraction *(Page 717)*

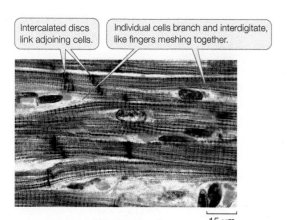

IN-TEXT ART *(Page 718)*

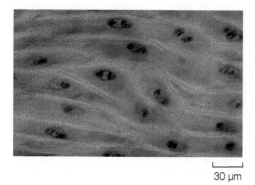

IN-TEXT ART *(Page 718)*

INVESTIGATION

FIGURE 36.7 Neurotransmitters and Stretch Alter the Membrane Potential of Smooth Muscle Cells Several factors influence the motility of the gut. Motility increases after a meal when the ingested food stretches the walls of the gut. Activity of the autonomic nervous system also controls gut motility; the sympathetic nervous system inhibits gut motility, and the parasympathetic nervous system stimulates it. The experimental setup below was used to study how stretching and autonomic neurotransmitters influence gut smooth muscle activity.

HYPOTHESIS

Neurotransmitters of the autonomic nervous system regulate contractions in the smooth muscles of the gut.

METHOD

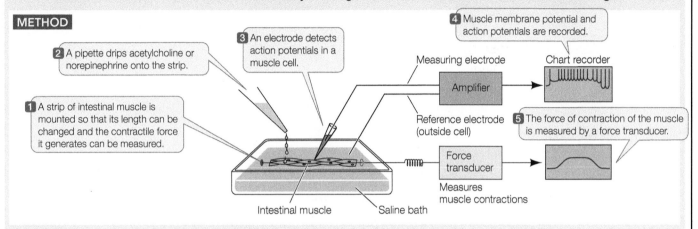

2 A pipette drips acetylcholine or norepinephrine onto the strip.

3 An electrode detects action potentials in a muscle cell.

4 Muscle membrane potential and action potentials are recorded.

Measuring electrode

Chart recorder

Amplifier

1 A strip of intestinal muscle is mounted so that its length can be changed and the contractile force it generates can be measured.

Reference electrode (outside cell)

5 The force of contraction of the muscle is measured by a force transducer.

Force transducer

Measures muscle contractions

Intestinal muscle   Saline bath

RESULTS

When acetylcholine is dripped onto the muscle, the cells depolarize, fire action potentials more rapidly, and increase their force of contraction.

Norepinephrine, on the other hand, causes the cells to hyperpolarize, decreasing their rate of firing, and decreasing their force of contraction.

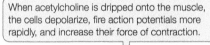

Apply acetylcholine   Wash out acetylcholine   Apply norepinephrine   Wash out norepinephrine

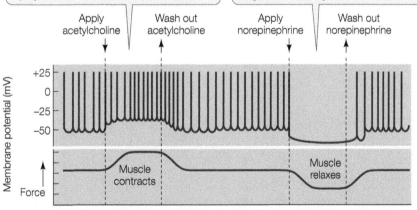

Membrane potential (mV)
+25
0
−25
−50

Muscle contracts

Muscle relaxes

Force

CONCLUSION

ANS neurotransmitters can alter membrane resting potentials and affect the rate at which smooth muscle cells fire action potentials, thus controlling smooth muscle contraction.

ANALYZE THE DATA

In another experiment, the muscle strip was pulled to lengthen it, and the following data were collected:

Length of strip	Membrane potential	Firing rate	Contractile force
10 mm	−50 mv	0.8 hz	5 g
20 mm	−40 mv	1.2 hz	10 g
30 mm	−35 mv	1.6 hz	15 g

A. What is the relationship between the amount the muscle was stretched and its membrane potential?
B. What is the relationship between membrane potential and firing rate?
C. How does firing rate influence the force of contraction?
D. What would happen to your stomach motility if following a large meal you were confronted by a robber?

Go to **yourBioPortal.com** for original citations, discussions, and relevant links for all INVESTIGATION figures.

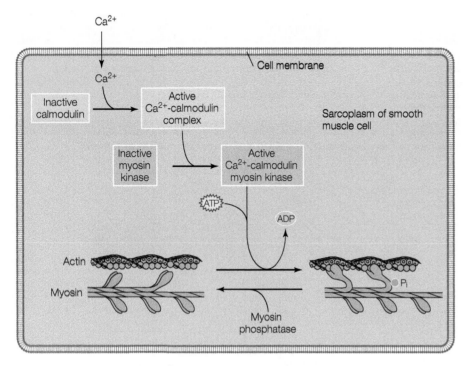

FIGURE 36.8   The Role of Ca²⁺ in Smooth Muscle Contraction *(Page 720)*

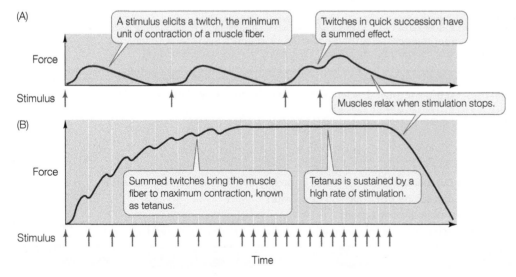

FIGURE 36.9   Twitches and Tetanus *(Page 721)*

(A) Cross sections of leg muscles

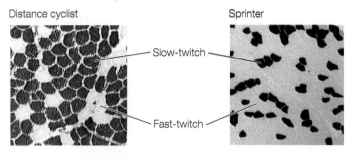

(B)

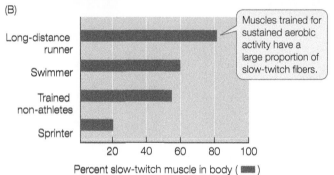

FIGURE 36.10 **Slow- and Fast-twitch Muscle Fibers** *(Page 722)*

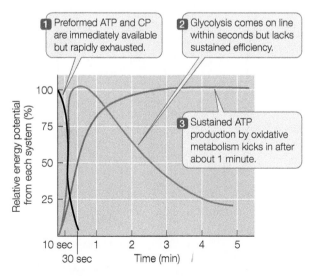

FIGURE 36.11 **Supplying Fuel for High Performance**
(Page 722)

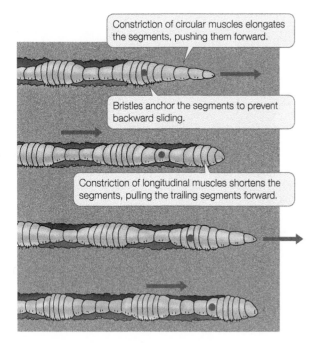

FIGURE 36.12   A Hydrostatic Skeleton *(Page 723)*

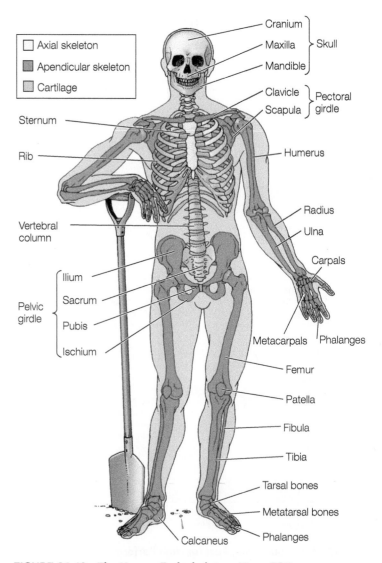

FIGURE 36.13   The Human Endoskeleton *(Page 724)*

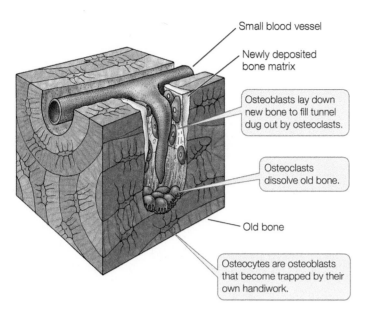

Small blood vessel

Newly deposited bone matrix

Osteoblasts lay down new bone to fill tunnel dug out by osteoclasts.

Osteoclasts dissolve old bone.

Old bone

Osteocytes are osteoblasts that become trapped by their own handiwork.

FIGURE 36.14   Bone Is Living Tissue *(Page 724)*

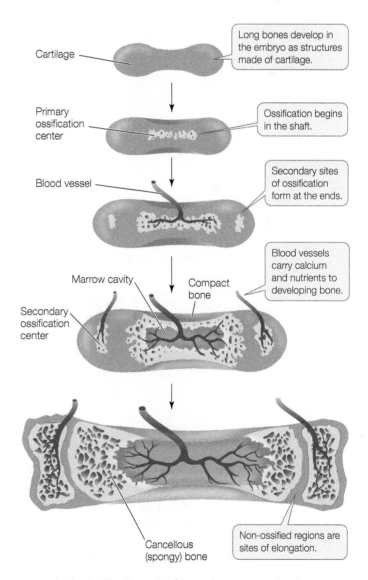

Cartilage

Long bones develop in the embryo as structures made of cartilage.

Primary ossification center

Ossification begins in the shaft.

Blood vessel

Secondary sites of ossification form at the ends.

Marrow cavity

Compact bone

Blood vessels carry calcium and nutrients to developing bone.

Secondary ossification center

Cancellous (spongy) bone

Non-ossified regions are sites of elongation.

FIGURE 36.15   The Growth of Long Bones *(Page 725)*

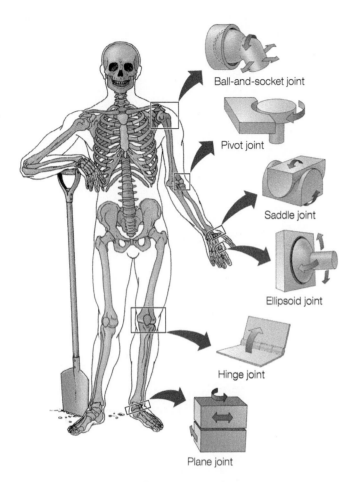

FIGURE 36.16 Types of Joints *(Page 725)*

Ball-and-socket joint

Pivot joint

Saddle joint

Ellipsoid joint

Hinge joint

Plane joint

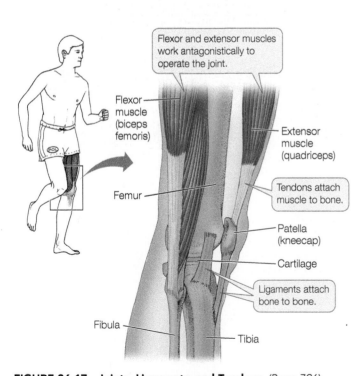

Flexor and extensor muscles work antagonistically to operate the joint.

Flexor muscle (biceps femoris)

Extensor muscle (quadriceps)

Tendons attach muscle to bone.

Femur

Patella (kneecap)

Cartilage

Ligaments attach bone to bone.

Fibula

Tibia

FIGURE 36.17 Joints, Ligaments, and Tendons *(Page 726)*

Lever system designed to maximize force
Load arm : effort arm = 2:1 ratio which generates much force over a small distance.

Lever system designed for speed
Load arm : effort arm = 5:1 ratio which moves low weights long distances with speed.

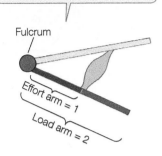

Fulcrum

Effort arm = 1
Load arm = 2

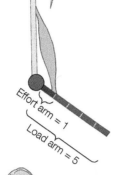

Effort arm = 1
Load arm = 5

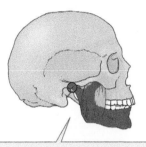

An example of a lever system designed for applying maximum force is the human jaw. The effort arm is long relative to the load arm.

An example of a lever system designed for speed is the human leg. The effort arm is short relative to the load arm.

FIGURE 36.18 Bones and Joints Work Like Systems of Levers *(Page 726)*

FIGURE 36.19 Champion Jumpers *(Page 727)*

Gas Exchange in Animals 37

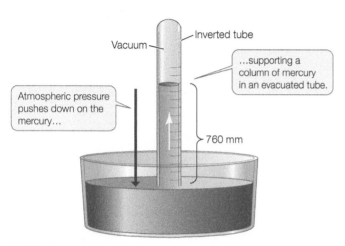

IN-TEXT ART *(Page 730)*

Pseudoceros ferrugineus

IN-TEXT ART *(Page 731)*

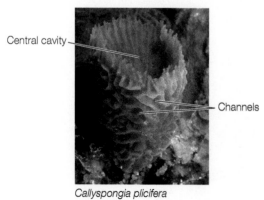

Callyspongia plicifera

IN-TEXT ART *(Page 731)*

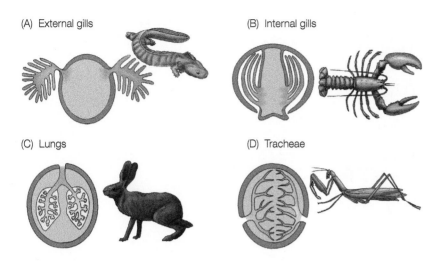

(A) External gills

(B) Internal gills

(C) Lungs

(D) Tracheae

FIGURE 37.1   Gas Exchange Systems *(Page 732)*

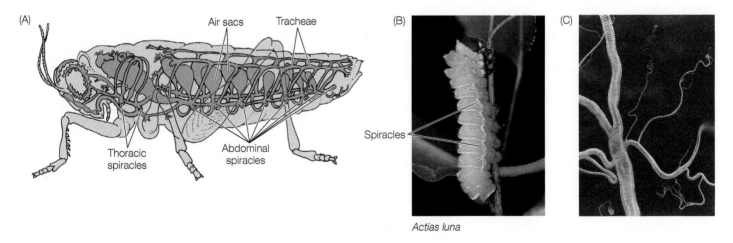

(A)

Air sacs

Tracheae

Thoracic spiracles

Abdominal spiracles

(B)

Spiracles

Actias luna

(C)

FIGURE 37.2   The Tracheal Gas Exchange System of Insects *(Page 733)*

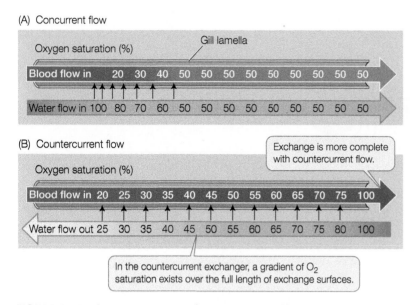

(A) Concurrent flow

Oxygen saturation (%)

Gill lamella

Blood flow in 20 30 40 50 50 50 50 50 50 50 50 50

Water flow in 100 80 70 60 50 50 50 50 50 50 50 50 50

(B) Countercurrent flow

Exchange is more complete with countercurrent flow.

Oxygen saturation (%)

Blood flow in 20 25 30 35 40 45 50 55 60 65 70 75 100

Water flow out 25 30 35 40 45 50 55 60 65 70 75 80 100

In the countercurrent exchanger, a gradient of O_2 saturation exists over the full length of exchange surfaces.

FIGURE 37.3 Countercurrent Exchange Is More Efficient *(Page 733)*

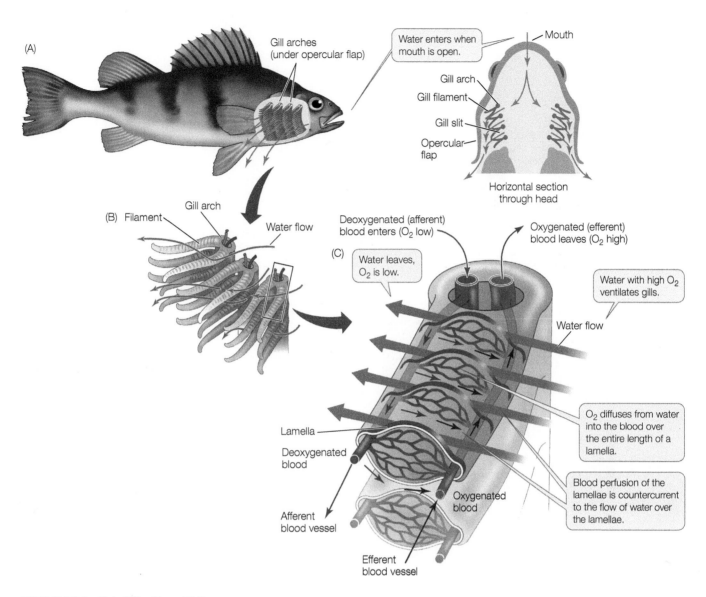

FIGURE 37.4 Fish Gills *(Page 734)*

(A) Avian air sacs and lungs

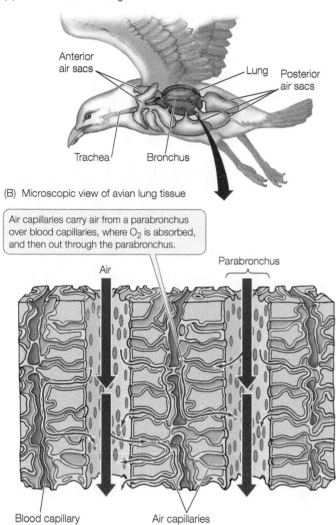

Anterior air sacs

Lung

Posterior air sacs

Trachea

Bronchus

(B) Microscopic view of avian lung tissue

Air capillaries carry air from a parabronchus over blood capillaries, where O_2 is absorbed, and then out through the parabronchus.

Air

Parabronchus

Blood capillary

Air capillaries

FIGURE 37.5   The Respiratory System of a Bird *(Page 735)*

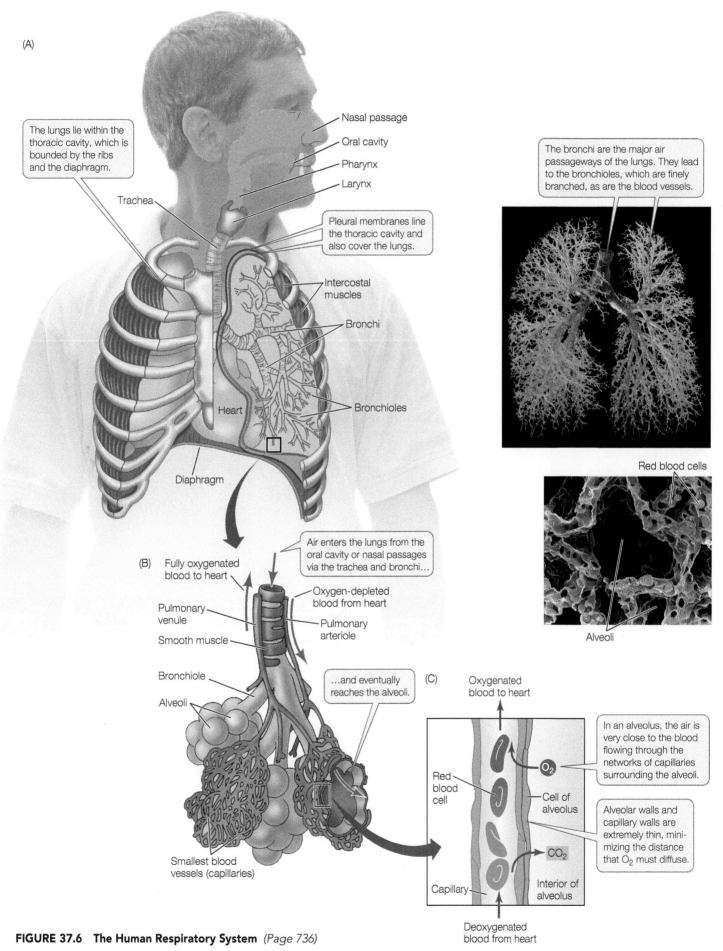

(A)

The lungs lie within the thoracic cavity, which is bounded by the ribs and the diaphragm.

Nasal passage

Oral cavity

Pharynx

Larynx

Trachea

Pleural membranes line the thoracic cavity and also cover the lungs.

The bronchi are the major air passageways of the lungs. They lead to the bronchioles, which are finely branched, as are the blood vessels.

Intercostal muscles

Bronchi

Heart

Bronchioles

Diaphragm

Red blood cells

Alveoli

(B) Fully oxygenated blood to heart

Air enters the lungs from the oral cavity or nasal passages via the trachea and bronchi...

Oxygen-depleted blood from heart

Pulmonary venule

Pulmonary arteriole

Smooth muscle

Bronchiole

Alveoli

...and eventually reaches the alveoli.

(C) Oxygenated blood to heart

In an alveolus, the air is very close to the blood flowing through the networks of capillaries surrounding the alveoli.

Red blood cell

O_2

Cell of alveolus

Alveolar walls and capillary walls are extremely thin, minimizing the distance that O_2 must diffuse.

CO_2

Smallest blood vessels (capillaries)

Capillary

Interior of alveolus

Deoxygenated blood from heart

FIGURE 37.6 The Human Respiratory System *(Page 736)*

RESEARCH TOOLS

FIGURE 37.7 Measuring Lung Ventilation A spirometer is a device that measures the volume of air a person breathes through a mouthpiece. The combined tidal volume, inspiratory reserve volume, and expiratory reserve volume are the lungs' vital capacity.

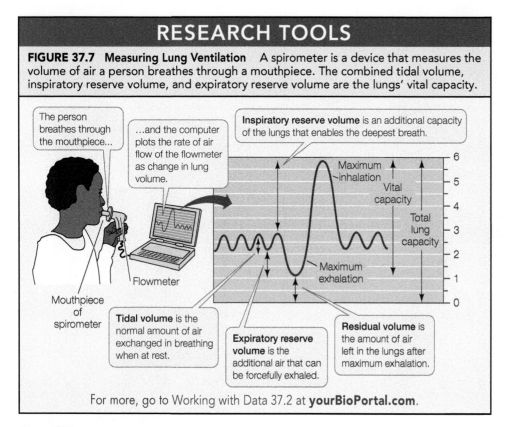

The person breathes through the mouthpiece...

...and the computer plots the rate of air flow of the flowmeter as change in lung volume.

Inspiratory reserve volume is an additional capacity of the lungs that enables the deepest breath.

Maximum inhalation

Vital capacity

Total lung capacity

Flowmeter

Maximum exhalation

Mouthpiece of spirometer

Tidal volume is the normal amount of air exchanged in breathing when at rest.

Expiratory reserve volume is the additional air that can be forcefully exhaled.

Residual volume is the amount of air left in the lungs after maximum exhalation.

For more, go to Working with Data 37.2 at **yourBioPortal.com**.

(Page 737)

(A)

(B)

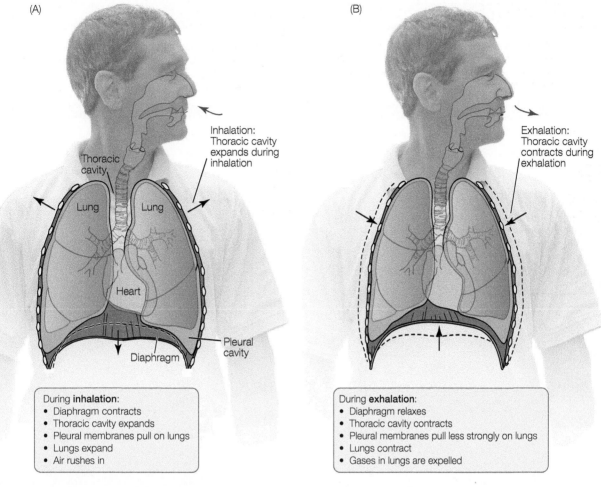

Thoracic cavity

Lung

Lung

Heart

Diaphragm

Inhalation:
Thoracic cavity
expands during
inhalation

Pleural
cavity

Exhalation:
Thoracic cavity
contracts during
exhalation

During **inhalation**:
• Diaphragm contracts
• Thoracic cavity expands
• Pleural membranes pull on lungs
• Lungs expand
• Air rushes in

During **exhalation**:
• Diaphragm relaxes
• Thoracic cavity contracts
• Pleural membranes pull less strongly on lungs
• Lungs contract
• Gases in lungs are expelled

FIGURE 37.8   Into the Lungs and Out Again *(Page 738)*

INVESTIGATION

FIGURE 37.9 Sensitivity of the Respiratory Control System Changes with Exercise What is the metabolic feedback signal that controls ventilation rate during exercise? In experiments with dogs running on treadmills with different slopes, the ventilation rate increases as the P_{CO_2} in the arterial blood increases. When the dogs run at different speeds instead, their ventilation rates are different but their arterial P_{CO_2}'s are the same. How can P_{CO_2} be the metabolic stimulus for breathing?

HYPOTHESIS

P_{CO_2} is the feedback stimulus controlling ventilation.

METHOD

1. Dogs are trained to run on a treadmill.
2. The dogs are equipped with instruments that measure respiratory rate and with arterial catheters that enable sampling of blood.
3. As a dog runs, either the slope of the treadmill or its speed is changed to increase the metabolic workload.
4. Ventilation rate (V; L/min) is plotted as a function of arterial P_{CO_2} (mm Hg).

Catheter for taking blood samples

To flowmeter and respiratory analyzer

RESULTS

When the workload is altered by slowly changing the slope of the treadmill (no change in speed), the ventilation rate is a function of P_{CO_2}.

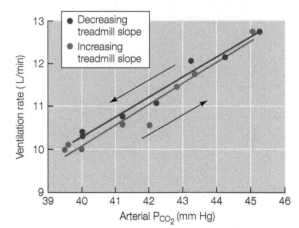

CONCLUSION

Arterial P_{CO_2} can be the metabolic feedback signal controlling ventilation in response to changes in workload.

ANALYZE THE DATA

Additional experiments were done in which the ventilation rate and arterial P_{CO_2} were measured when the treadmill speed was changed. The average values when the dog was running at 3 mph were P_{CO_2} = 39.0 and V = 9. The data for the first seven breaths after the treadmill speed was increased to 6 mph were:

Breath	P_{CO_2}	V
1	38.0	13.0
2	37.0	14.0
3	36.5	11.2
4	37.2	11.2

Breath	P_{CO_2}	V
5	37.2	12.0
6	36.8	13.0
7	37.2	13.0

After the dog had run at 6 mph for several minutes, the values averaged P_{CO_2} = 41.0 and V = 15.0. Plot these data and use the information to answer the following questions:

A. Do these data support the hypothesis that P_{CO_2} is the feedback signal controlling ventilation rate? Why or why not?
B. How do you explain the average values after the dog had been running at the higher speed for a few minutes?
C. Relate these results to those obtained in the experiment in which the slope of the treadmill was gradually raised and lowered. Explain the differences between the results in terms of the P_{CO_2} sensing mechanism.

Go to **yourBioPortal.com** for original citations, discussions, and relevant links for all INVESTIGATION figures.

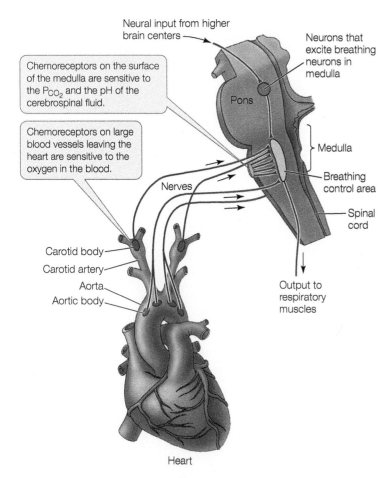

Neural input from higher brain centers

Neurons that excite breathing neurons in medulla

Chemoreceptors on the surface of the medulla are sensitive to the P_{CO_2} and the pH of the cerebrospinal fluid.

Pons

Chemoreceptors on large blood vessels leaving the heart are sensitive to the oxygen in the blood.

Medulla

Nerves

Breathing control area

Spinal cord

Carotid body
Carotid artery
Aorta
Aortic body

Output to respiratory muscles

Heart

FIGURE 37.10 Feedback Information Controls Breathing *(Page 741)*

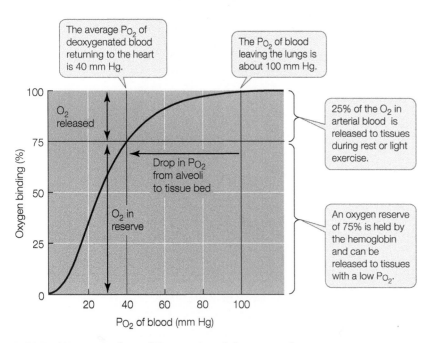

The average P_{O_2} of deoxygenated blood returning to the heart is 40 mm Hg.

The P_{O_2} of blood leaving the lungs is about 100 mm Hg.

O_2 released

25% of the O_2 in arterial blood is released to tissues during rest or light exercise.

Drop in P_{O_2} from alveoli to tissue bed

O_2 in reserve

An oxygen reserve of 75% is held by the hemoglobin and can be released to tissues with a low P_{O_2}.

Oxygen binding (%)

P_{O_2} of blood (mm Hg)

FIGURE 37.11 Binding of O₂ to Hemoglobin Depends on P$_{O_2}$ *(Page 742)*

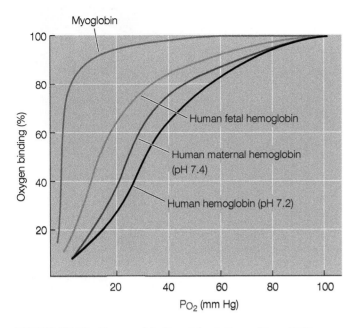

FIGURE 37.12 Oxygen-binding Adaptations *(Page 742)*

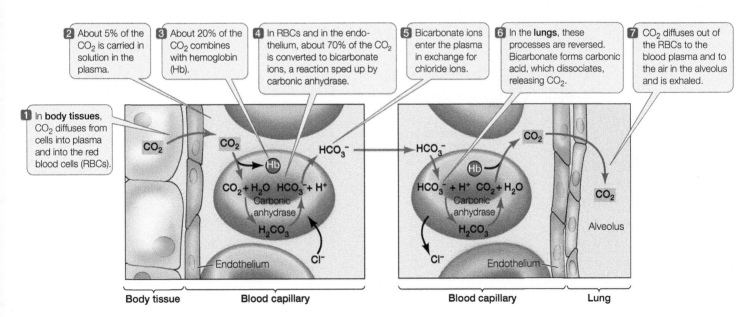

FIGURE 37.13 Carbon Dioxide Is Transported as Bicarbonate Ions *(Page 743)*

(A) Open circulatory system: mollusk

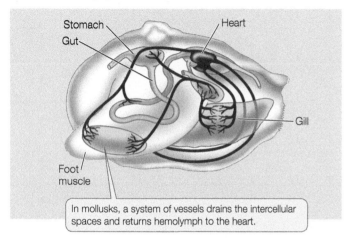

Stomach

Heart

Gut

Gill

Foot
muscle

In mollusks, a system of vessels drains the intercellular
spaces and returns hemolymph to the heart.

(B) Closed circulatory system: annelid worm

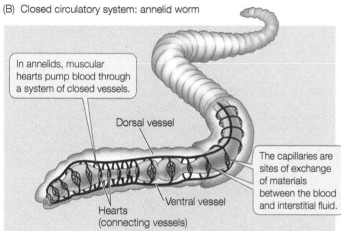

In annelids, muscular
hearts pump blood through
a system of closed vessels.

Dorsal vessel

The capillaries are
sites of exchange
of materials
between the blood
and interstitial fluid.

Ventral vessel

Hearts
(connecting vessels)

FIGURE 38.1 Circulatory Systems *(Page 747)*

From heart

To heart

Large artery | Small artery | Arterioles | Capillaries | Venules | Vein

IN-TEXT ART *(Page 747)*

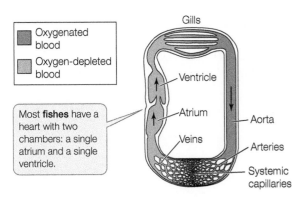

Gills

Oxygenated blood

Oxygen-depleted blood

Most **fishes** have a heart with two chambers: a single atrium and a single ventricle.

Ventricle

Atrium

Veins

Aorta

Arteries

Systemic capillaries

IN-TEXT ART *(Page 748)*

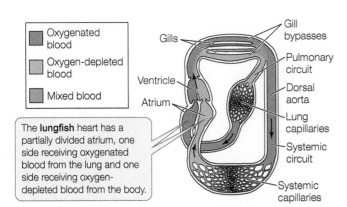

Oxygenated blood

Oxygen-depleted blood

Mixed blood

Gills

Gill bypasses

Pulmonary circuit

Ventricle

Atrium

Dorsal aorta

Lung capillaries

Systemic circuit

The **lungfish** heart has a partially divided atrium, one side receiving oxygenated blood from the lung and one side receiving oxygen-depleted blood from the body.

Systemic capillaries

IN-TEXT ART *(Page 749)*

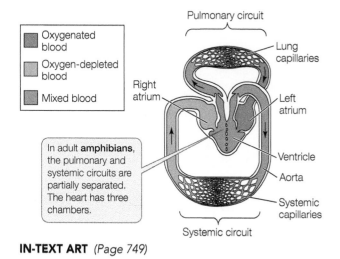

Pulmonary circuit

Lung capillaries

Right atrium

Left atrium

Ventricle

Aorta

Systemic capillaries

Systemic circuit

Oxygenated blood

Oxygen-depleted blood

Mixed blood

In adult **amphibians**, the pulmonary and systemic circuits are partially separated. The heart has three chambers.

IN-TEXT ART *(Page 749)*

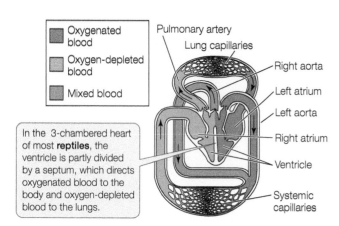

Pulmonary artery

Lung capillaries

Right aorta

Left atrium

Left aorta

Right atrium

Ventricle

Systemic capillaries

Oxygenated blood

Oxygen-depleted blood

Mixed blood

In the 3-chambered heart of most **reptiles**, the ventricle is partly divided by a septum, which directs oxygenated blood to the body and oxygen-depleted blood to the lungs.

IN-TEXT ART *(Page 749)*

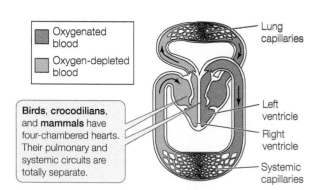

Lung capillaries

Left ventricle

Right ventricle

Systemic capillaries

Oxygenated blood

Oxygen-depleted blood

Birds, **crocodilians**, and **mammals** have four-chambered hearts. Their pulmonary and systemic circuits are totally separate.

IN-TEXT ART *(Page 750)*

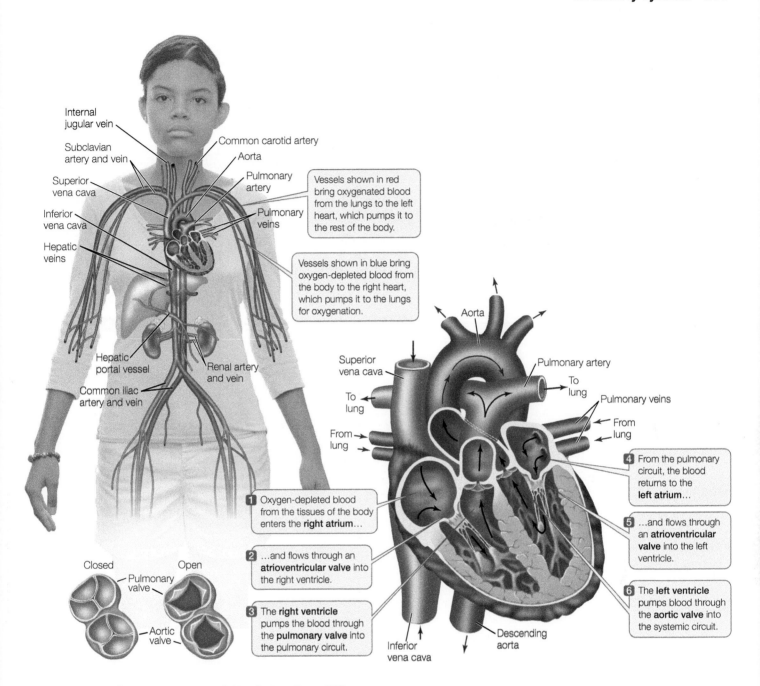

Internal jugular vein

Subclavian artery and vein

Superior vena cava

Inferior vena cava

Hepatic veins

Common carotid artery

Aorta

Pulmonary artery

Pulmonary veins

Vessels shown in red bring oxygenated blood from the lungs to the left heart, which pumps it to the rest of the body.

Vessels shown in blue bring oxygen-depleted blood from the body to the right heart, which pumps it to the lungs for oxygenation.

Hepatic portal vessel

Common Iliac artery and vein

Renal artery and vein

Aorta

Superior vena cava

Pulmonary artery

To lung

To lung

From lung

From lung

Pulmonary veins

From lung

From lung

1 Oxygen-depleted blood from the tissues of the body enters the **right atrium**…

2 …and flows through an **atrioventricular valve** into the right ventricle.

3 The **right ventricle** pumps the blood through the **pulmonary valve** into the pulmonary circuit.

4 From the pulmonary circuit, the blood returns to the **left atrium**…

5 …and flows through an **atrioventricular valve** into the left ventricle.

6 The **left ventricle** pumps blood through the **aortic valve** into the systemic circuit.

Closed

Open

Pulmonary valve

Aortic valve

Inferior vena cava

Descending aorta

FIGURE 38.2   The Human Heart and Circulation *(Page 751)*

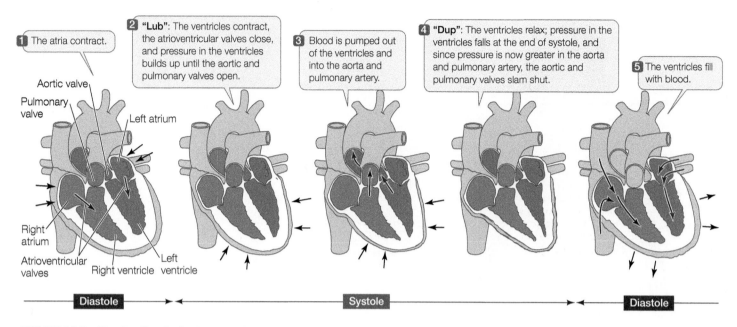

FIGURE 38.3 The Cardiac Cycle *(Page 752)*

INVESTIGATION

FIGURE 38.4 The Autonomic Nervous System Controls Heart Rate The membrane potentials of pacemaker cells spontaneously depolarize until action potential threshold is reached. Neurotransmitter signals from the two divisions of the autonomic nervous system speed up and slow down the rate at which the pacemaker membrane potential drifts upward, thereby controlling the rate at which pacemaker cells fire action potentials.

HYPOTHESIS

The ANS neurotransmitters norepinephrine (NE) and acetylcholine (ACh) influence the membrane potentials of pacemaker cells by altering the properties of the ion channels that determine membrane potential.

METHOD
1. Culture living sinoatrial node tissue in a dish. Insert an intracellular recording electrode into pacemaker cells.
2. Measure the membrane potential of pacemaker cells during a resting heartbeat (the control) and after applications of the ANS neurotransmitters NE (sympathetic) and ACh (parasympathetic).

RESULTS

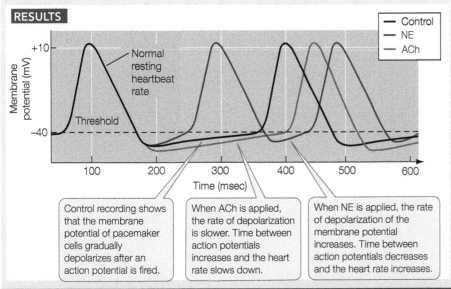

Control recording shows that the membrane potential of pacemaker cells gradually depolarizes after an action potential is fired.

When ACh is applied, the rate of depolarization is slower. Time between action potentials increases and the heart rate slows down.

When NE is applied, the rate of depolarization of the membrane potential increases. Time between action potentials decreases and the heart rate increases.

CONCLUSION

The ANS neurotransmitters NE and ACh influence heart rate by altering the membrane resting potentials of pacemaker cells.

ANALYZE THE DATA

Additional experiments were performed using specific Ca^{2+}, Na^+, and K^+ channel blockers to investigate the roles of these ion channels in generating action potentials (spikes) in pacemaker cells. The table shows the results.

Treatment	Spike height	Spike width	Interspike intervals
Control	+10 mv	100 msec	300 msec
Add Ca^{2+} channel blocker		Action potentials cease	
Add NE	+10 mv	100 msec	200 msec
Add ACh	+10 mv	100 msec	350 msec
Add Na^+ channel blocker and NE	+10 mv	100 msec	250 msec
Add K^+ channel blocker	+10 mv	100 msec	250 msec

A. What ion channel is responsible for the spikes?

B. How do the ANS neurotransmitters alter the characteristics of the pacemaker membrane potential?

C. What ion channels are likely involved in the actions of the ANS neurotransmitters?

Go to **yourBioPortal.com** for original citations, discussions, and relevant links for all INVESTIGATION figures.

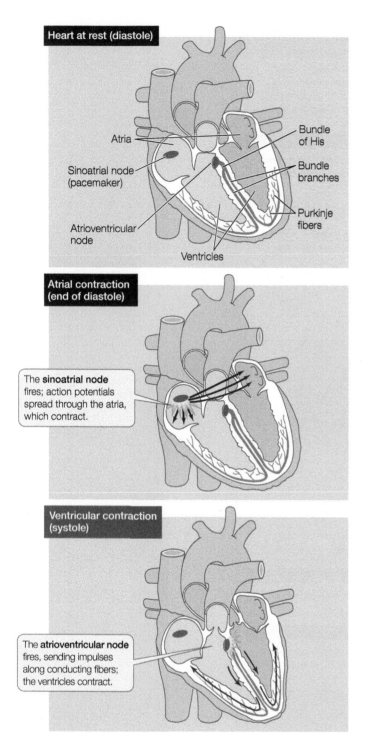

Heart at rest (diastole)

Atria

Sinoatrial node
(pacemaker)

Atrioventricular
node

Ventricles

Bundle
of His

Bundle
branches

Purkinje
fibers

**Atrial contraction
(end of diastole)**

The **sinoatrial node** fires; action potentials spread through the atria, which contract.

**Ventricular contraction
(systole)**

The **atrioventricular node** fires, sending impulses along conducting fibers; the ventricles contract.

FIGURE 38.5 The Heartbeat *(Page 754)*

(A)

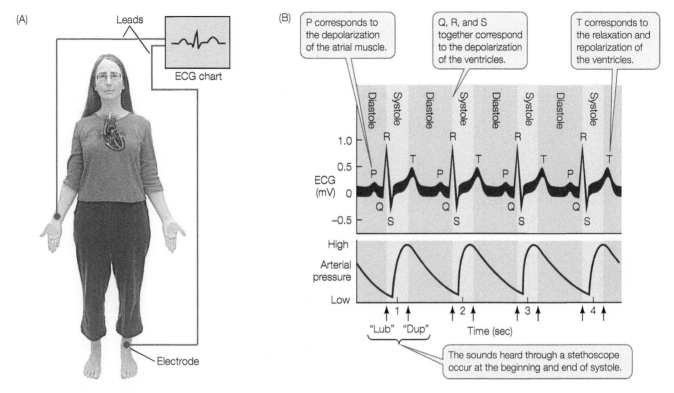

FIGURE 38.6 The Electrocardiogram *(Page 755)*

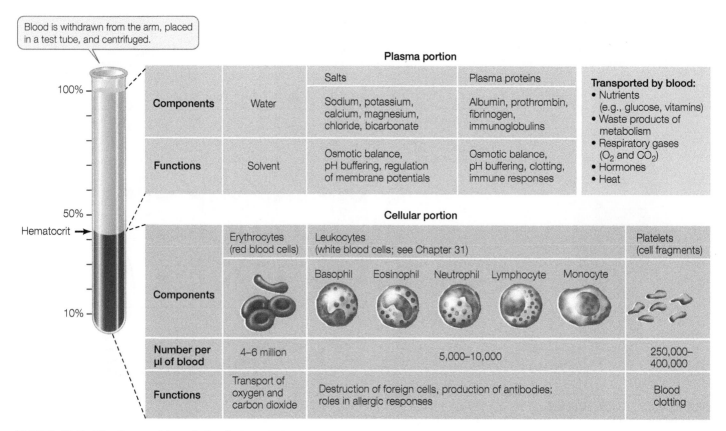

Blood is withdrawn from the arm, placed in a test tube, and centrifuged.

100%

50%

Hematocrit →

10%

Plasma portion

Components	Water	Salts		Plasma proteins
		Sodium, potassium, calcium, magnesium, chloride, bicarbonate		Albumin, prothrombin, fibrinogen, immunoglobulins
Functions	Solvent	Osmotic balance, pH buffering, regulation of membrane potentials		Osmotic balance, pH buffering, clotting, immune responses

Transported by blood:
- Nutrients (e.g., glucose, vitamins)
- Waste products of metabolism
- Respiratory gases (O_2 and CO_2)
- Hormones
- Heat

Cellular portion

	Erythrocytes (red blood cells)	Leukocytes (white blood cells; see Chapter 31)					Platelets (cell fragments)
Components		Basophil	Eosinophil	Neutrophil	Lymphocyte	Monocyte	
Number per µl of blood	4–6 million	5,000–10,000					250,000–400,000
Functions	Transport of oxygen and carbon dioxide	Destruction of foreign cells, production of antibodies; roles in allergic responses					Blood clotting

FIGURE 38.7 The Composition of Blood *(Page 756)*

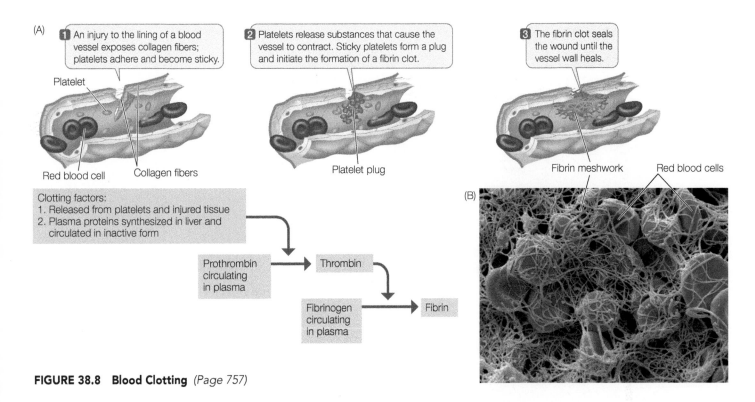

(A)

1 An injury to the lining of a blood vessel exposes collagen fibers; platelets adhere and become sticky.

Platelet

Red blood cell   Collagen fibers

2 Platelets release substances that cause the vessel to contract. Sticky platelets form a plug and initiate the formation of a fibrin clot.

Platelet plug

3 The fibrin clot seals the wound until the vessel wall heals.

Fibrin meshwork   Red blood cells

(B)

Clotting factors:
1. Released from platelets and injured tissue
2. Plasma proteins synthesized in liver and circulated in inactive form

Prothrombin circulating in plasma → Thrombin

Fibrinogen circulating in plasma → Fibrin

FIGURE 38.8 Blood Clotting *(Page 757)*

(A)

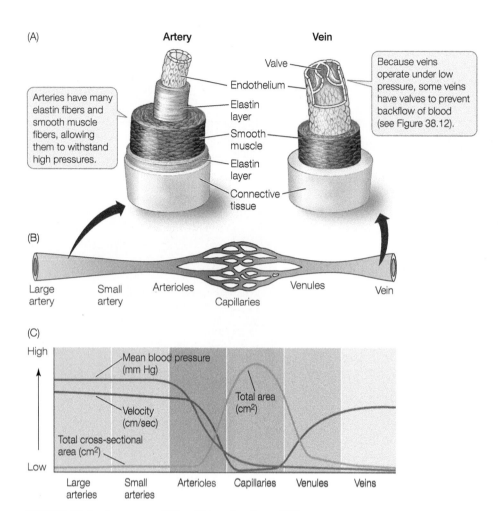

Artery

Vein

Valve

Endothelium

Elastin layer

Smooth muscle

Elastin layer

Connective tissue

Arteries have many elastin fibers and smooth muscle fibers, allowing them to withstand high pressures.

Because veins operate under low pressure, some veins have valves to prevent backflow of blood (see Figure 38.12).

(B)

Large artery

Small artery

Arterioles

Capillaries

Venules

Vein

(C)

High

Mean blood pressure (mm Hg)

Total area (cm²)

Velocity (cm/sec)

Total cross-sectional area (cm²)

Low

Large arteries

Small arteries

Arterioles

Capillaries

Venules

Veins

FIGURE 38.9 Anatomy of Blood Vessels *(Page 758)*

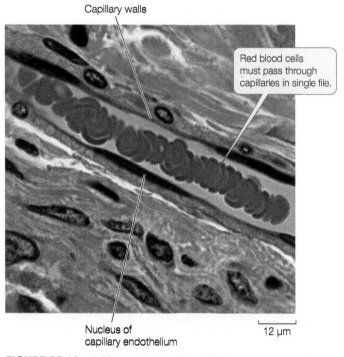

Capillary walls

Red blood cells must pass through capillaries in single file.

Nucleus of capillary endothelium

12 µm

FIGURE 38.10 A Narrow Lane *(Page 759)*

(A)

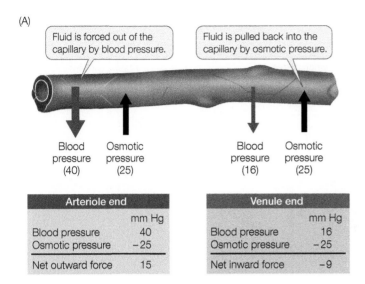

Arteriole end	
	mm Hg
Blood pressure	40
Osmotic pressure	−25
Net outward force	15

Venule end	
	mm Hg
Blood pressure	16
Osmotic pressure	−25
Net inward force	−9

(B)

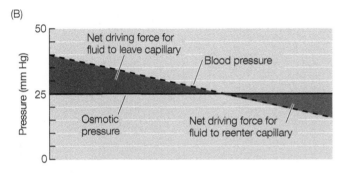

FIGURE 38.11 Starling's Forces *(Page 759)*

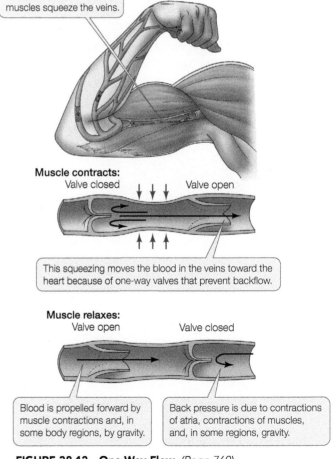

FIGURE 38.12 One-Way Flow *(Page 760)*

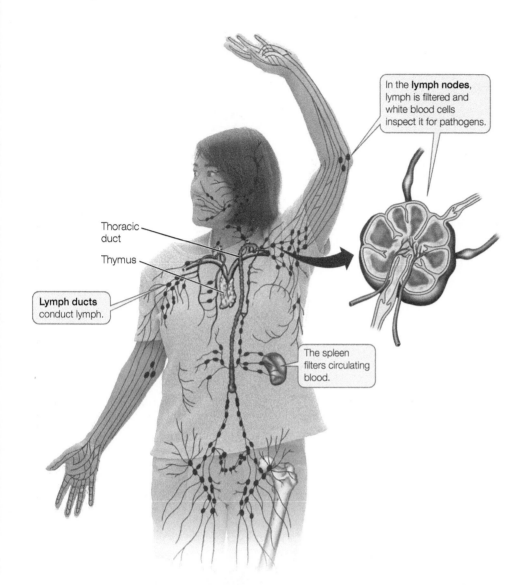

In the **lymph nodes**, lymph is filtered and white blood cells inspect it for pathogens.

Thoracic duct

Thymus

Lymph ducts conduct lymph.

The spleen filters circulating blood.

FIGURE 38.13 The Human Lymphatic System *(Page 761)*

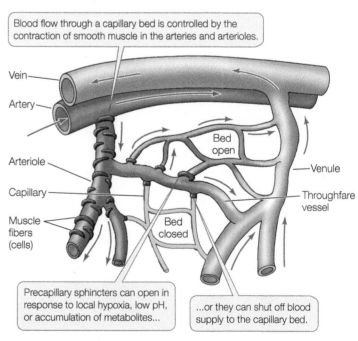

Blood flow through a capillary bed is controlled by the contraction of smooth muscle in the arteries and arterioles.

Vein

Artery

Arteriole

Capillary

Muscle fibers (cells)

Bed open

Bed closed

Venule

Throughfare vessel

Precapillary sphincters can open in response to local hypoxia, low pH, or accumulation of metabolites...

...or they can shut off blood supply to the capillary bed.

FIGURE 38.14 Local Control of Blood Flow *(Page 761)*

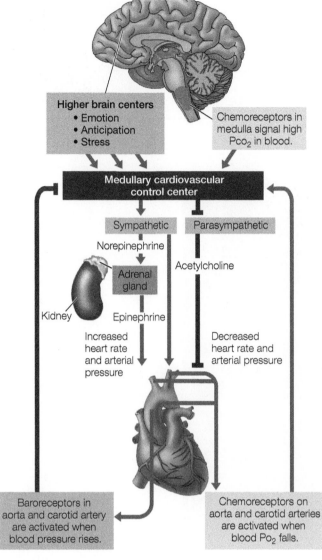

FIGURE 38.15   Regulating Cardiac Output
(Page 762)

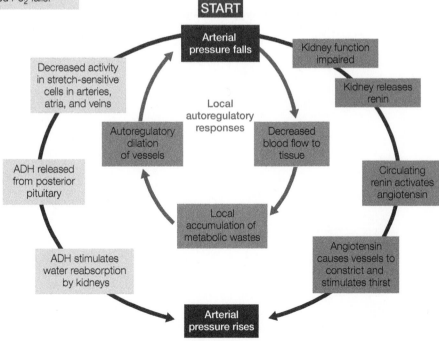

FIGURE 38.16   Influences of Local and Systemic Mechanisms on Blood Pressure
(Page 763)

Nutrition, Digestion, and Absorption

FIGURE 39.1   Heterotrophs Get Energy from Autotrophs *(Page 766)*

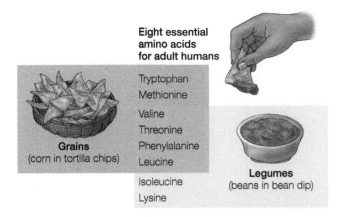

Eight essential amino acids for adult humans

Tryptophan
Methionine
Valine
Threonine
Phenylalanine
Leucine
Isoleucine
Lysine

Grains
(corn in tortilla chips)

Legumes
(beans in bean dip)

FIGURE 39.2   A Strategy for Vegetarians *(Page 767)*

TABLE 39.1	Mineral Elements Required by Animals	
ELEMENT	**SOURCE IN HUMAN DIET**	**MAJOR FUNCTIONS**
MACRONUTRIENTS		
Calcium (Ca)	Dairy foods, eggs, green leafy vegetables, whole grains, legumes, nuts, meat	Found in bones and teeth; blood clotting; nerve and muscle action; enzyme activation
Chlorine (Cl)	Table salt (NaCl), meat, eggs, vegetables, dairy foods	Water balance; digestion (as HCl); principal negative ion in extracellular fluid
Magnesium (Mg)	Green vegetables, meat, whole grains, nuts, milk	Required by many enzymes; found in bones and teeth
Phosphorus (P)	Dairy, eggs, meat, whole grains, legumes, nuts	Found in nucleic acids, ATP, and phospholipids; bone formation; buffers; metabolism of sugars
Potassium (K)	Meat, whole grains, fruits, vegetables	Nerve and muscle action; protein synthesis; principal positive ion in cells
Sodium (Na)	Table salt, dairy foods, meat, eggs	Nerve and muscle action; water balance; principal positive ion in extracellular fluid
Sulfur (S)	Meat, eggs, dairy foods, nuts, legumes	Found in proteins and coenzymes; detoxification of harmful substances
MICRONUTRIENTS		
Chromium (Cr)	Meat, dairy, whole grains, legumes, yeast	Glucose metabolism
Cobalt (Co)	Meat, tap water	Found in vitamin B_{12}; formation of red blood cells
Copper (Cu)	Liver, meat, fish, shellfish, legumes, whole grains, nuts	Found in active site of many redox enzymes and electron carriers; production of hemoglobin; bone formation
Fluorine (F)	Most water supplies	Found in teeth; helps prevent decay
Iodine (I)	Fish, shellfish, iodized salt	Found in thyroid hormones
Iron (Fe)	Liver, meat, green vegetables, eggs, whole grains, legumes, nuts	Found in active sites of many redox enzymes and electron carriers, hemoglobin, and myoglobin
Manganese (Mn)	Organ meats, whole grains, legumes, nuts, tea, coffee	Activates many enzymes
Molybdenum (Mo)	Organ meats, dairy, whole grains, green vegetables, legumes	Found in some enzymes
Selenium (Se)	Meat, seafood, whole grains, eggs, milk, garlic	Fat metabolism
Zinc (Zn)	Liver, fish, shellfish, and many other foods	Found in some enzymes and some transcription factors; insulin physiology

TABLE 39.2	Vitamins in the Human Diet		
VITAMIN	**SOURCE**	**FUNCTION**	**DEFICIENCY SYMPTOMS**
WATER-SOLUBLE			
B$_1$ (thiamin)	Liver, legumes, whole grains	Coenzyme in cellular respiration	Beriberi, loss of appetite, fatigue
B$_2$ (riboflavin)	Dairy, meat, eggs, green leafy vegetables	Coenzyme in FAD	Lesions in corners of mouth, eye irritation, skin disorders
Niacin	Meat, fowl, liver, yeast	Coenzyme in NAD and NADP	Pellagra, skin disorders, diarrhea, mental disorders
B$_6$ (pyridoxine)	Liver, whole grains, dairy foods	Coenzyme in amino acid metabolism	Anemia, slow growth, skin problems, convulsions
Pantothenic acid	Liver, eggs, yeast	Found in acetyl CoA	Adrenal problems, reproductive problems
Biotin	Liver, yeast, bacteria in gut	Found in coenzymes	Skin problems, loss of hair
B$_{12}$ (cobalamin)	Liver, meat, dairy foods, eggs	Formation of nucleic acids, proteins, and red blood cells	Pernicious anemia
Folic acid	Vegetables, eggs, liver, whole grains	Coenzyme in formation of heme and nucleotides	Anemia
C (ascorbic acid)	Citrus fruits, tomatoes, potatoes	Formation of connective tissues; antioxidant	Scurvy, slow healing, poor bone growth
FAT-SOLUBLE			
A (retinol)	Fruits, vegetables, liver, dairy	Found in visual pigments	Night blindness
D (cholecalciferol)	Fortified milk, fish oils, sunshine	Absorption of calcium and phosphate	Rickets
E (tocopherol)	Meat, dairy foods, whole grains	Muscle maintenance, antioxidant	Anemia
K (menadione)	Intestinal bacteria, liver	Blood clotting	Blood-clotting problems

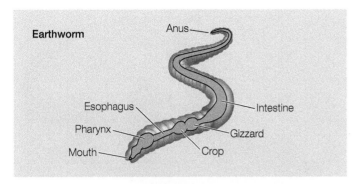

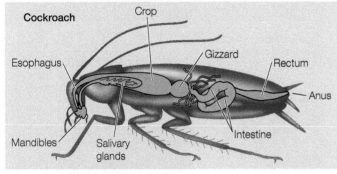

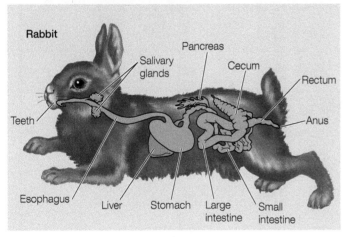

FIGURE 39.3 Compartments for Digestion and Absorption
(Page 770)

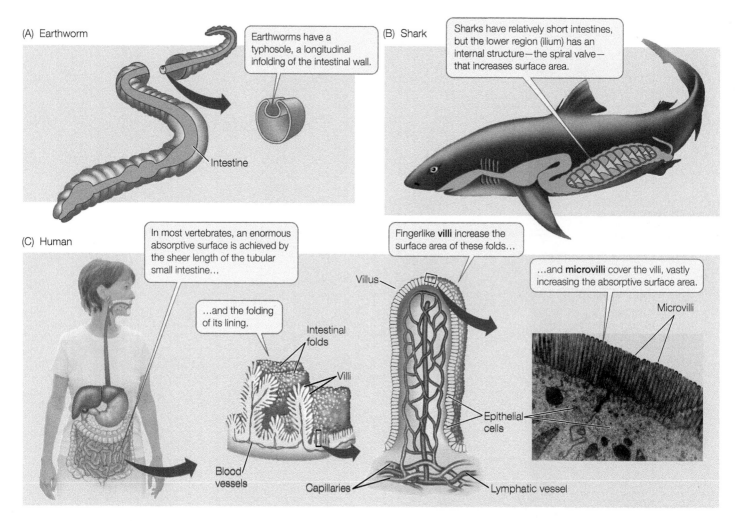

(A) Earthworm

Earthworms have a typhosole, a longitudinal infolding of the intestinal wall.

Intestine

(B) Shark

Sharks have relatively short intestines, but the lower region (ilium) has an internal structure—the spiral valve—that increases surface area.

(C) Human

In most vertebrates, an enormous absorptive surface is achieved by the sheer length of the tubular small intestine...

...and the folding of its lining.

Intestinal folds

Villi

Blood vessels

Fingerlike **villi** increase the surface area of these folds...

Villus

Epithelial cells

Capillaries

Lymphatic vessel

...and **microvilli** cover the villi, vastly increasing the absorptive surface area.

Microvilli

FIGURE 39.4 Intestinal Surface Area and Nutrient Absorption *(Page 771)*

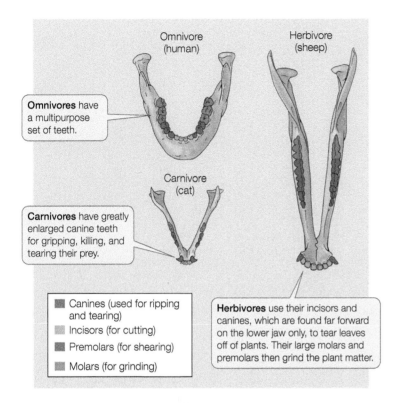

Omnivore (human)

Herbivore (sheep)

Omnivores have a multipurpose set of teeth.

Carnivore (cat)

Carnivores have greatly enlarged canine teeth for gripping, killing, and tearing their prey.

■ Canines (used for ripping and tearing)
■ Incisors (for cutting)
■ Premolars (for shearing)
■ Molars (for grinding)

Herbivores use their incisors and canines, which are found far forward on the lower jaw only, to tear leaves off of plants. Their large molars and premolars then grind the plant matter.

FIGURE 39.5 Mammalian Teeth *(Page 772)*

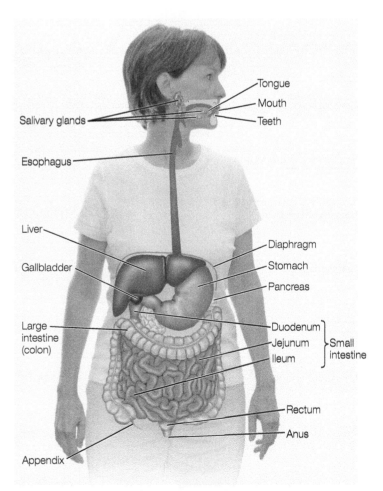

Tongue
Mouth
Teeth
Salivary glands
Esophagus
Liver
Diaphragm
Gallbladder
Stomach
Pancreas
Large intestine (colon)
Duodenum
Jejunum — Small intestine
Ileum
Rectum
Anus
Appendix

FIGURE 39.6 The Vertebrate Digestive System *(Page 773)*

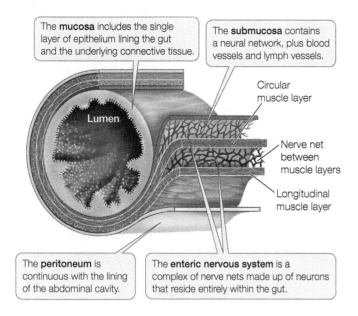

The **mucosa** includes the single layer of epithelium lining the gut and the underlying connective tissue.

The **submucosa** contains a neural network, plus blood vessels and lymph vessels.

Circular muscle layer

Lumen

Nerve net between muscle layers

Longitudinal muscle layer

The **peritoneum** is continuous with the lining of the abdominal cavity.

The **enteric nervous system** is a complex of nerve nets made up of neurons that reside entirely within the gut.

FIGURE 39.7 Tissue Layers of the Vertebrate Gut *(Page 773)*

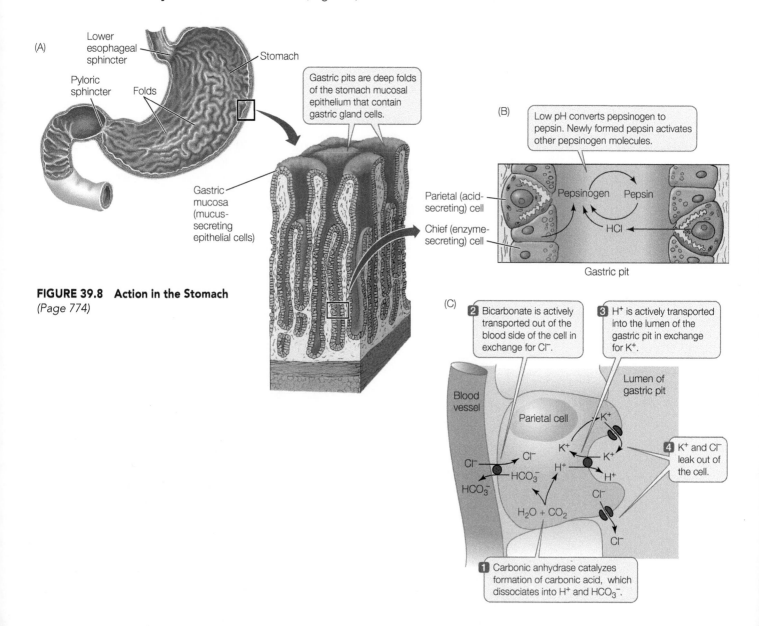

(A)

Lower esophageal sphincter

Stomach

Pyloric sphincter

Folds

Gastric pits are deep folds of the stomach mucosal epithelium that contain gastric gland cells.

Gastric mucosa (mucus-secreting epithelial cells)

FIGURE 39.8 Action in the Stomach *(Page 774)*

(B)

Low pH converts pepsinogen to pepsin. Newly formed pepsin activates other pepsinogen molecules.

Parietal (acid-secreting) cell

Chief (enzyme-secreting) cell

Pepsinogen   Pepsin

HCl

Gastric pit

(C)

2 Bicarbonate is actively transported out of the blood side of the cell in exchange for Cl^-.

3 H^+ is actively transported into the lumen of the gastric pit in exchange for K^+.

Lumen of gastric pit

Blood vessel

Parietal cell

K^+

K^+

K^+

4 K^+ and Cl^- leak out of the cell.

Cl^- Cl^-

HCO_3^-

HCO_3^-

H^+

H^+

Cl^-

$H_2O + CO_2$

Cl^-

1 Carbonic anhydrase catalyzes formation of carbonic acid, which dissociates into H^+ and HCO_3^-.

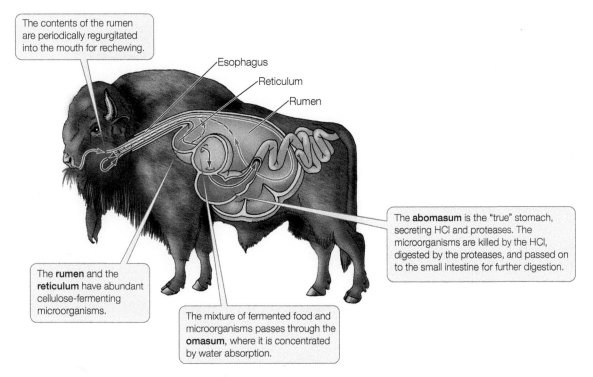

The contents of the rumen are periodically regurgitated into the mouth for rechewing.

Esophagus

Reticulum

Rumen

The **abomasum** is the "true" stomach, secreting HCl and proteases. The microorganisms are killed by the HCl, digested by the proteases, and passed on to the small intestine for further digestion.

The **rumen** and the **reticulum** have abundant cellulose-fermenting microorganisms.

The mixture of fermented food and microorganisms passes through the **omasum**, where it is concentrated by water absorption.

FIGURE 39.9   A Ruminant's Stomach *(Page 775)*

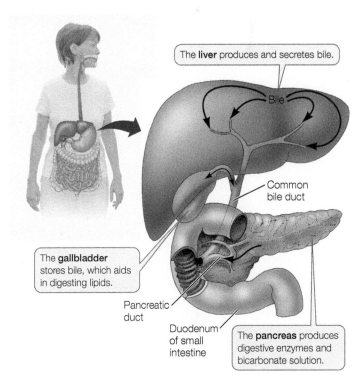

The **liver** produces and secretes bile.

Bile

Common bile duct

The **gallbladder** stores bile, which aids in digesting lipids.

Pancreatic duct

Duodenum of small intestine

The **pancreas** produces digestive enzymes and bicarbonate solution.

FIGURE 39.10   The Liver, Gallbladder, and Pancreas *(Page 776)*

(A) Digestion of fats

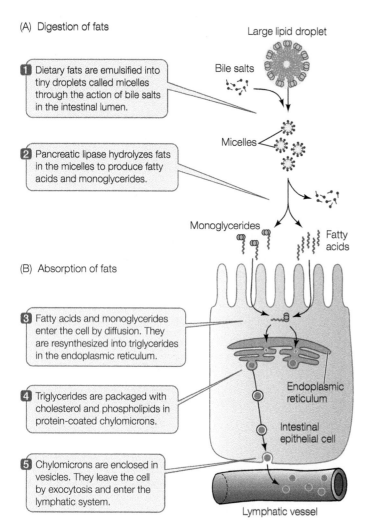

Large lipid droplet

Bile salts

1 Dietary fats are emulsified into tiny droplets called micelles through the action of bile salts in the intestinal lumen.

Micelles

2 Pancreatic lipase hydrolyzes fats in the micelles to produce fatty acids and monoglycerides.

Monoglycerides

Fatty acids

(B) Absorption of fats

3 Fatty acids and monoglycerides enter the cell by diffusion. They are resynthesized into triglycerides in the endoplasmic reticulum.

Endoplasmic reticulum

4 Triglycerides are packaged with cholesterol and phospholipids in protein-coated chylomicrons.

Intestinal epithelial cell

5 Chylomicrons are enclosed in vesicles. They leave the cell by exocytosis and enter the lymphatic system.

Lymphatic vessel

FIGURE 39.11   Digestion and Absorption of Fats (Page 776)

TABLE 39.3	Major Digestive Enzymes of Humans
SOURCE/ENZYME	**ACTION**
SALIVARY GLANDS	
Salivary amylase	Starch → Maltose
STOMACH	
Pepsin	Proteins → Peptides; autocatalysis
PANCREAS	
Pancreatic amylase	Starch → Maltose
Lipase	Fats → Fatty acids and glycerol
Nuclease	Nucleic acids → Nucleotides
Trypsin	Proteins → Peptides; zymogen activation
Chymotrypsin	Proteins → Peptides
Carboxypeptidase	Peptides → Shorter peptide and amino acids
SMALL INTESTINE	
Aminopeptidase	Peptides → Shorter peptides and amino acids
Dipeptidase	Dipeptides → Amino acids
Enterokinase	Trypsinogen → Trypsin
Nuclease	Nucleic acids → Nucleotides
Maltase	Maltose → Glucose
Lactase	Lactose → Galactose and glucose
Sucrase	Sucrose → Fructose and glucose

(Page 777)

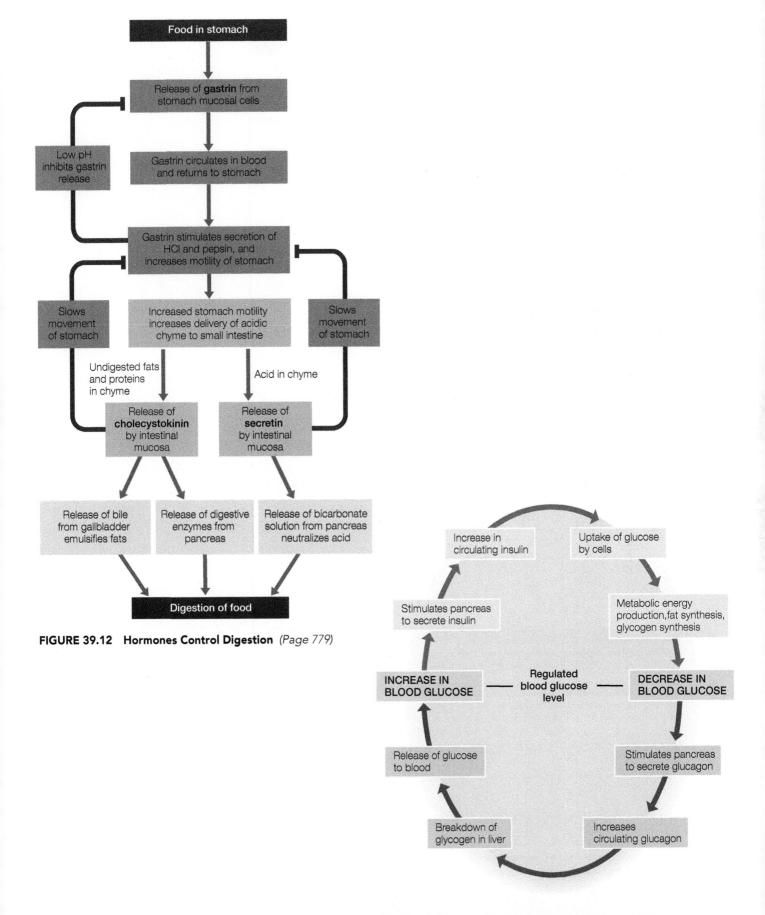

FIGURE 39.12   Hormones Control Digestion *(Page 779)*

FIGURE 39.13   Regulating Glucose Levels in the Blood *(Page 779)*

INVESTIGATION

FIGURE 39.14 A Single-Gene Mutation Leads to Obesity in Mice In mice the *Ob* gene codes for the protein leptin, a satiety factor that signals the brain when enough food has been consumed. The recessive *ob* allele is a loss-of-function allele, so *ob/ob* mice do not produce leptin; they do not experience satiety and become obese. The *Db* gene encodes the leptin receptor, so mice homozygous for the recessive loss-of-function allele *db*, even if they produce leptin, cannot use it and so become obese.

HYPOTHESIS

Mice who cannot produce the satiety signal protein leptin will not become obese if they are able to obtain leptin from an outside source.

METHOD
1. Create two strains of genetically obese laboratory mice, one of which lacks functional leptin (genotype *ob/ob*) and one which lacks the receptor for leptin (genotype *db/db*).
2. Create parabiotic pairs by surgically joining the circulatory systems of a non-obese (wild-type) mouse with a partner from one of the obese strains.
3. Allow mice to feed at will.

Parabiotic pair

Wild-type mouse   Genetically obese mouse
(*Ob/–* and *Db/–*)   (either *ob/ob* or *db/db*)

RESULTS
Parabiotic *ob/ob* mice obtain leptin from the wild-type partner and lose fat. Parabiotic *db/db* mice remain obese because they lack the leptin receptor and thus the leptin they obtain from their partner has no effect.

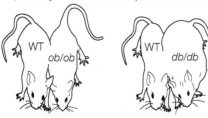

CONCLUSION

The protein leptin is a satiety signal that acts to prevent overeating and resultant obesity.

ANALYZE THE DATA

In a further experiment, leptin was purified and injected into *ob/ob* and *Ob/Ob* (wild-type) mice daily. The data in the table were collected before the injections began (baseline) and 10 days later.

Parameter	Baseline		Day 10	
	ob/ob	*Ob/Ob*	*ob/ob*	*Ob/Ob*
Food intake (g/day)	12.0	5.5	5.0	6.0
Body mass (g)	64	35	50	38
Metabolic rate (ml O$_2$/kg/hr)	900	1150	1100	1150
Body temperature (°C)	34.8	37.0	37.0	37.0

A. Do the data support the hypothesis that leptin is a satiety signal? Why or why not?
B. Discuss what factors might explain the loss of body mass in the *ob/ob* mice.

Go to **yourBioPortal.com** for original citations, discussions, and relevant links for all INVESTIGATION figures.

Salt and Water Balance and Nitrogen Excretion

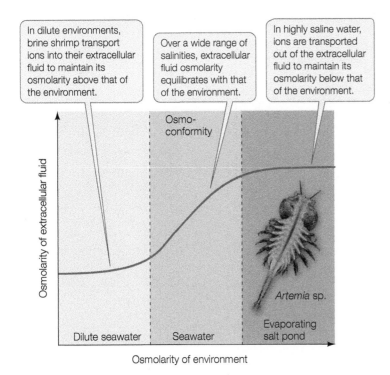

In dilute environments, brine shrimp transport ions into their extracellular fluid to maintain its osmolarity above that of the environment.

Over a wide range of salinities, extracellular fluid osmolarity equilibrates with that of the environment.

In highly saline water, ions are transported out of the extracellular fluid to maintain its osmolarity below that of the environment.

Osmolarity of extracellular fluid

Osmo-conformity

Artemia sp.

Dilute seawater | Seawater | Evaporating salt pond

Osmolarity of environment

FIGURE 40.1 Osmoconformity Has Limits *(Page 785)*

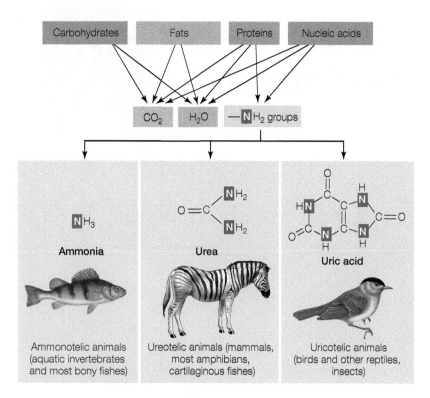

FIGURE 40.2 Waste Products of Metabolism *(Page 787)*

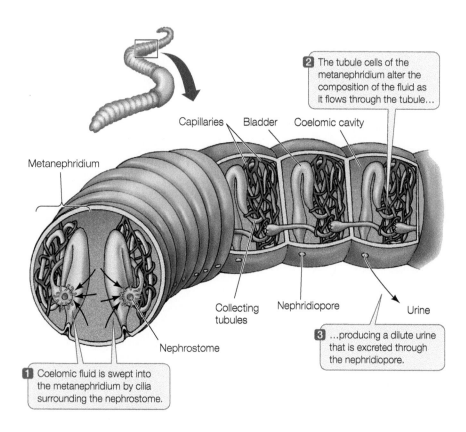

FIGURE 40.3 Metanephridia in Earthworms *(Page 788)*

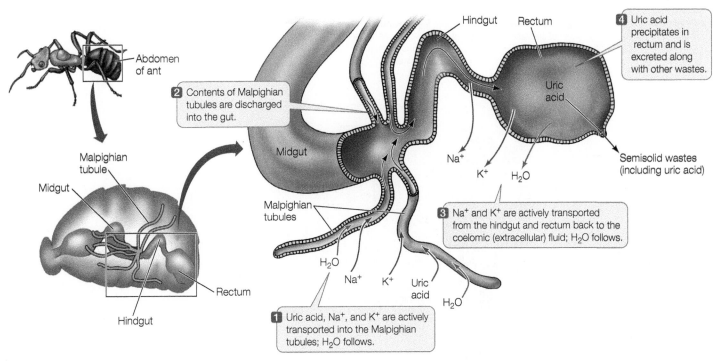

Abdomen of ant

2 Contents of Malpighian tubules are discharged into the gut.

Hindgut   Rectum

4 Uric acid precipitates in rectum and is excreted along with other wastes.

Uric acid

Midgut

Malpighian tubule

Midgut

Rectum

Hindgut

Malpighian tubules

Na+

K+   H2O

Semisolid wastes (including uric acid)

3 Na+ and K+ are actively transported from the hindgut and rectum back to the coelomic (extracellular) fluid; H2O follows.

H2O

Na+

K+

Uric acid

H2O

1 Uric acid, Na+, and K+ are actively transported into the Malpighian tubules; H2O follows.

FIGURE 40.4   Malpighian Tubules in Insects *(Page 789)*

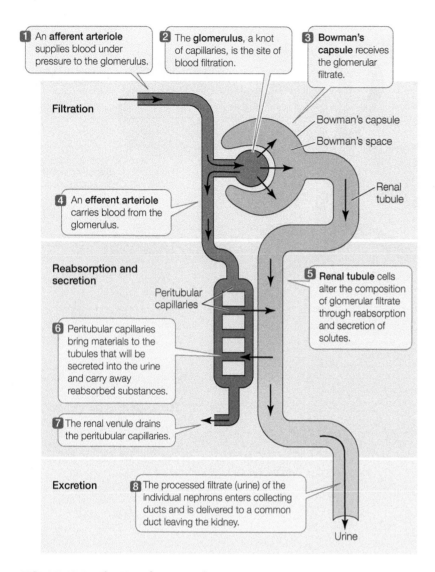

1 An **afferent arteriole** supplies blood under pressure to the glomerulus.

2 The **glomerulus**, a knot of capillaries, is the site of blood filtration.

3 **Bowman's capsule** receives the glomerular filtrate.

Filtration

Bowman's capsule

Bowman's space

Renal tubule

4 An **efferent arteriole** carries blood from the glomerulus.

Reabsorption and secretion

Peritubular capillaries

5 **Renal tubule** cells alter the composition of glomerular filtrate through reabsorption and secretion of solutes.

6 Peritubular capillaries bring materials to the tubules that will be secreted into the urine and carry away reabsorbed substances.

7 The renal venule drains the peritubular capillaries.

Excretion

8 The processed filtrate (urine) of the individual nephrons enters collecting ducts and is delivered to a common duct leaving the kidney.

Urine

FIGURE 40.5 The Vertebrate Nephron *(Page 789)*

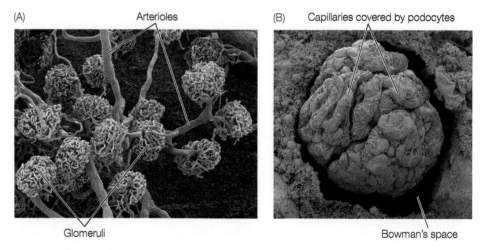

(A) Arterioles

Glomeruli

(B) Capillaries covered by podocytes

Bowman's space

FIGURE 40.6 A Tour of the Nephron *(Page 790)*

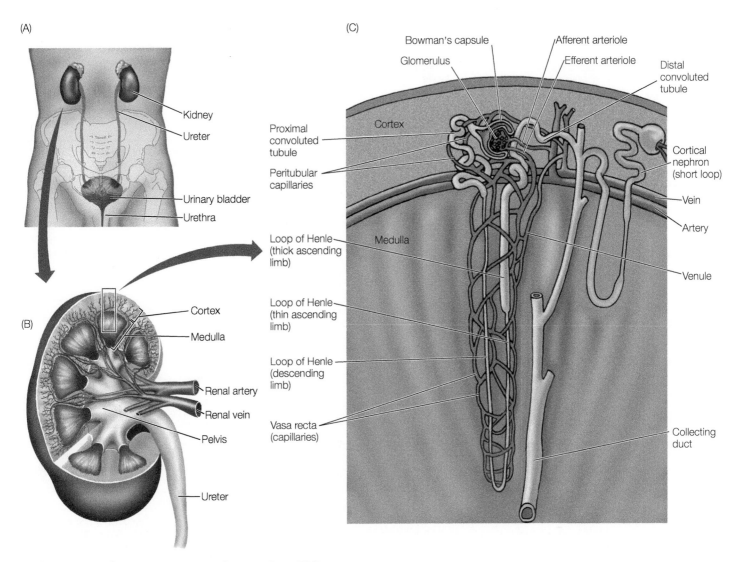

FIGURE 40.7 The Human Excretory System *(Page 792)*

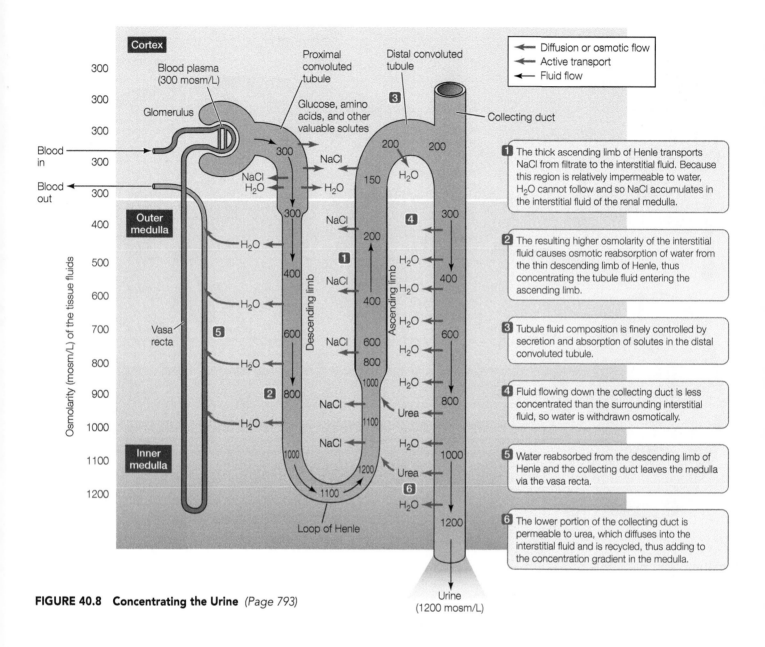

FIGURE 40.8 Concentrating the Urine *(Page 793)*

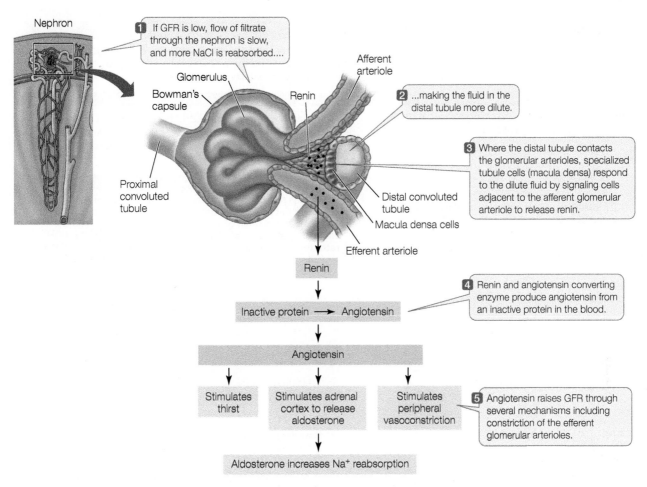

Nephron

1 If GFR is low, flow of filtrate through the nephron is slow, and more NaCl is reabsorbed....

Glomerulus

Bowman's capsule

Renin

Afferent arteriole

2 ...making the fluid in the distal tubule more dilute.

3 Where the distal tubule contacts the glomerular arterioles, specialized tubule cells (macula densa) respond to the dilute fluid by signaling cells adjacent to the afferent glomerular arteriole to release renin.

Proximal convoluted tubule

Distal convoluted tubule

Macula densa cells

Efferent arteriole

Renin

4 Renin and angiotensin converting enzyme produce angiotensin from an inactive protein in the blood.

Inactive protein ⟶ Angiotensin

Angiotensin

Stimulates thirst

Stimulates adrenal cortex to release aldosterone

Stimulates peripheral vasoconstriction

5 Angiotensin raises GFR through several mechanisms including constriction of the efferent glomerular arterioles.

Aldosterone increases Na⁺ reabsorption

FIGURE 40.9 Renin-Angiotensin-Aldosterone System Helps Regulate GFR (Page 796)

INVESTIGATION

FIGURE 40.10 ADH Induces Insertion of Aquaporins into Plasma Membranes Aquaporin proteins make some regions of renal tubules permeable to water. One aquaporin, AQP-2, is responsible for the permeability of the collecting duct cells. How does antidiuretic hormone (ADH) act on these proteins to control the level of permeability in renal cells?

HYPOTHESIS

ADH controls permeability by changing the location of aquaporin proteins.

METHOD
1. Isolate collecting ducts from rat kidney.
2. Use immunochemical staining to localize AQP-2 in collecting duct cells with and without ADH, and after ADH is applied and then washed away.
3. Measure the water permeability of the collecting duct cells under the same three conditions.

RESULTS

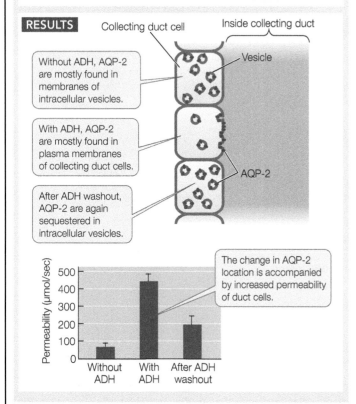

Collecting duct cell   Inside collecting duct

Without ADH, AQP-2 are mostly found in membranes of intracellular vesicles.

Vesicle

With ADH, AQP-2 are mostly found in plasma membranes of collecting duct cells.

After ADH washout, AQP-2 are again sequestered in intracellular vesicles.

AQP-2

The change in AQP-2 location is accompanied by increased permeability of duct cells.

CONCLUSION

In the absence of ADH, AQP-2 is sequestered intracellularly. When ADH is present, these water channels are inserted into the plasma membranes, making the cells more permeable to water.

ANALYZE THE DATA

The results showed that ADH controls the location of AQP-2 in collecting duct cells, but does it also affect the amount of AQP-2? The Brattleboro strain of rats does not produce ADH, and the DI strain of mice has a defect in the signaling pathway of the ADH receptor. The amount of AQP-2 produced in response to ADH and an ADH receptor antagonist was studied in these animals. Values were normalized to baseline amounts in normal animals.

Treatment	Amount of AQP-2			
	Normal rat	Brattleboro rat	Normal mouse	DI mouse
Baseline	1.0	0.5	1.0	0.1
ADH	1.0	1.5	1.0	0.1
ADH receptor antagonist	0.5	0.5	0.5	0.1

A. How does ADH affect the amount of AQP-2 in normal and Brattleboro rats? Explain the difference in the responses of the two rat strains.

B. Why does ADH not have an effect on the amount of AQP-2 in DI mice?

C. Considering these data as a whole, construct a hypothesis to explain why Brattleboro mice can maintain AQP-2 levels at 50% of normal. How would you test your hypothesis?

Go to **yourBioPortal.com** for original citations, discussions, and relevant links for all INVESTIGATION figures.

FIGURE 40.11   Salt excretion in a marine bird (Page 797)

(A) Before conditioning

Food is an unconditioned stimulus (US) that produces an unconditioned response (UR).

Sound is a neutral stimulus that produces no response.

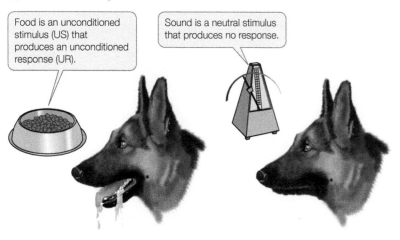

(B) Conditioning

Conditioning repeatedly presents the US immediately following presentation of the neutral stimulus.

+

(C) After conditioning

The neutral stimulus has become a conditioned stimulus (CS) that by itself produces the conditioned response (CR).

FIGURE 41.1 The Conditioned Reflex *(Page 800)*

(A)

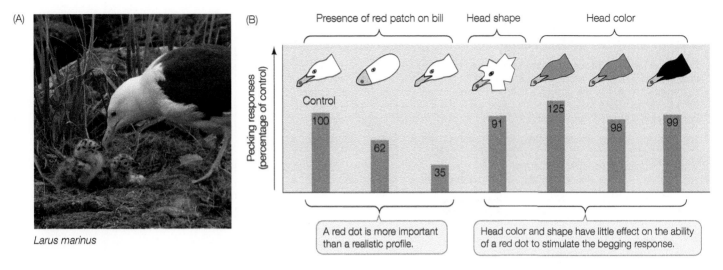

Larus marinus

(B)

Presence of red patch on bill   Head shape   Head color

Pecking responses (percentage of control)

Control
100

62

35

91

125

98

99

A red dot is more important than a realistic profile.

Head color and shape have little effect on the ability of a red dot to stimulate the begging response.

FIGURE 41.2 Releasing a Fixed Action Pattern *(Page 801)*

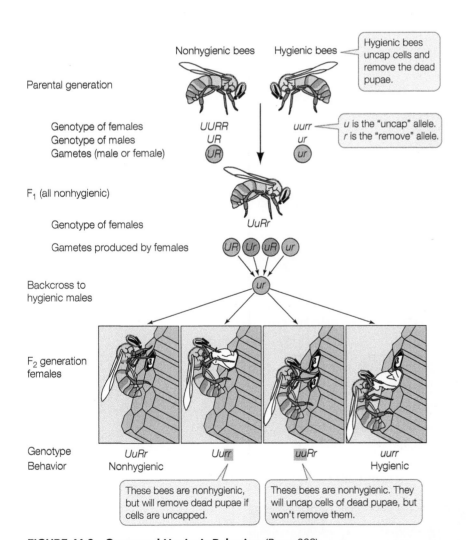

Nonhygienic bees   Hygienic bees

Hygienic bees uncap cells and remove the dead pupae.

Parental generation

Genotype of females   UURR   uurr
Genotype of males   UR   ur
Gametes (male or female)   UR   ur

u is the "uncap" allele.
r is the "remove" allele.

F₁ (all nonhygienic)

Genotype of females   UuRr

Gametes produced by females   UR Ur uR ur

Backcross to hygienic males   ur

F₂ generation females

Genotype   UuRr   Uurr   uuRr   uurr
Behavior   Nonhygienic   Hygienic

These bees are nonhygienic, but will remove dead pupae if cells are uncapped.

These bees are nonhygienic. They will uncap cells of dead pupae, but won't remove them.

FIGURE 41.3 Genes and Hygienic Behavior *(Page 802)*

INVESTIGATION

FIGURE 41.4   The Mouse Vomeronasal Organ Identifies Gender   The mouse VNO is located adjacent to the nasal passages. It contains pheromone receptors whose input travels to a specific region of the olfactory bulb (the accessory olfactory bulb). Dulac used knockout mice to demonstrate that pheromone receptors in the VNO are involved in stimulating mating behaviors in male mice (pursuit of females and aggression toward other males).

HYPOTHESIS

When the receptors in a male's VNO bind to sex pheromones produced by other mice, the receptors stimulate mating behavior.

METHOD

1. Create knockout mice in which a gene necessary for VNO receptor signaling is inactivated.
2. Place knockout male mice with wild-type females and wild-type males and observe their behavior.

Brain   Olfactory lobe of brain   Vomeronasal nerves   Nasal cavity   Nostril   Nasal epithelium   Vomeronasal organ

RESULTS

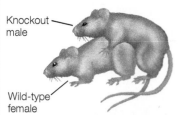

Knockout males pursued and mated with wild-type females

Knockout male   Wild-type female

Knockout males also pursued and attempted to mate with wild-type males

Wild-type male   Knockout male

CONCLUSION

Properly functioning VNO receptors appear to be essential not for sexual attraction, but for gender identification.

ANALYZE THE DATA

Mice have two pheromone receptors in the VNO, VN1 and VN2. Knockout males in which either the VN1 or VN2 receptor was inactivated were exposed to either a wild-type male, a castrated male, or a female. The results are shown in the table. M indicates that the test male tried to mate with the introduced individual, O means that he did not react to the individuals, and A indicates that he was aggressive towards that individual.

Introduced individual	Genotype of resident male		
	Wild type	VN1 knockout	VN2 knockout
Male	A	O	M
Castrated male	O	O	M
Female	M	M	M

A. What behavioral trait is dependent on a functional VN1 receptor?

B. What behavioral trait is dependent on a functional VN2 receptor?

C. If a male mouse lacked both a VN1 receptor and a VN2 receptor, how would he react to an introduced wild-type male?

Go to **yourBioPortal.com** for original citations, discussions, and relevant links for all INVESTIGATION figures.

(A) Female rats

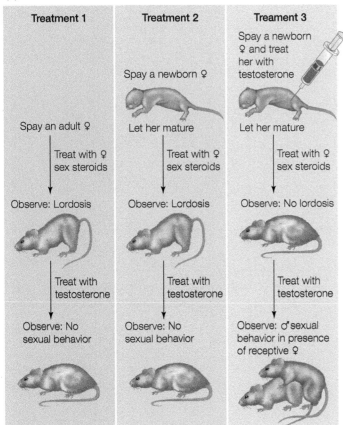

(B) Male rats

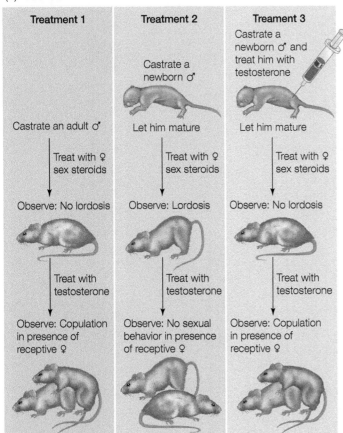

FIGURE 41.5 Hormonal Control of Sexual Behavior *(Page 804)*

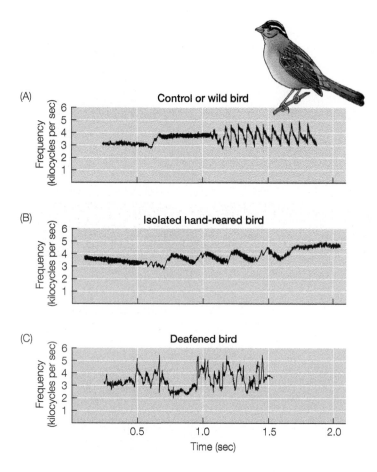

(A) Control or wild bird

(B) Isolated hand-reared bird

(C) Deafened bird

FIGURE 41.6 Sensitive Periods for Song Learning *(Page 805)*

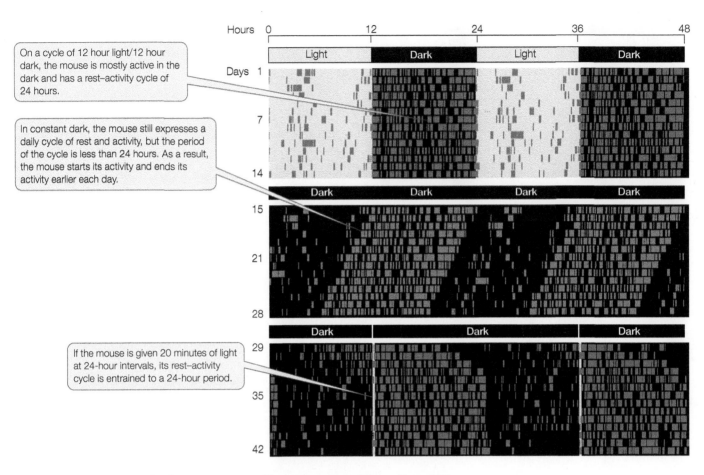

FIGURE 41.7   Circadian Rhythms Are Entrained by Environmental Cues *(Page 807)*

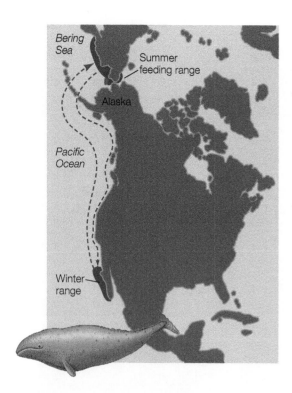

FIGURE 41.8 Piloting *(Page 808)*

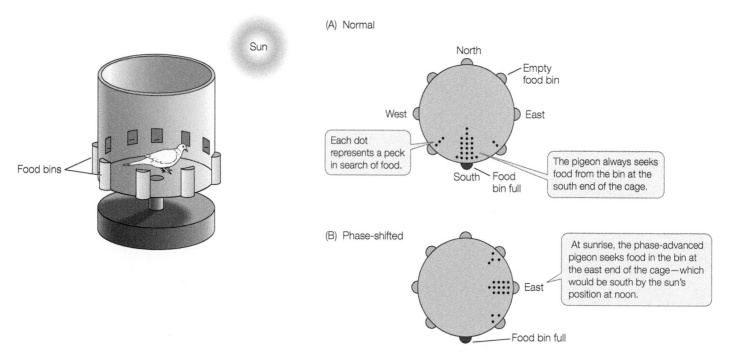

FIGURE 41.9 A Time-Compensated Solar Compass *(Page 809)*

(A)

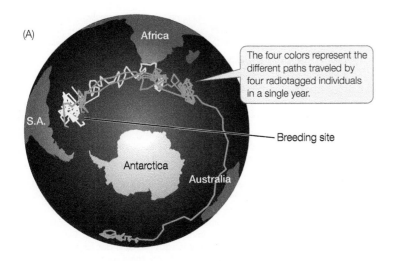

The four colors represent the different paths traveled by four radiotagged individuals in a single year.

Breeding site

S.A.

Africa

Antarctica

Australia

FIGURE 41.10   **Coming Home** (Page 810)

(B) *Thalassarche chrysostoma*

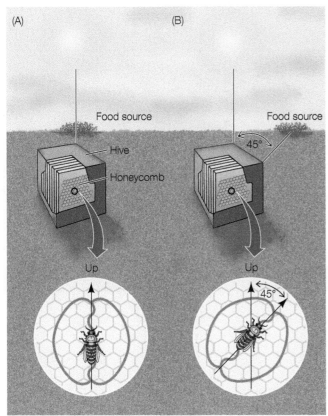

(A)   (B)

Food source   Food source
                        45°
Hive
Honeycomb

Up   Up
                       45°

Pattern of waggle dance   Pattern of waggle dance

FIGURE 41.11   The Waggle Dance of the Honey Bee
(Page 811)

INVESTIGATION

FIGURE 41.12 The Costs of Defending a Territory
By using testosterone implants to increase territorial behavior, Moore and Marler measured the costs to male Yarrow's spiny lizards (*Sceloporus jarrovii*) of defending a territory during the summer, when they do not normally do so.

HYPOTHESIS

Yarrow's spiny lizards do not defend a territory during summer because the energetic costs of territorial behavior in that season outweigh the benefits.

METHOD

1. During the summer, when female lizards are not sexually receptive, insert testosterone capsules under the skin of some males; leave other males untreated as controls.
2. Observe the patterns of territorial behavior and the survival rate of the two groups of males.

RESULTS

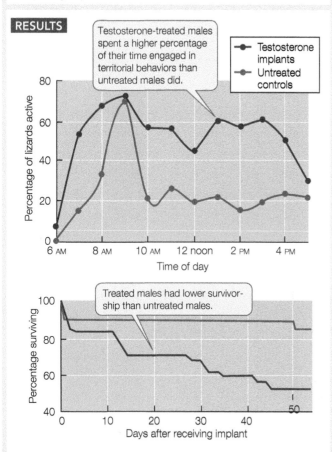

Testosterone-treated males spent a higher percentage of their time engaged in territorial behaviors than untreated males did.

- Testosterone implants
- Untreated controls

Treated males had lower survivorship than untreated males.

CONCLUSION

For these lizards, the cost of defending territories during summer significantly reduces their survival rate without increasing their reproductive success.

ANALYZE THE DATA

Given the trade-off between time spent in territorial behavior and time available for foraging, researchers hypothesized that the cost of territoriality should be reflected in decreased growth rates. Two measures of body size in a lizard are length (tip of snout to urogenital vent) and weight. Lizards were captured and implanted with testosterone capsules or empty capsules. The individual lizards varied widely in size at the time of capture, but the average size was the same for the two treatment groups. Three months later the lizards were recaptured and their sizes measured (see table).

Controls		Testosterone implants	
Weight (g)	Length (mm)	Weight (g)	Length (mm)
3.9	73	3.1	73
4.9	78	3.2	76
5.1	78	3.2	79
4.3	80	4.2	78
4.8	80	4.1	79
4.6	82	4.8	80
5.8	84	3.5	82
5.2	85	4.5	84
8.2	86	4.2	87
5.5	90	7.5	102
6.9	90		
6.4	91		
8.1	93		
7.0	94		
7.0	96		

A. For each treatment, calculate the mean and standard deviation for the two size measures.

B. Using statistical tests from Appendix B, what can you conclude from these data?

C. Since the lizards varied greatly in size at the beginning of the experiment, how could you use regression analysis to compare the two experimental groups?

Go to **yourBioPortal.com** for original citations, discussions, and relevant links for all INVESTIGATION figures.

Leontopithecus rosalia

FIGURE 41.13   Polyandry in a Small Primate *(Page 815)*

FIGURE 41.14   Helpers at the Nest *(Page 816)*

Heterocephalus glaber

FIGURE 41.15 A Eusocial Mammal *(Page 817)*

FIGURE 41.16 Group Living Provides Protection from Predators *(Page 817)*

Organisms in Their Environment

42

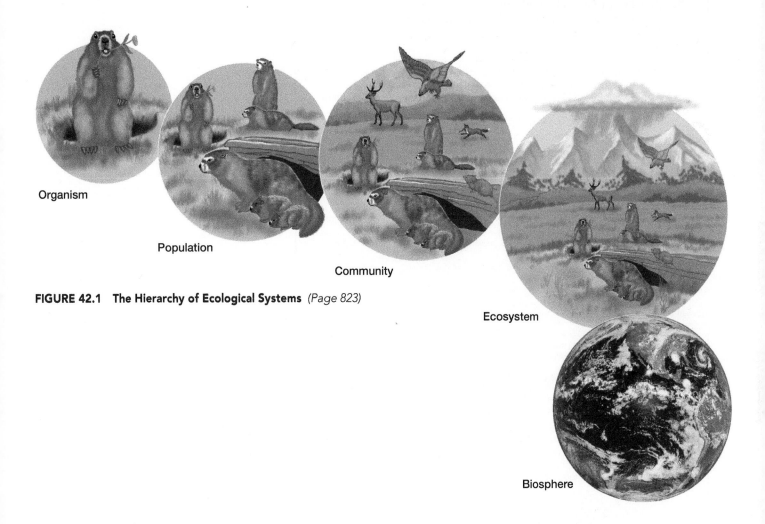

Organism

Population

Community

Ecosystem

Biosphere

FIGURE 42.1 **The Hierarchy of Ecological Systems** *(Page 823)*

INVESTIGATION

FIGURE 42.2 The Microbial Community of the Human Gut Depends on the Host's Diet To treat certain digestive disorders, doctors try to increase the relative abundance of beneficial *Bifidobacterium* bacteria in the human gut. This manipulation of the nutritional environment as a way of adjusting the species composition of the gut community is known as *prebiotic therapy*.

HYPOTHESIS

The abundance of beneficial *Bifidobacterium* bacteria in the human gut can be increased relative to pathogenic bacteria by including oligofructose in the diet.

METHOD

1. Feed 8 healthy human subjects a standardized experimental diet for 45 days. On days 1–15 supplement the diet with 15 g sucrose/day ("Sucrose 1"); on days 16–30, substitute 15 g oligofructose for the sucrose; on days 31–45 return to 15 g sucrose ("Sucrose 2").
2. Collect stool samples during each 15-day period and assay for bacterial composition and energy content.

RESULTS

The number of bifidobacteria was highest on the oligofructose diet.

The numbers of these potentially pathogenic bacteria were lowest on the oligofructose diet.

Type of bacteria	Number of bacteria ($\log_{10}$/g stool; mean ± SD)		
	Sucrose 1	Oligofructose	Sucrose 2
Bifidobacteria	**8.8 ± 0.5**	**9.5 ± 0.7**[a]	**8.9 ± 0.9**[b]
Lactobacilli	6.8 ± 1.2	7.0 ± 1.4	7.1 ± 1.0
Coliforms	6.0 ± 1.2	5.9 ± 0.7	5.8 ± 1.0
Gram-positive cocci	5.8 ± 1.0	5.8 ± 0.9	5.5 ± 0.8
Bacteroides	9.4 ± 0.8	8.8 ± 1.1[a]	8.9 ± 0.9[c]
Fusobacteria	8.5 ± 0.7	7.7 ± 0.9[a]	8.1 ± 0.8[c]
Clostridia	8.0 ± 1.2	7.5 ± 0.9[c]	7.7 ± 0.7

[a]Significantly different from sucrose 1 ($P < 0.01$).
[b]Significantly different from oligofructose ($P < 0.01$).
[c]Significantly different from sucrose 1 ($P < 0.05$).

CONCLUSION

Oligofructose stimulated the growth of bifidobacteria at the expense of potentially pathogenic bacteria.

ANALYZE THE DATA

Researchers measured the energy content of the subjects' stools and compared it with the energy content of the ingested oligofructose. The stools contained no oligofructose because it had been fermented—converted into bacterial biomass and waste heat.

	Energy (kJ/day)
Ingested as oligofructose	240
Excreted in stools	77

A. Was all of the oligofructose energy excreted?
B. What happened to the energy that wasn't excreted?
C. What do these observations suggest about the role of gut bacteria in host nutrition?
D. Why did the researchers follow the oligofructose diet with "Sucrose 2"? (Hint: If the microbial community in Sucrose 2 had not moved back toward its composition in Sucrose 1, would the Conclusion be different?)

Go to **yourBioPortal.com** for original citations, discussions, and relevant links for all INVESTIGATION figures.

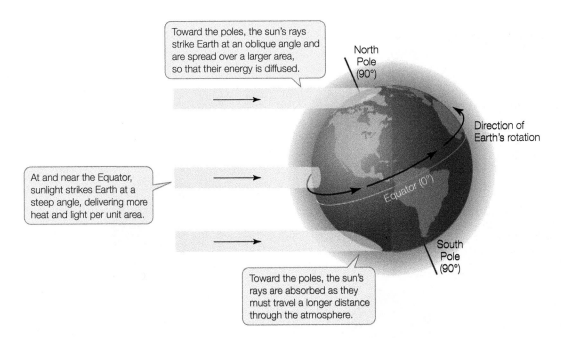

FIGURE 42.3 Solar Energy Input Varies with Latitude *(Page 826)*

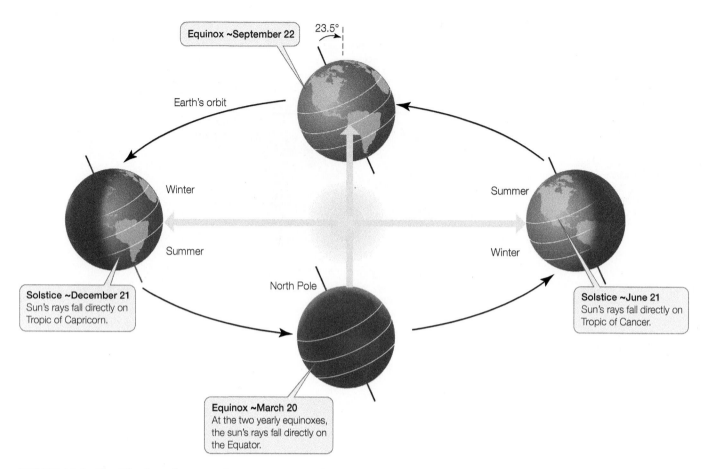

FIGURE 42.4   The Tilt of Earth's Axis of Rotation Causes the Seasons *(Page 826)*

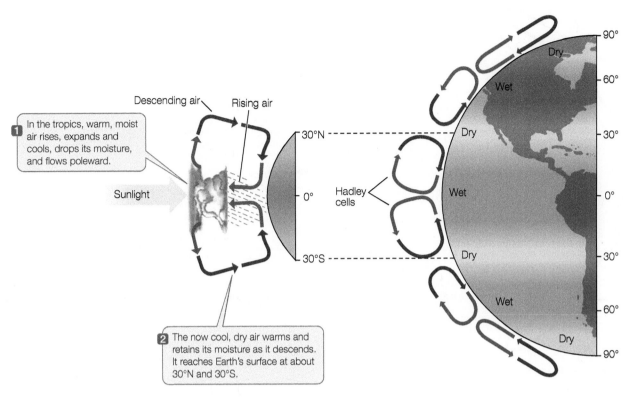

FIGURE 42.5   Global Atmospheric Circulation *(Page 827)*

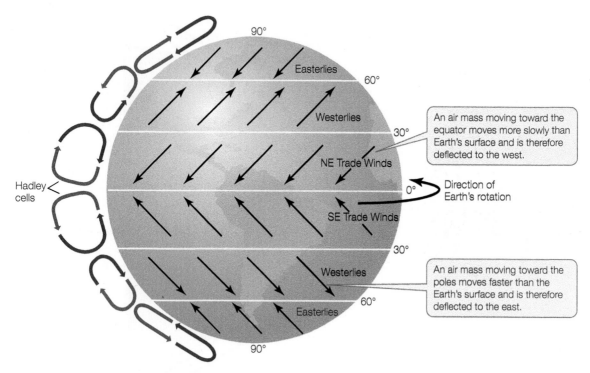

FIGURE 42.6 **Direction of Prevailing Surface Winds** *(Page 828)*

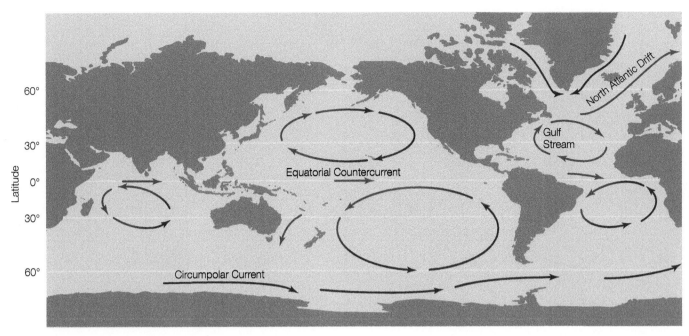

FIGURE 42.7   Ocean Currents *(Page 828)*

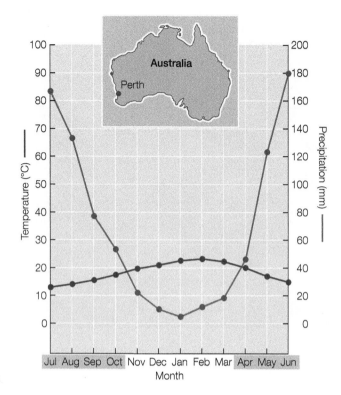

FIGURE 42.8   Walter Climate Diagrams Summarize Climate in an Ecologically Relevant Way *(Page 829)*

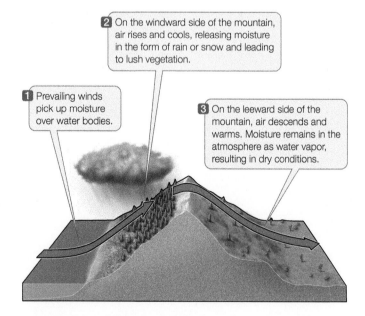

2 On the windward side of the mountain, air rises and cools, releasing moisture in the form of rain or snow and leading to lush vegetation.

1 Prevailing winds pick up moisture over water bodies.

3 On the leeward side of the mountain, air descends and warms. Moisture remains in the atmosphere as water vapor, resulting in dry conditions.

FIGURE 42.9   A Rain Shadow *(Page 830)*

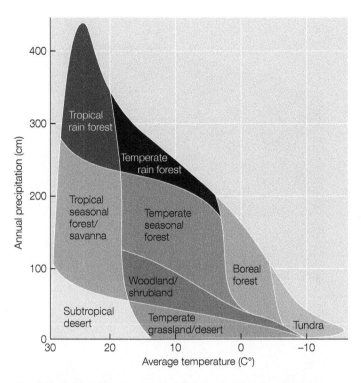

FIGURE 42.10 Temperature and Precipitation Gradients Determine Terrestrial Biomes *(Page 831)*

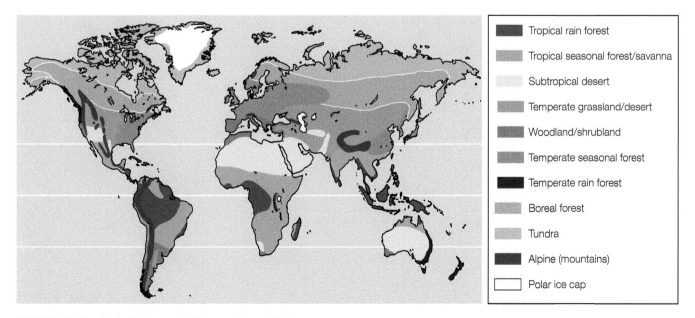

FIGURE 42.11 Global Terrestrial Biomes *(Page 831)*

(A)

(B)

(C)

(D)

FIGURE 42.12 Same Biome, Different Continents *(Page 832)*

TABLE 42.1   Major Aquatic Biomes

BIOME[a]	DESCRIPTION
FRESHWATER	
Rivers and streams	Flowing water. Many fast-flowing, small *source streams* form on high ground, feeding into networks of ever larger, slower-flowing streams and rivers. Biota adapted to constantly moving water.
Wetlands	Glades, swamps, and marshes. Rich biota adapted to water-saturated soil and/or standing fresh water.
Ponds and lakes	Significant bodies of standing fresh water. Ponds are smaller and shallower, subject to drying. Biotic zones determined by distance from shore and light penetration (see Figure 42.13A).
ESTUARIES[b]	
Salt marshes	Cool-temperate stands of salt-tolerant grasses, herbaceous plants, and low-growing shrubs. Crucial to nutrient cycling and coastal protection; rich habitat supporting diverse aquatic and terrestrial life.
Mangrove forests	Tropical and warm subtropical coasts and river deltas. Dominated by mangrove trees with aerial roots (see Figure 28.11A). Rich in animal life; protect against coastal erosion.
MARINE	
Intertidal	Sandy or rocky coastlines subject to rising and falling tides; organisms adapted to withstand both submerged and dry conditions, as well as the force of waves and moving water.
Kelp forests	Found in shallow coastal waters of temperate and cold regions. Dominated by large, leaflike brown algae (kelp) that support a wide variety of marine life.
Seagrass beds	"Meadows" of monocot grasses (see Figure 21.29C) found in shallow, light-filled temperate and tropical waters.
Coral reefs	Rich, highly endangered ecosystems of shallow tropical waters. Dependent on cnidarian corals (see Figure 23.9C) and their photosynthetic endosymbionts (see Concept 20.4).
Open ocean	The *pelagic zone* (see Figure 42.13B) is rich in photosynthetic planktonic organisms that support a host of marine animals. Below the level of light penetration, the *abyssal zone* supports a fauna largely dependent on detritus that sinks down from pelagic regions.
Hydrothermal vents	Abyssal ecosystems warmed by volcanic emissions. Chemolithotrophic prokaryotes (see Concept 19.3) nourish large annelid worms (see Figure 23.17B) and other invertebrates.

[a] A *benthic* region—silt, sand, or other substrate and the organisms encompassed there—occurs in all three biome types.

[b] *Estuaries* are coastal biomes where the water is brackish (i.e., fresh and salt water mix).

(Page 833)

(A) Lake depth zones

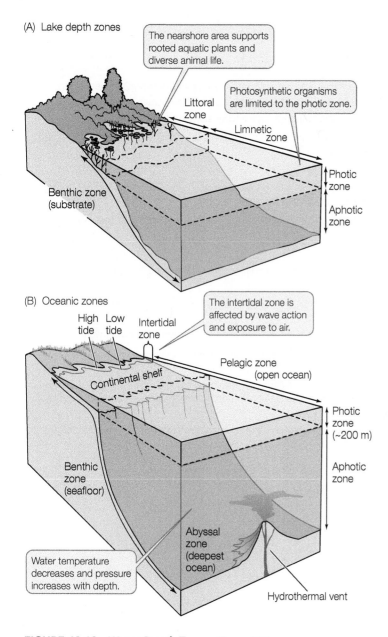

The nearshore area supports rooted aquatic plants and diverse animal life.

Photosynthetic organisms are limited to the photic zone.

Littoral zone

Limnetic zone

Photic zone

Aphotic zone

Benthic zone (substrate)

(B) Oceanic zones

The intertidal zone is affected by wave action and exposure to air.

High tide   Low tide

Intertidal zone

Pelagic zone (open ocean)

Continental shelf

Photic zone (~200 m)

Aphotic zone

Benthic zone (seafloor)

Abyssal zone (deepest ocean)

Water temperature decreases and pressure increases with depth.

Hydrothermal vent

FIGURE 42.13 Water-Depth Zones *(Page 834)*

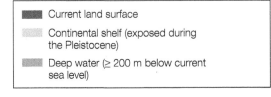

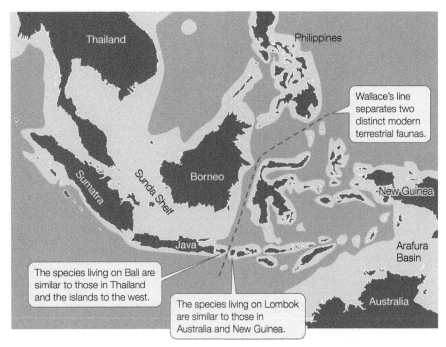

FIGURE 42.14 Wallace's Line *(Page 835)*

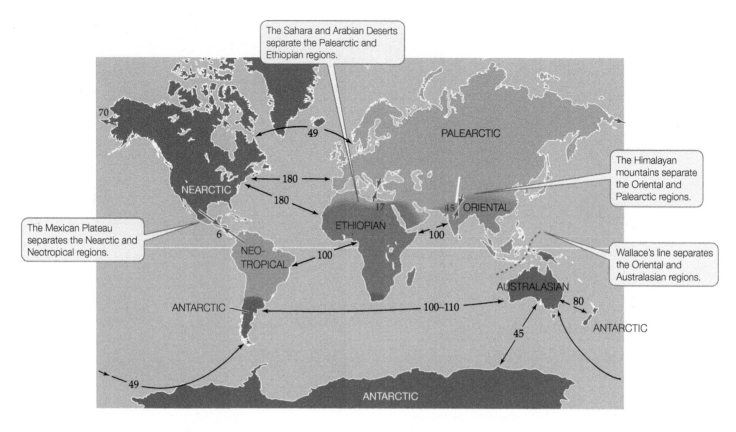

FIGURE 42.15 **Movement of the Continents Shaped Earth's Biogeographic Regions** *(Page 835)*

Nothofagus sp.

FIGURE 42.16   Distribution of *Nothofagus* *(Page 836)*

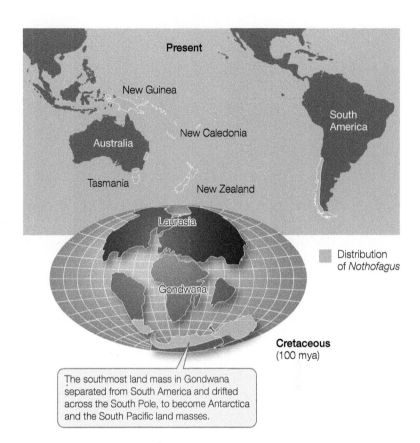

Present

New Guinea

Australia

New Caledonia

Tasmania

New Zealand

South America

Laurasia

Gondwana

Distribution of *Nothofagus*

Cretaceous (100 mya)

The southmost land mass in Gondwana separated from South America and drifted across the South Pole, to become Antarctica and the South Pacific land masses.

FIGURE 42.17   Human Agricultural Practices Produce a Uniform Landscape *(Page 838)*

FIGURE 42.18 Harmonious Grazers *(Page 840)*

Populations | 43

(A)

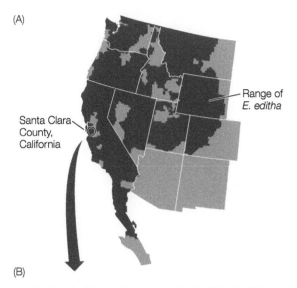

Santa Clara County, California

Range of *E. editha*

(B)

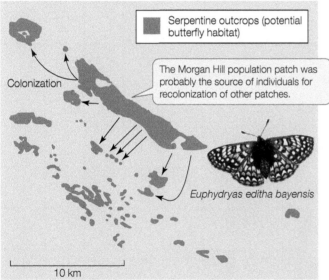

Serpentine outcrops (potential butterfly habitat)

Colonization

The Morgan Hill population patch was probably the source of individuals for recolonization of other patches.

Euphydryas editha bayensis

10 km

FIGURE 43.1 Species Are Patchily Distributed on Several Spatial Scales *(Page 843)*

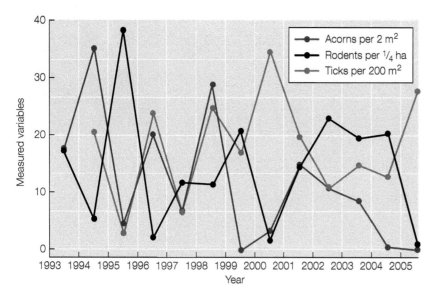

FIGURE 43.2   Population Densities Are Dynamic and Interconnected
(Page 844)

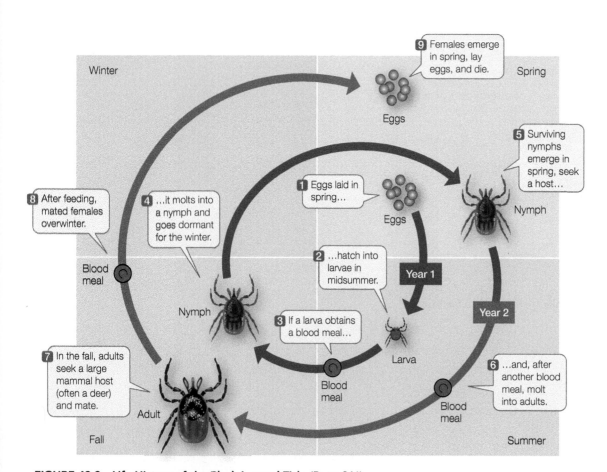

FIGURE 43.3   Life History of the Black-Legged Tick (Page 846)

TABLE 43.1	Life Table for the 1978 Cohort of Cactus Ground Finch on Isla Daphne		
CALENDAR YEAR	**AGE OF BIRD (YEARS)**	**SURVIVORSHIP**[a]	**FECUNDITY**[b]
1978	0 (hatchlings)	1.00	0.00
1979	1	0.43	0.05
1980	2	0.37	0.67
1981	3	0.33	1.50
1982	4	0.31	0.66
1983 Increased rain	5	0.30	5.50
1984	6	0.20	0.69
1985 Drought	7	0.11	0.00
1986	8	0.07	0.00
1987	9	0.07	2.20
1988	10	0.05	0.00
1989	11	0.05	0.00

[a] Survivorship = the proportion of the original cohort (here, 210 birds) surviving from fledging to age x.

[b] Fecundity = average number of young fledged per female of age x.

(Page 847)

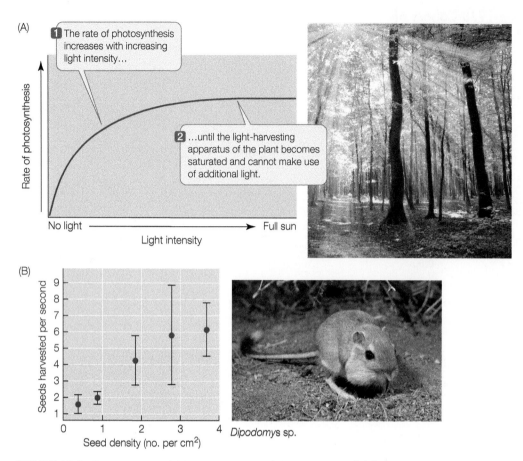

FIGURE 43.4 Resource Acquisition Increases with Resource Availability *(Page 847)*

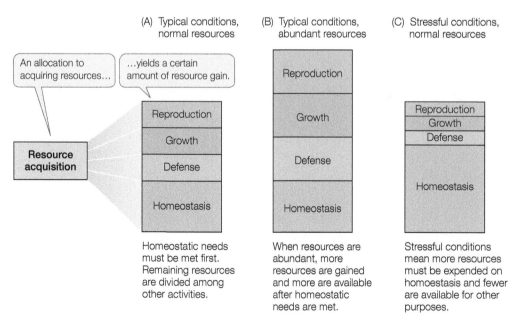

FIGURE 43.5 The Principle of Allocation *(Page 848)*

INVESTIGATION

FIGURE 43.6 Climate Warming Stresses Spiny Lizards
Barry Sinervo and colleagues investigated whether higher daytime temperatures can reduce the number of hours that Mexican blue spiny lizards (*Sceloporus serrifer*) can remain outside their burrows without overheating. The researchers knew that climate warming was taking place in Mexico, and that the lizards cannot feed while inside their burrows.

HYPOTHESIS

Spiny lizards are able to forage for fewer hours on hotter days.

METHOD

1. Construct model "lizards" that have the same thermal properties as actual lizards.

2. At 4 sites in the Yucatán, place model lizards in various sunny and shady perches known to be used by real lizards in 1975. In 2008, monitor body temperature of the models and record maximum daily air temperatures throughout the breeding season (March and April).

3. For each day, calculate the number of daylight hours when the body temperature T_b of the thermal models exceeded 31°C—the temperature at which *S. serrifer* are known to retreat to their burrows and become inactive.

4. Determine whether the number of inactive hours increased with maximum air temperature.

RESULTS

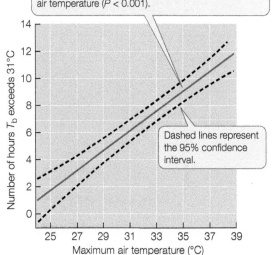

The number of hours during which lizards were inactive—and hence could not forage—increased by 0.74 hours for each °C of increase in daily maximum air temperature ($P < 0.001$).

Dashed lines represent the 95% confidence interval.

CONCLUSION

Climate warming can decrease the number of hours per day when *S. serrifer* can forage without overheating.

ANALYZE THE DATA

Between 1975 and 2008, the *S. serrifer* populations went extinct at two of the four sites surveyed. Examine the graph at right and answer the questions below.

A. How did the hours available for foraging differ between sites where the lizards had gone extinct versus where they persisted?

B. How might that difference in foraging time influence lizard fecundity, survivorship, and per capita growth rates?

C. Could global warming have caused the extinctions of the lizard populations? Explain your answer.

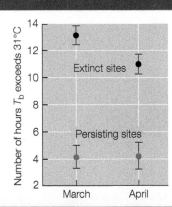

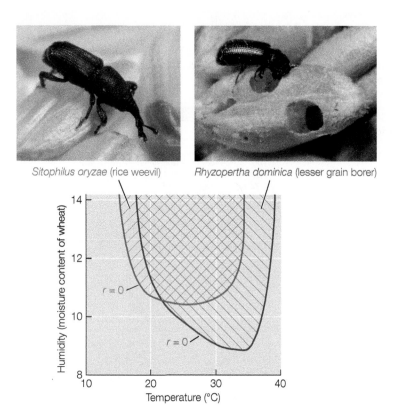

Sitophilus oryzae (rice weevil) *Rhyzopertha dominica* (lesser grain borer)

FIGURE 43.7 Environmental Conditions Affect Per Capita Growth Rates and Species Distributions *(Page 850)*

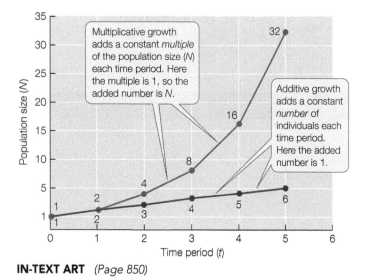

Multiplicative growth adds a constant *multiple* of the population size (*N*) each time period. Here the multiple is 1, so the added number is *N*.

Additive growth adds a constant *number* of individuals each time period. Here the added number is 1.

IN-TEXT ART *(Page 850)*

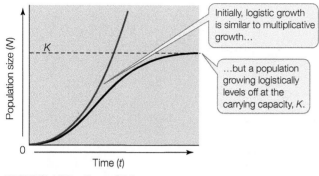

IN-TEXT ART *(Page 851)*

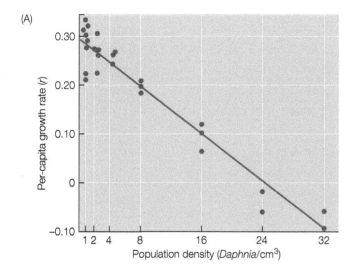

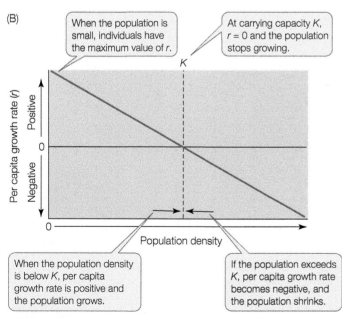

FIGURE 43.8 Per Capita Growth Rate Decreases with Population Density *(Page 852)*

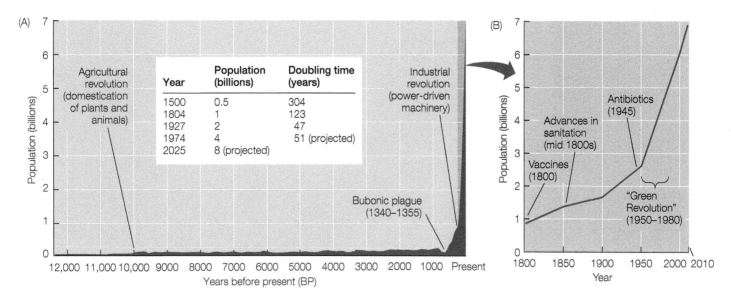

FIGURE 43.9 **Human Population Growth** (Page 853)

The table in panel (A):

Year	Population (billions)	Doubling time (years)
1500	0.5	304
1804	1	123
1927	2	47
1974	4	51 (projected)
2025	8 (projected)	

FIGURE 43.10 **A Metapopulation Has Many Subpopulations**
(Page 854)

INVESTIGATION

FIGURE 43.11 Corridors Can Rescue Some Populations Data from the experiments summarized here suggest that corridors between patches of habitat increase the chances of recolonization, and thus of subpopulation persistence.

HYPOTHESIS

Subpopulations of a fragmented metapopulation are more likely to persist if there is no barrier to recolonization.

METHOD

1. On replicate moss-covered boulders, scrape off the continuous cover of moss to create a "landscape" of moss "mainland" with patches surrounded by bare rock. A central 50 cm × 50 cm moss "mainland" (M) is surrounded by 12 circular patches of moss, each 10 cm² (subpopulations). In the "insular" treatment (I), the patches are surrounded by bare rock (which is inhospitable to moss-dwelling small arthropods, and thus a barrier to recolonization). In the "corridor" treatment (C), the patches are connected to the mainland by a 7 × 2 cm strip of live moss. In the "broken-corridor" treatment (B), the configuration is the same as the "corridor" treatment, except that the moss strip is cut by a 2-cm strip of bare rock.

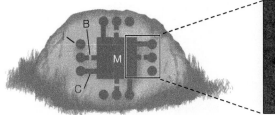

2. After 6 months, determine the number of small arthropod species present in each of the mainlands and small patches.

RESULTS

Patches connected to the mainland by corridors retained as many species as did the mainland to which they were connected. Fewer species remained in the broken-corridor and insular treatments.

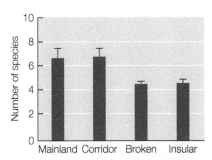

CONCLUSION

Barriers to recolonization reduce the number of subpopulations that persist in a metapopulation.

ANALYZE THE DATA

A. What percentage of the species present in the mainlands was lost, on average, in the corridor patches?

B. What percentage of the species present in the mainlands was lost, on average, in the insular and broken-corridor patches? What does this percentage tell you about the average risk of extinction for the subpopulation of each arthropod species in each patch?

C. The broken-corridor treatment controls for another factor that can affect extinction risk. What is this factor?

For more, go to Working with Data 43.1 at **yourBioPortal.com**.

Go to **yourBioPortal.com** for original citations, discussions, and relevant links for all INVESTIGATION figures.

FIGURE 43.12 A Corridor for Large Mammals *(Page 857)*

Ecological and Evolutionary Consequences of Species Interactions

(A)

Major Types of Species Interactions

TYPE OF INTERACTION	EFFECT ON SPECIES 1	EFFECT ON SPECIES 2
Competition	–	–
Consumer–resource: Predation, herbivory, parasitism	+	–
Mutualism	+	+
Commensalism	+	0
Amensalism	–	0

(C)

Consumer–resource
The American bison feeds on the grasses of the Great Plains.

Amensalism, Commensalism
The large mammal unwittingly destroys insects and their nests. The buffalo birds feed on insects disturbed by the bison's passage.

(D) *Tegeticula yuccasella*

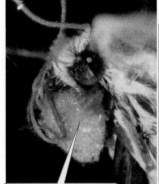

...and deposits the pollen on the stigma of another flower.

Mutualism
The female yucca moth collects and carries pollen grains in specialized mouthparts...

Female moths subsequently lay eggs in the plant's ovary. The resulting larvae eat some of the developing seeds.

(B)

Competition
Green plants compete for light. The leaves of tall trees have reduced the light available to the plants growing on the forest floor.

FIGURE 44.1 Types of Interspecific Interactions *(Page 861)*

Amphiprion ocellaris

FIGURE 44.2 Interactions between Species Are Not Always Clear-Cut *(Page 862)*

(A)

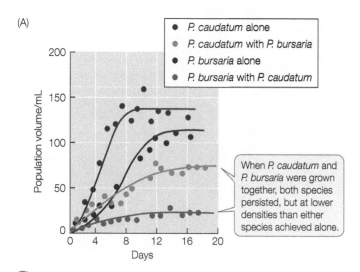

● *P. caudatum* alone
● *P. caudatum* with *P. bursaria*
● *P. bursaria* alone
● *P. bursaria* with *P. caudatum*

When *P. caudatum* and *P. bursaria* were grown together, both species persisted, but at lower densities than either species achieved alone.

(B)

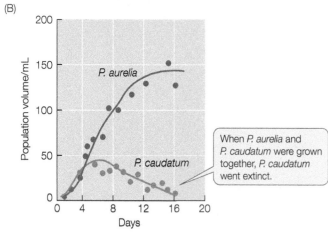

P. aurelia

P. caudatum

When *P. aurelia* and *P. caudatum* were grown together, *P. caudatum* went extinct.

FIGURE 44.3 Interspecific Competition Affects Population Growth *(Page 863)*

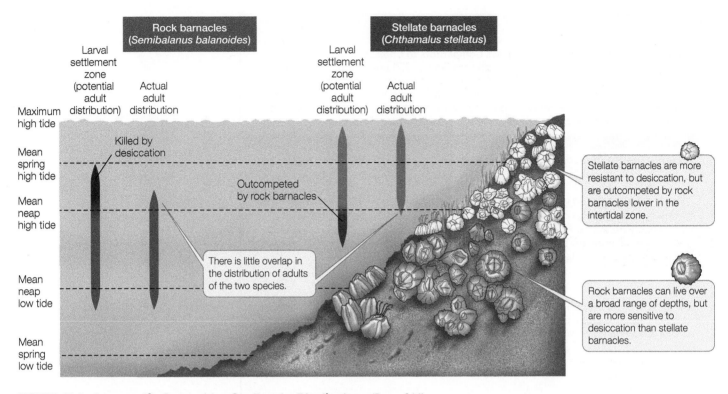

FIGURE 44.4   Interspecific Competition Can Restrict Distributions *(Page 864)*

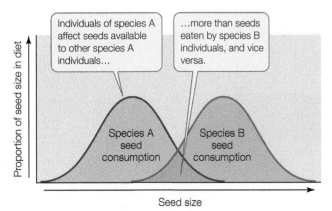

FIGURE 44.5   Resource Partitioning Can Result in Intraspecific Competition Being Greater than Interspecific Competition *(Page 865)*

INVESTIGATION

FIGURE 44.6 Resource Partitioning Allows Competitors to Coexist In the Galápagos archipelago, seed-eating finches (*Geospiza* spp.; see Figure 17.7) use their beaks to crack open seeds, which are often in short supply. Individuals with big beaks can crack large, hard seeds that individuals with small beaks cannot eat, whereas small-beaked birds are more efficient at eating small, soft seeds. Dolph Schluter and Peter Grant documented how 15 of the islands differed in both their seed resources and in which *Geospiza* species were present.

HYPOTHESIS

Multiple species of *Geospiza* coexist only where they can partition seed resources.

METHOD

1. Determine which species of seed can be eaten efficiently by *Geospiza* with different beak sizes.
2. Measure the abundances of seeds of different sizes on 15 islands.
3. Characterize the availability of food for finches with different beak sizes, expressing availability as the population density that can be supported on each island (a measure of carrying capacity).
4. Determine the average beak sizes of finch species present on each island.

RESULTS

Islands supported between 1 and 3 finch species (shown here for 6 of the 15 islands). The number of species present (indicated by colored dots) increased with the number of seed sizes available (reflected in the number of distinct peaks in carrying capacity).

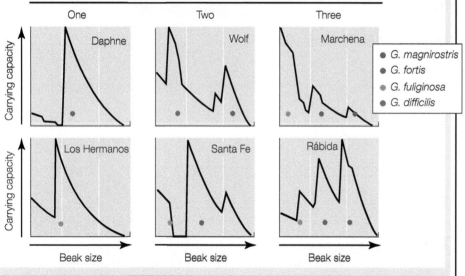

CONCLUSION

Coexisting *Geospiza* species differ in beak sizes and thus in resource use.

ANALYZE THE DATA

A. The average beak sizes of finch species present on an island (indicated by the locations of the colored dots) closely match the peaks in carrying capacity. Why might this be so?
B. Why do peaks in seed availability have no more than one associated finch species?
C. Why might some peaks in seed availability lack an associated finch species?
   (Hint: See Concept 45.1.)

Go to **yourBioPortal.com** for original citations, discussions, and relevant links for all INVESTIGATION figures.

Geospiza fuliginosa

Xylocopa darwinii

Nectar Use and Size of *G. fuliginosa*

ISLAND	TIME SPENT FEEDING ON FLOWER NECTAR (%)	MEAN SIZE (WINGSPAN, mm)
Bees Absent		
Pinta	10	59.8
Marchena	28	58.2
Bees Present		
Fernandina	1	64.8
Santa Cruz	14	64.0
San Salvador	0	63.8
Española	0	64.7
Isabela	7	64.5

FIGURE 44.7 Finch Morphology Evolves in Response to Competition with Carpenter Bees *(Page 867)*

(A)

Episyrphus balteatus

(B) *Anodorhyncus hyacinthinus*

Vespula vulgaris

FIGURE 44.8 Defense Mechanisms and "Arms Races" *(Page 867)*

FIGURE 44.9 **Using Mimicry to Avoid Being Eaten** *(Page 868)*

FIGURE 44.10 **An Invasive Species** *(Page 870)*

FIGURE 44.11   A Fungal Garden *(Page 871)*

Ecological Communities

FIGURE 45.1 Vegetation Recolonized Krakatau *(Page 874)*

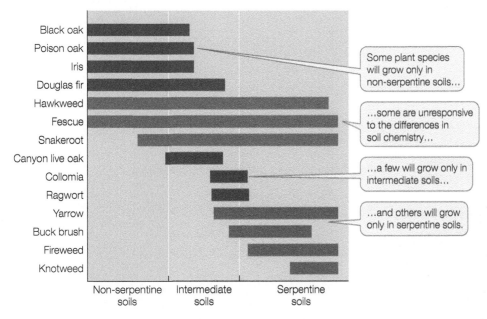

FIGURE 45.2 Species Turnover along an Environmental Gradient *(Page 875)*

FIGURE 45.3 Many Animals Associate with Habitats of a Particular Structure *(Page 876)*

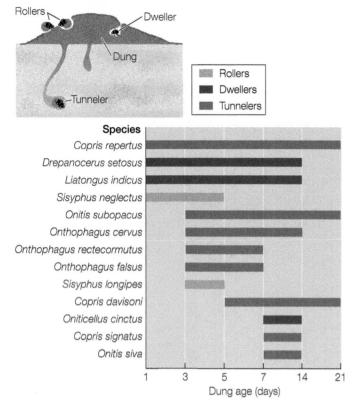

FIGURE 45.4 Dung Beetle Species Composition Changes over Time
(Page 876)

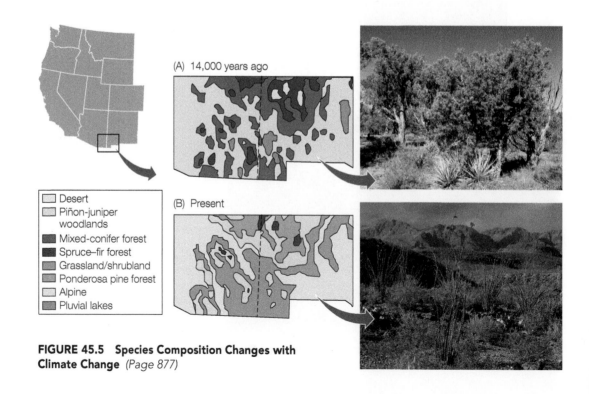

FIGURE 45.5 Species Composition Changes with Climate Change (Page 877)

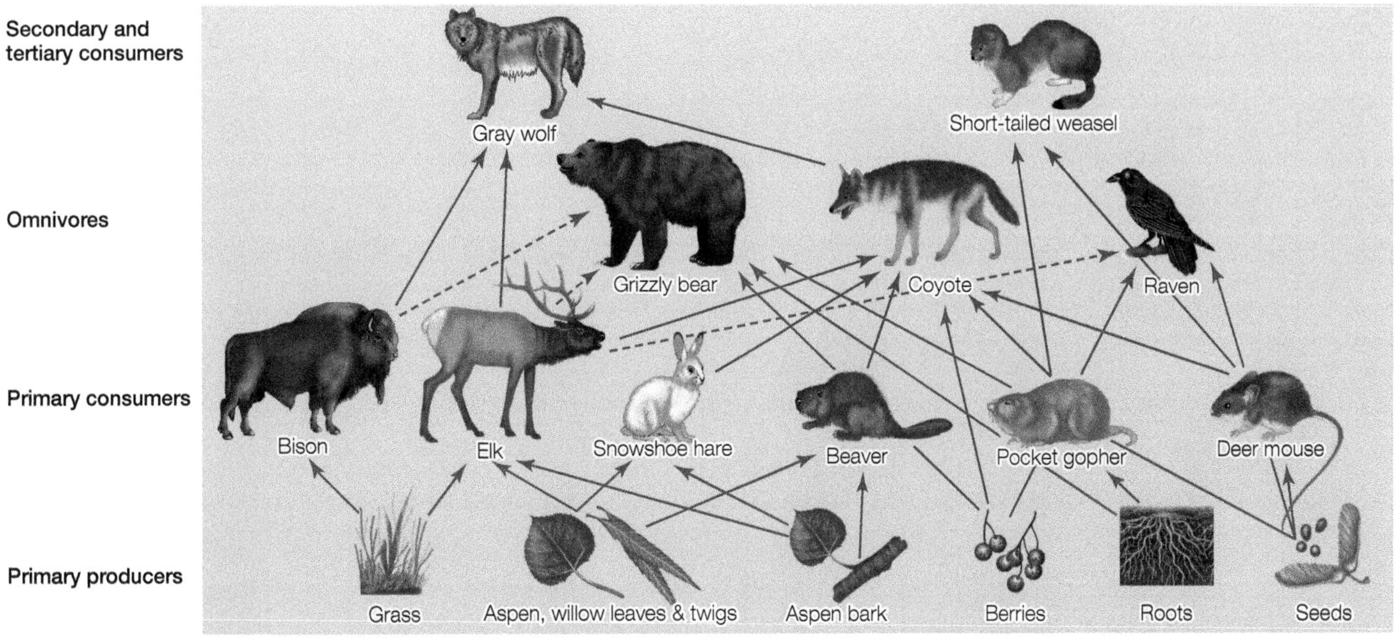

FIGURE 45.6 A Food Web in the Yellowstone Grasslands *(Page 878)*

TABLE 45.1	The Major Trophic Levels		
TROPHIC LEVEL	**SOURCE OF ENERGY**	**EXAMPLES**	
Primary producers (photosynthesizers)	Solar energy	Green plants, photosynthetic bacteria and protists	
Primary consumers (herbivores)	Tissues of primary producers	Elk, grasshoppers, gypsy moth larvae, pollinating bees, geese	
Secondary consumers (carnivores)	Tissues of herbivores	Spiders, great tits, cheetahs, parasites	
Tertiary consumers (carnivores)	Tissues of carnivores	Tuna, killer whales, parasites	
Omnivores	Several trophic levels	Coyotes, opossums, crabs, robins, white-footed mice	
Decomposers (detritivores)	Dead bodies and waste products of other organisms	Fungi, many bacteria, vultures, earthworms, dung beetles	

(Page 879)

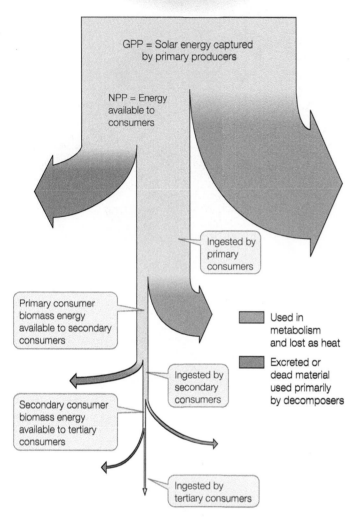

FIGURE 45.7 Energy Flow through Ecological Communities
(Page 879)

(A)

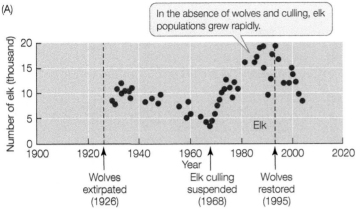

In the absence of wolves and culling, elk populations grew rapidly.

Number of elk (thousand)

Elk

Wolves extirpated (1926)

Year

Elk culling suspended (1968)

Wolves restored (1995)

(B)

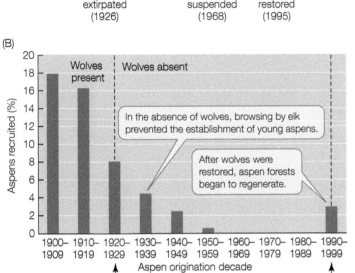

Wolves present   Wolves absent

Aspens recruited (%)

In the absence of wolves, browsing by elk prevented the establishment of young aspens.

After wolves were restored, aspen forests began to regenerate.

Aspen origination decade

Wolves extirpated (1926)

Wolves restored (1995)

(C) *Populus tremuloides*

FIGURE 45.8   Removing Wolves Initiated a Trophic Cascade *(Page 880)*

Community A

Community A is less diverse than community B because it contains three equally abundant species rather than four.

Community B

With four equally abundant species, community B is the most diverse.

Community C

Community C is less diverse than community B because it has an uneven distribution of the four species.

FIGURE 45.9   Species Richness and Species Evenness Contribute to Diversity *(Page 881)*

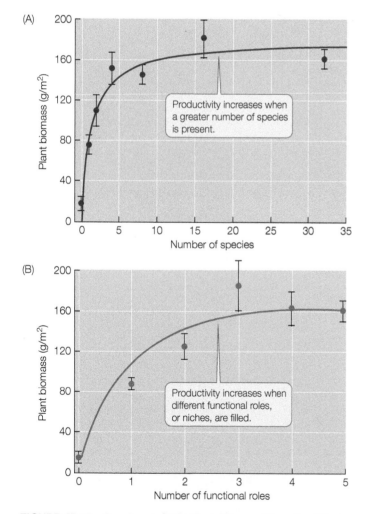

(A)

Plant biomass (g/m^2)

Number of species

Productivity increases when a greater number of species is present.

(B)

Plant biomass (g/m^2)

Number of functional roles

Productivity increases when different functional roles, or niches, are filled.

FIGURE 45.10   Species and Functional Group Diversity Affect Grassland Productivity *(Page 882)*

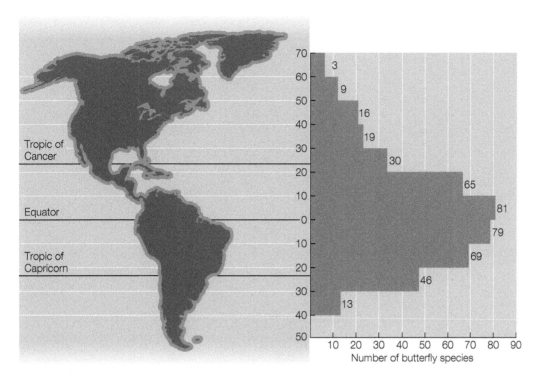

FIGURE 45.11   Species Richness Increases toward the Equator *(Page 883)*

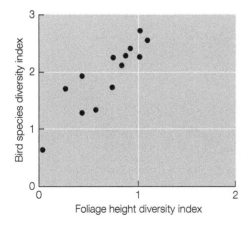

**FIGURE 45.12   Structurally Complex Habitats
Support Greater Diversity** *(Page 883)*

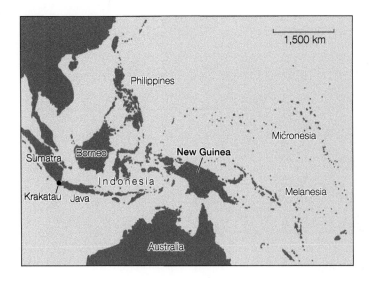

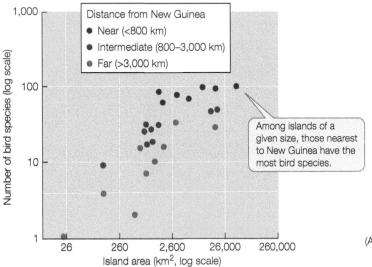

Among islands of a given size, those nearest to New Guinea have the most bird species.

FIGURE 45.13   Area and Isolation Influence Species Richness on Islands *(Page 884)*

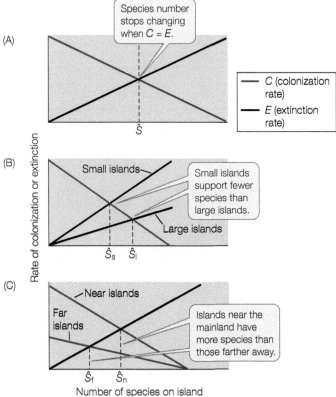

(A) Species number stops changing when $C = E$.

— C (colonization rate)
— E (extinction rate)

(B) Small islands

Small islands support fewer species than large islands.

Large islands

(C) Near islands

Far islands

Islands near the mainland have more species than those farther away.

Number of species on island

FIGURE 45.14   MacArthur and Wilson's Theory of Island Biogeography *(Page 884)*

INVESTIGATION

FIGURE 45.15   The Theory of Island Biogeography Can Be Tested   By experimentally removing all the arthropods on four small mangrove islands of equal size but different distance from the mainland, Simberloff and Wilson were able to observe the process of recolonization and compare the results with the predictions of island biogeography theory.

HYPOTHESIS

The rate at which experimentally defaunated islands accumulate species initially, and their equilibrium species number, will decrease with distance from a mainland source of colonists.

METHOD

1. Census the terrestrial arthropods on 4 small mangrove islands of equal size (11–12 m diameter) but different distance from a mainland source of colonists.
2. Erect scaffolding and tent the islands. Fumigate with methyl bromide (a chemical that kills arthropods but does not harm plants).

3. Remove tenting. Monitor recolonization for the following 2 years, periodically censusing terrestrial arthropod species.

RESULTS

Recolonization was fastest on the closer islands, slowest on the one farthest from the mainland. Two years after defaunation, each island had about the same number of species it had before the experiment.

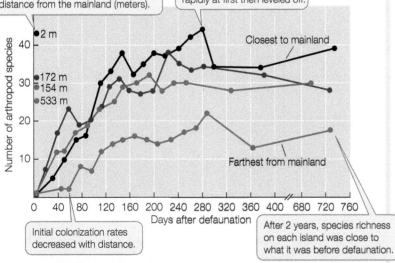

The number of species present before defaunation (dots) decreased with distance from the mainland (meters).

Species number increased rapidly at first then leveled off.

Closest to mainland

Farthest from mainland

Initial colonization rates decreased with distance.

After 2 years, species richness on each island was close to what it was before defaunation.

CONCLUSION

The data support the theory that species richness on islands represents a dynamic balance between colonization and extinction rates.

For more, go to Working with Data 45.1 at **yourBioPortal.com**.

Go to **yourBioPortal.com** for original citations, discussions, and relevant links for all INVESTIGATION figures.

TABLE 45.2	Some Major Ecosystem Goods and Services	
GOOD OR SERVICE	COMMUNITY PROCESS	EXAMPLES
Food production	Trophic interactions	Production of wild food, production of crops and livestock
Materials production	Trophic interactions	Production of lumber, fuel, fiber
Pollination and seed dispersal	Plant–pollinator and plant–disperser interactions	Plant reproduction and dispersal
Maintenance of fertile soil	Decomposition; composition of vegetation; plant- and animal-microbe mutualisms	Nitrogen fixation, nutrient recycling, erosion control
Waste treatment	Decomposition	Breakdown of toxins and wastes
Pest control	Predator–prey, host–parasite, and competitive interactions	Removal of pests and pest breeding sites
Water supply	Regulation of water infiltration and runoff by vegetation structure and animal activity	Retention of water in watersheds, reservoirs, and aquifers
Climate regulation	Metabolic gas exchange	Regulation of greenhouse gases and cloud formation
Disturbance control	Composition and biomass of vegetation	Damping of storm winds and wave surges; flood control
Recreational and cultural opportunities	Ecological processes; species diversity	Ecotourism, outdoor recreation; aesthetic, educational, spiritual, scientific values

(Page 887)

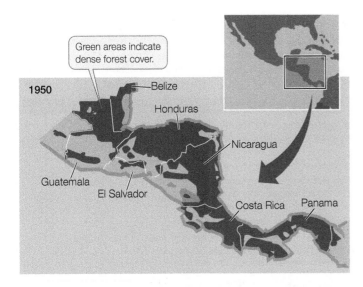

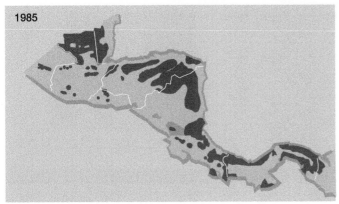

FIGURE 45.16   Habitat Fragmentation in Tropical Forests
(Page 888)

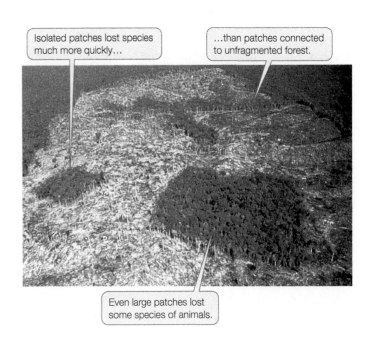

FIGURE 45.17   A Large-Scale Study of Habitat Fragmentation
(Page 888)

INVESTIGATION

FIGURE 45.18 Species Richness Can Enhance Wetland Restoration In one large-scale field experiment, ecologists compared different methods for restoring denuded areas of the Tijuana Estuary, a wetlands environment near San Diego, California. They found that several measures of community function improved more rapidly in species-rich than in species-poor plantings.

HYPOTHESIS

Faster progress toward restoring the community's original condition will be made by planting mixtures of species than by planting single species alone.

METHOD

1. In an area of wetland denuded of vegetation, mark off replicate small experimental plots, all of the same size.

2. Choose 8 native species typical of the region. Plant some plots with each of the 8 species by itself, others with different 3-species subsets, and others with different 6-species subsets. Plant the same total number of seedlings per plot. Leave some plots unplanted as controls.

3. Return over the next 18 months to measure the vegetation and soil nitrogen levels.

RESULTS

Vegetation covered the bare ground more quickly in those plots with higher species richness. Those same plots developed complex vertical structure more quickly and accumulated more nitrogen in plant roots per m² of area.

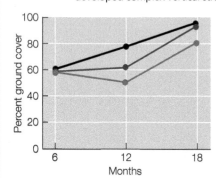
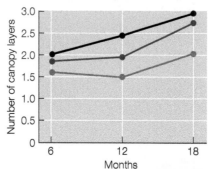
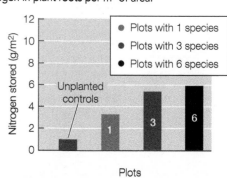

CONCLUSION

Planting a mixture of species leads to more rapid restoration of wetlands

ANALYZE THE DATA

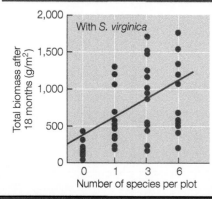
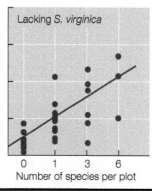

A. The unplanted control plots (above) showed non-zero values of stored nitrogen after 18 months. Is this a surprise? Why or why not?

B. One of the 8 species in the study, *Salicornia virginica*, contributed a disproportionate share of the biomass, cover, and nitrogen in mixtures in which it was included. In the two graphs at left, each circle represents the performance of a particular plot; the lines graph the average values. Based on these two graphs, what do you conclude about the mechanism for the higher success of species-rich plantings? Is the dominance of *S. virginica* the likely explanation?

Go to **yourBioPortal.com** for original citations, discussions, and relevant links for all INVESTIGATION figures.

FIGURE 45.19   Traditional Coffee Cultivation and Community Diversity *(Page 890)*

The Global Ecosystem   46

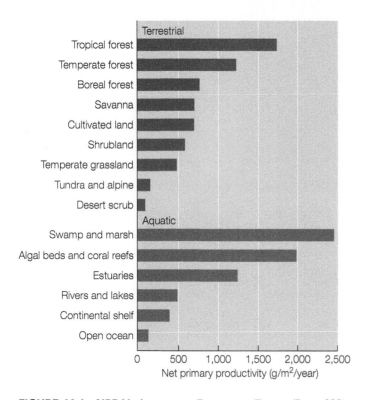

FIGURE 46.1   NPP Varies among Ecosystem Types *(Page 893)*

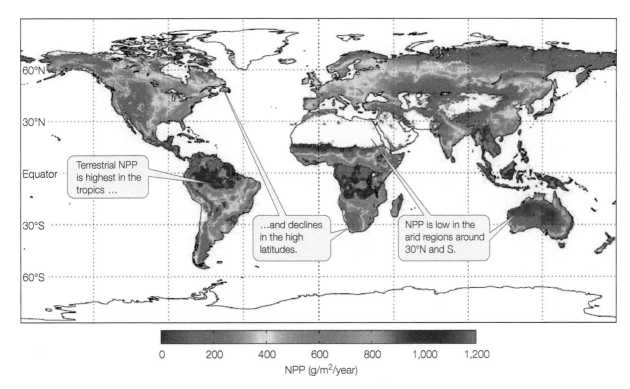

FIGURE 46.2   Terrestrial NPP Corresponds to Climate *(Page 894)*

(A) Temperature

(B) Precipitation

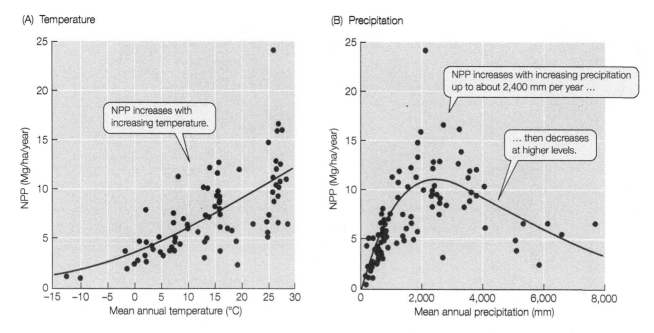

FIGURE 46.3   Terrestrial NPP Varies with Temperature and Precipitation *(Page 894)*

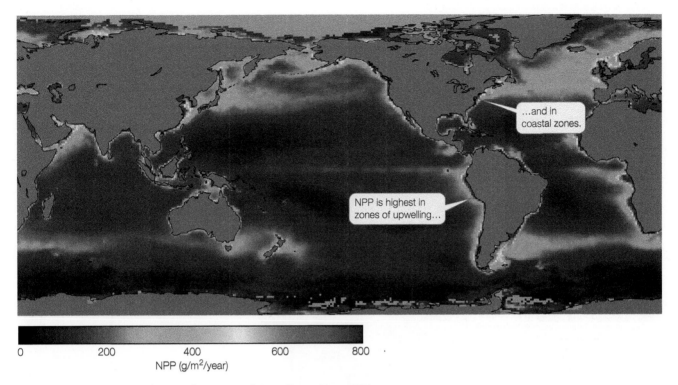

FIGURE 46.4   Marine NPP Is Highest around Coastlines *(Page 895)*

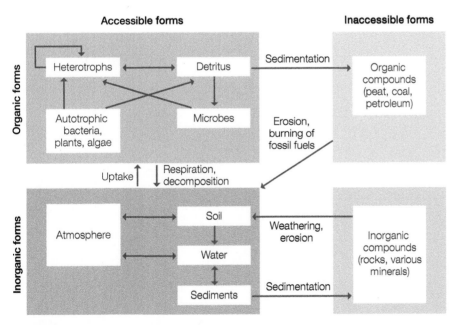

FIGURE 46.5   Chemical Elements Cycle among Compartments of the Biosphere
(Page 896)

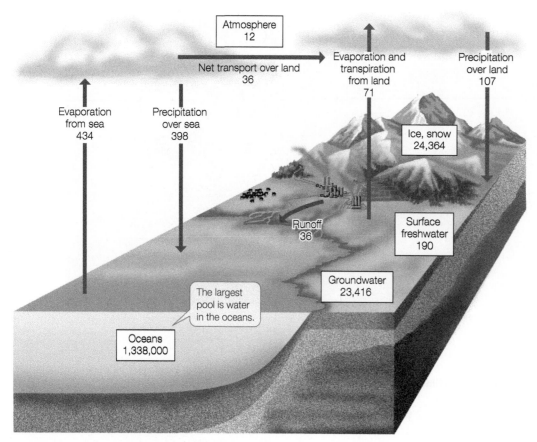

FIGURE 46.6 The Global Water Cycle *(Page 897)*

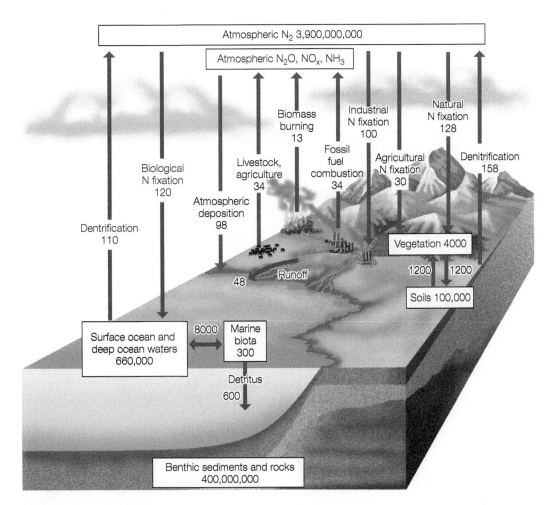

FIGURE 46.7 The Global Nitrogen Cycle *(Page 898)*

INVESTIGATION

FIGURE 46.8 Where Does the Extra Nitrogen Come From? Leaf-cutter ants require more nitrogen than is contained in the fresh leaves they feed to their fungal garden. Perhaps the fungus concentrates nitrogen from the leaves into the fungal structures that the ants eat. If so, spent leaf material in the refuse dump outside the ant nest should be lower in nitrogen than fresh leaves—but the opposite turns out to be true. One possible explanation for this nitrogen enrichment is that ants eat protein-rich insects as well as fungus, and fertilize the fungal garden with their feces. Another is that the fungus absorbs additional nitrogen from the soil. A third possibility is that ant nests harbor nitrogen-fixing organisms.

HYPOTHESIS

Nitrogen-fixing organisms in ant nests supply nitrogen to leaf-cutter ants

METHOD

1. Bring ant colonies into the laboratory and allow them to function in an environment with no insects and no soil (i.e., where the only non-atmospheric source of N is fresh leaves).
2. Measure the nitrogen content of leaves, fungus, ants, and leaf refuse.

RESULTS

The cultivated fungus, the bodies of worker ants, the contents of the refuse dump, and fresh leaves all differed significantly from each other in nitrogen content.

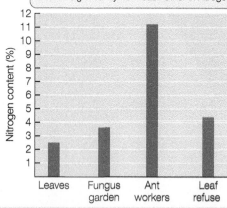

CONCLUSION

Nitrogen is being fixed within the ant nest.

ANALYZE THE DATA

Scientists measured activity of nitrogenase, an enzyme in the bacterial metabolic pathway that fixes atmospheric nitrogen. The results are shown in the figure below. Different letters indicate significant differences in nitrogen content.

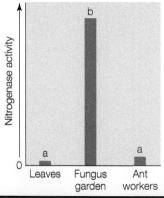

A. Where in the nest is nitrogen fixation occurring?

B. Taken together, the two graphs in this figure support the hypothesis that the fungus concentrates nitrogen in the fungal structures eaten by the ants. Explain. (Hint: Consider that the four values in the Results graph are all significantly different from each other.)

C. Can the researchers now conclude that the extra nitrogen comes from nitrogen-fixing bacteria?

Go to **yourBioPortal.com** for original citations, discussions, and relevant links for all INVESTIGATION figures.

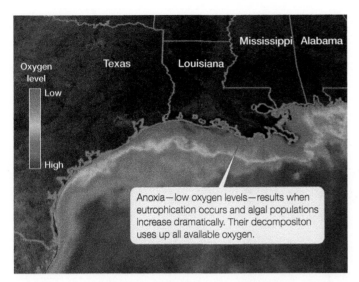

FIGURE 46.9 High Nutrient Input Creates Dead Zones *(Page 900)*

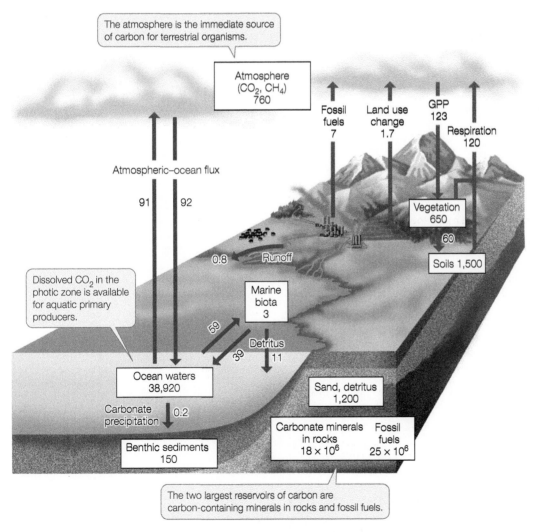

FIGURE 46.10 The Global Carbon Cycle *(Page 900)*

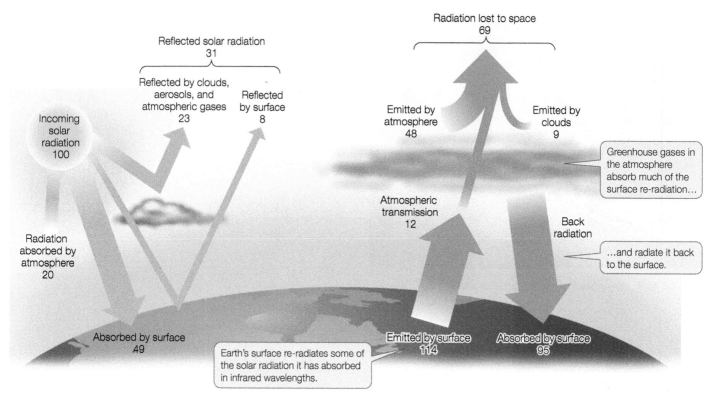

FIGURE 46.11 **Earth's Radiation Balance** *(Page 902)*

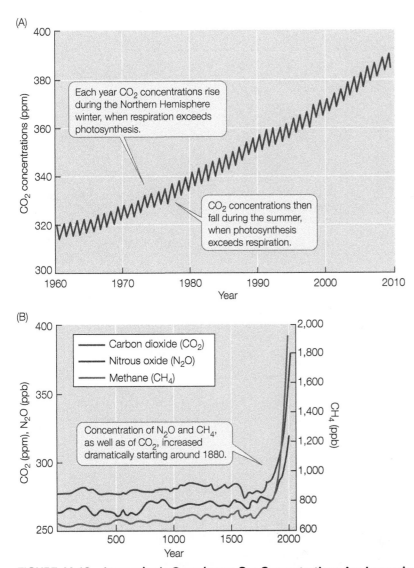

(A)

Each year CO_2 concentrations rise during the Northern Hemisphere winter, when respiration exceeds photosynthesis.

CO_2 concentrations then fall during the summer, when photosynthesis exceeds respiration.

(B)

— Carbon dioxide (CO_2)
— Nitrous oxide (N_2O)
— Methane (CH_4)

Concentration of N_2O and CH_4, as well as of CO_2, increased dramatically starting around 1880.

FIGURE 46.12 Atmospheric Greenhouse Gas Concentrations Are Increasing
(Page 903)

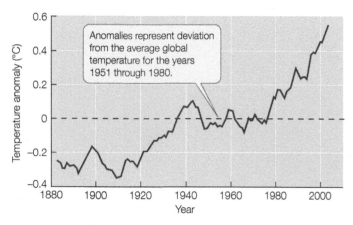

FIGURE 46.13 Global Temperatures Are Increasing *(Page 903)*

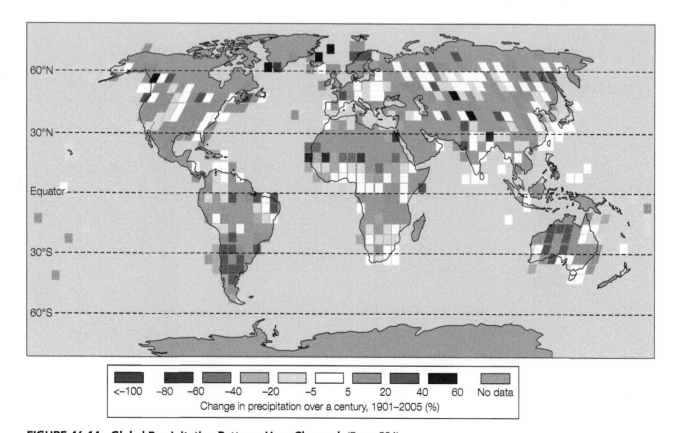

FIGURE 46.14 Global Precipitation Patterns Have Changed *(Page 904)*

FIGURE 46.15   Climate Change Affects Life Histories
(Page 906)